D1246763

FAST FORWARD

The Technologies & Companies Shaping our Future

FAST FORWARD

The Technologies & Companies Shaping our Future

BY JIM MELLON & AL CHALABI

Read other books by Jim Mellon & Al Chalabi

Available to buy now on:
amazon.co.uk

About the Authors

JIM MELLON is an investor with interests in several industries. After leaving Oxford, where he studied PPE, Jim worked in Asia and the US for two fund management companies, GT and Thornton, before establishing his own business in 1991, which includes listed fund management company Charlemagne Capital and an Asian mining group, Regent Pacific.

Jim is the controlling shareholder and Chairman of Manx Financial Corporation, and a controlling shareholder of Plethora Plc, a property business, as well as of Webis Holdings. He is a co-founder of the mining groups Uramin and Red Dragon Resources. Jim's private company, Burnbrae, is a substantial landlord in Germany and the Isle of Man, and owns the hotel chain Sleepwell Hotels. Jim is also a Director of Summit Plc, Port Erin Plc, and Condor Gold Plc, all London-listed companies

Jim spends most of his time working on start-up ideas and on investing. Jim lives in the Isle of Man, Brussels and Ibiza. Jim is an honorary fellow of Oriel College, Oxford.

AL CHALABI is an entrepreneur and business advisor with a diverse professional background. He grew up in the UK and studied Aeronautical Engineering at the University of Southampton. Al started his career in Canada, working as an engineer in process automation systems. After his MBA, he worked as a management consultant, specialising in technology, strategy and operations, based out of Hong Kong.

Since 2008, Al has been running CASP-R, a firm he founded to provide independent research and advisory services to investors and corporations, with a focus on real estate and technology. He is a founding member of Prospect Ventures, a Hong Kong-based angel investor group that provides seed and growth funding to Asian-based tech companies.

Al lives in Hong Kong with his partner Fiona and two children.

This edition first published 2014

Registered Office:
Fruitful Publications, Viking House, Nelson Street, Douglas, Isle Of Man, IM1 2AH

For customer services and information about how to apply for permission to reuse the copyright material in this book please see our website at www.fastforwardbook.com

A catalogue record for this book is available from the British Library.

ISBN 978-0-9930478-0-0

Designed by Lee Akers @ www.cfdmedia.co.uk
Printed by CPI Group (UK) Ltd, Croydon, CR0 4YY

Contents

Contents

FAST FORWARD

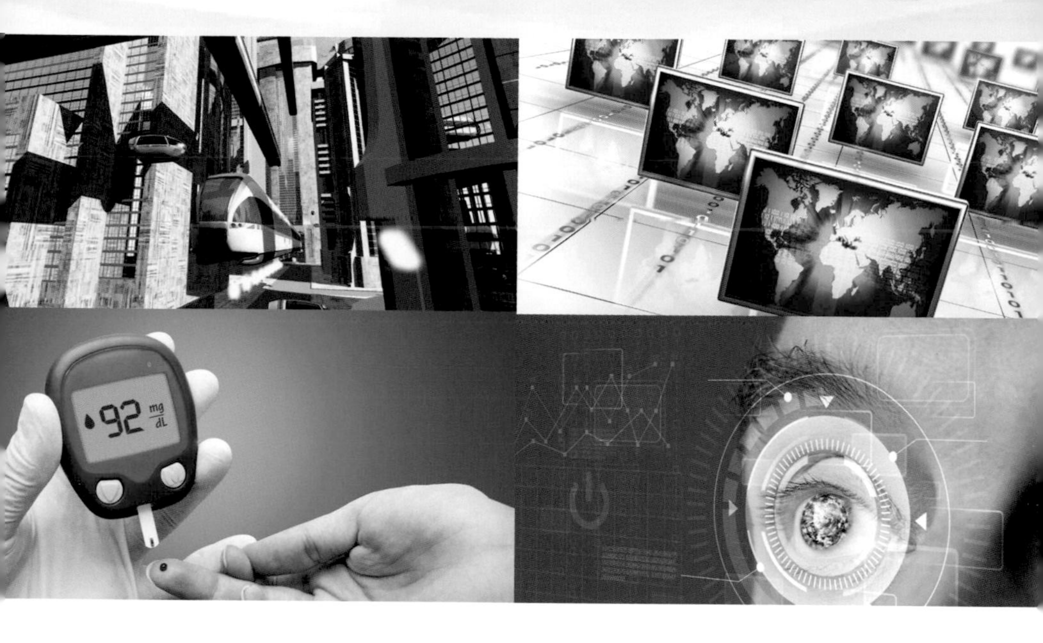

Acknowledgements

We would like to extend our thanks to the following for all the help and support we have received in making this book:

Andy Smith, for reviewing the Life Sciences information.

Can Curune, for providing a great writing environment...and for all the coffee and teas.

Trish Wilson, for her help in getting the show on the road.

David and Angelina Thurston, for coming up with the great title of the book.

Professor Maha Hussain of the University of Michigan for her review and comments on the Life Sciences chapter.

Michele Bina for his valuable feedback on the energy chapter.

Lee Akers and Karl Coleman for their brilliant work in layout design and social media promotion.

Introduction

A couple of summers ago, we sat on the terrace of Jim's house in Ibiza and sketched out an idea for a follow-up book to *Cracking the Code.*

We hit on the theme of human redundancy in a world of increasing automation and of more sophisticated artificial intelligence, and their impact on society in the coming decades. Luckily, we didn't write that particular book, because at the beginning of 2014, Erik Brynjolfsson and Andrew McAfee published their scholarly *The Second Machine Age*, which covers exactly that topic. A few months later came the book that many have bought and few will read: *Capital in the 21st Century* by Thomas Piketty, the economist *du jour.* In this book, Mr Piketty expresses his controversial views on capitalism, and the long term political consequences of abundant capital and rising inequality.

The life sciences sector has enjoyed a huge bull market since *Cracking the Code* was published in 2012. We are not claiming credit for that of course, but undoubtedly its publication was timely for us and we have invested successfully in the sector, and enjoyed very good returns (refer to Appendix A to see the portfolios we suggested in *Cracking the Code* along with their respective returns over a two year period).

In this new book, we set out to identify new *Big Ideas* to serve as investment *Money Fountains* for us and our readers. As we went about our research, it soon became apparent that there were a number of exciting sectors that were undergoing a major transformation.

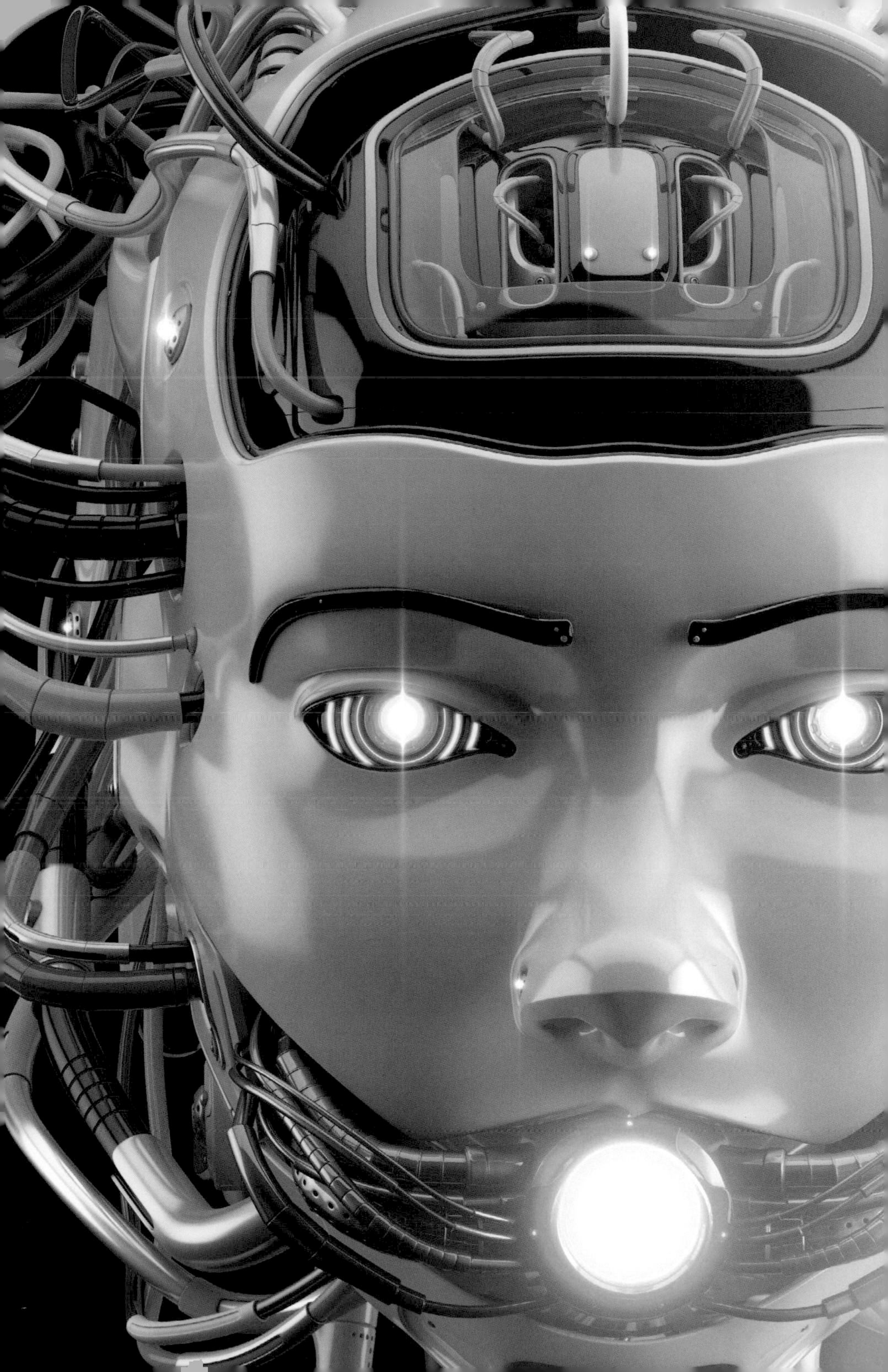

These sectors were benefiting from increased machine intelligence and expanded human knowledge.

We just had to include a chapter on life sciences given how much has happened since our last book. The sector remains one of the most exciting and interesting. All the sectors we have chosen are characterised by truly amazing new technologies, some of them will be familiar to some readers, others will be totally new and seemingly fantastical. All of them offer interesting investment opportunities for the far-sighted and patient; and all will transform the world we know today, and will do it much faster than most people think. Productivity growth, which has been poor around the world for some time now, is likely to accelerate, adding real economic benefits to most populations.

There will, of course, be consequences to these transformations, ranging from geopolitical to demographic, and they will change the way humans work and conduct their lives. Some of these consequences will be negative, and there is no doubt that some of what we have expounded before in our newsletters is about to happen, i.e. that human redundancy will be widespread in the new world of automation, at least in terms of current job functions. This book primes our readers for the future disruptions, giving them an opportunity to take advantage of the positive changes, while reducing the impact of the negative ones. In addition, the way in which investments are being made is changing, and not necessarily in favour of private investors.

Increased use of robotics and automation will certainly make life harder for emerging nations that have relied on cheap labour-based exports, forcing them to sustain and grow their economies through internal consumption. Africa, in particular, will experience difficulties adjusting to this era of automation; a continent which by far has the highest population growth in the world. A new study by UNICEF reports that by 2100, almost half of the children under 18 in the world will be African, up from a quarter today. By then Africa is forecast to have 4.2 billion people, up fourfold from today, with Nigeria alone having a population of just below one billion. It will be hard to find useful jobs for many of these people, as automation sweeps across the rest of the world.

Overall though, as we come close to the publication of this book, we are optimistic that all of these transformative technologies will result in a giant leap forward for mankind, extending life expectancies, improving the quality of our lives and expanding opportunities for those who seize them.

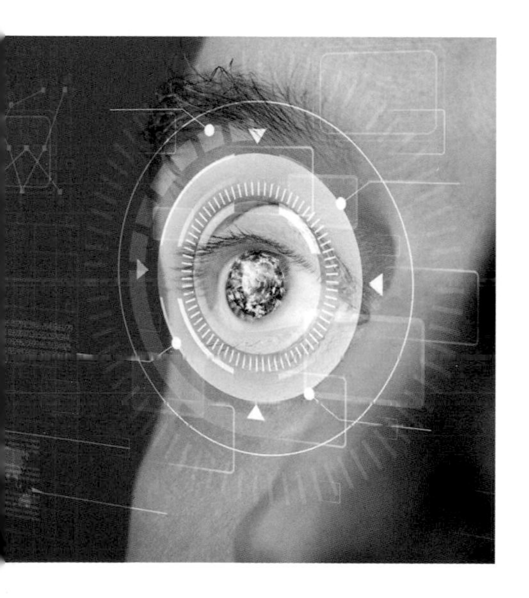

Renowned futurist and technology inventor Ray Kurzweil[1] posits that once artificial intelligence (AI) surpasses human intelligence, by around 2045, it is curtains for the human race. Such a milestone is known as the *Singularity* and when we reach it, a superior intelligence would be able to continuously redesign itself to be ever more intelligent, rendering us humans redundant. We will then have transcended our biological destiny, but not necessarily to the benefit of mankind.

Although we do not subscribe to this gloomy future of a *trans-humanist* world, some people are treating the Singularity as a quasi-religious event, with worshippers believing that 2045 will mark the day of reckoning with AI. The trans-humanist movement *Terasem* has emerged as a new-age religion based on the convergence of technology and faith. Terasem believes that *"life is purposeful, death is optional. God is technological. Love is essential."*

There is no doubt that *super-intelligence* is on the way, defined by Nick Bostrom in the New Scientist as *"any intellect that greatly exceeds the cognitive performance of humans in virtually all domains."*

[1] *Ray Kurzweil is currently Google's Director of Engineering.*

This might take the form of much faster processing speeds than we are capable of, or it may be a collective intelligence that harnesses many people's combined intelligence to form a single super-intelligence; or the future super-intelligence could just be qualitatively superior to any known human intelligence – a sort of Singularity. None of these outcomes need frighten us; in fact, they probably will be benign and lead to advances in technology and the life sciences at a pace that we cannot contemplate today. Our view is that machine intelligence in the future will be there to serve our own goals.

Everyone looking at technological progress agrees that the world has entered an era of accelerated change that is being driven by technologies whose tentacles are permeating every aspect of our lives. In this book we discuss these changes, some of which are already well-publicised in the popular press, such as the "sharing economy", the "Internet of Things", driverless vehicles, electric cars, robots, and the enabling power of the internet itself.

We also delve into areas that haven't received as much media attention but are certainly shaping our future; for instance, new forms of payment, improvements in energy technology, and the renaissance of the space industry.

Our coverage of these new technologies is accompanied by ideas for investors on how to profit from them. However, in almost all of the disruptive technologies we researched, we discovered that the big boys are crowding out the individual investor from many of the best opportunities. This is partly down to the concentration of capital and technological power lying in relatively few hands. So when a new technology comes along that is developed outside of what we might describe as the *behemoth brothers* (the likes of *Google, Apple, Alibaba, Softbank and Facebook*) it often gets snapped up by one of them before investors get a chance to purchase equity in public markets. If some of these companies do manage to go public without being swallowed up by one of the behemoth brothers, they are often already very large and much of the upside is already priced into the share price, rewarding only the early stage venture capital investors, who are often drawn from the same magic circle of names. A few good examples of this are *Twitter, Alibaba* and *LinkedIn*; all three went public at eye watering valuations, with their early supercharged growth days well behind them.

As we describe in more detail later, Google has bought many of the interesting companies in robotics and in the *Internet of Things*; Facebook has done the same in virtual reality, and Amazon and Softbank are doing the same in areas related to their businesses. Of course investors can buy shares of the acquirers – for example, we think Google remains an excellent long term investment despite its size.

However, as big tech continues to swallow up many of the exciting, emerging tech companies, it becomes increasingly difficult for individuals to invest in disruptive technology companies; the notable exception being the life sciences sector. That having been said, we have managed to identify a long list of potential investments for our readers to consider as a result of our extensive research.

This effective consolidation in the technology sector is a reflection of a broader trend, where capital is multiplying in the hands of those who are riding the wave of technological innovation, while many others are being left behind. This is a view very much espoused by Thomas Piketty, who would like to see taxation and other measures used more aggressively to redress the apparent widening gap between the rich and poor.

Bain & Company, a consultancy, suggests that we are in an era of "capital superabundance." Bain estimates that total financial assets globally today are almost 10 times the value of the global output of all goods and services, and that global capital will grow by another 50 per cent by 2020. The world is awash with capital and one of the effects is that for most investors, the returns on capital will steadily diminish.

The so-called "one per cent," or the elite and the powerful, are very much in the spotlight of public debate these days.

There is no question that wealth is more concentrated than it has been for nearly a century, but in some ways this is a reflection of success and progress. Over the past 20 years, one billion people have been taken out of poverty in the developing world, and not all of them in China. Certainly, the widening income gap between CEOs and the average employee is cause for concern; it currently stands at 300 times, up from 70 times in 1990. But overall, there is no doubt that the world today is richer, better and with less abject poverty, much of which is due to globalisation, international trade and technological innovation.

Indeed, if we go back to 1928, when John Maynard Keynes wrote a piece called "Economic Possibilities for our Grandchildren", he suggested that in 2028 the economies of the developed world would be vastly bigger, and the global economy would be seven times bigger. It looks like he will be proven right; today US GDP in real terms is 16 times bigger than it was then, and per capita GDP is six times higher.

But not everything in his piece was right; he was wrong in suggesting that one of the consequences of this richer society would be 15 hour work weeks and an abundance of leisure time. Indeed, he was worried that too many people would be unable to profit from this surplus of free time, leading to a sort of collective nervous breakdown.

Although the quality of life has improved for almost everyone on the planet since 1928, work weeks are still nowhere near 15 hours. Brigid Schulte authored a book called "Overwhelmed, Work, Love and Play when no one has the Time" in which she bemoans the lack of free time for the average American, describing it as the *"overwhelm."*

But things are changing and Schulte may just get her wish for more free time, and not necessarily in a bad way.

What is clearly happening that is of vital importance to us as investors is that labour, in the traditional sense, is being replaced by capital, which is itself getting cheaper as machines make more machines faster and more cheaply.

The pace of change in the fundamental structures of most economic systems is getting faster; from 1948 to 2000 the share of labour of the total US economy was fairly static at about 64 per cent. Today it has fallen to around 57 per cent, and that is a direct consequence of automation, and the concentration of economic rewards in fewer hands. Thomas Picketty describes this as "capital deepening" where capital becomes more important than labour, for instance robots replacing workers. Another example is China, where it is thought one quarter of manufacturing jobs (about 30 million) have been lost since 1996, despite a 75 per cent increase in output. An early backer of Amazon, Nick Hanauer claims that the "pitchforks" are coming as incomes and wealth become more concentrated at the top end of societies, and that the US risks becoming like eighteenth century France unless something is done about it. We think Hanauer and Picketty are too pessimistic; just as the *Luddites* in nineteenth century Britain believed that machines would replace human workers and strove to shut down technological progress.

The compression of incomes and wealth is a symptom of the abundance and relative cheapness of capital, which is due to the innovation and efforts of the relatively few disruptors and organisers. But that doesn't mean that the bulk of the population don't benefit from improvements in technology – most people already have a mobile phone, half of the world's population is online, health and life expectancy have improved almost everywhere, and fewer people around the world face starvation.

The fact is that innovators, doers and disruptors need consumers to buy the goods their companies produce. Users of Facebook, for instance, recognise that they are the product, or at least their "eyeballs" are. We are in a world where the more people use a particular platform, the more valuable it becomes. This is known as the *network effect.*

Pater Tenebrarum, an independent analyst with a popular blog called *Acting Man*, doesn't believe that disruption necessarily leads to job destruction; it just creates different types of jobs. He uses the music industry as an example, where up until the mid-1980s the then standard 24-track recording machines cost $80,000 each. Today's superior system (about 20 times better) costs just $2,500 in devalued dollars and the industry is considerably larger, both in terms of employment and turnover. In other words, one industry is wiped out, while another re-emerges stronger, more capable, and more useful to people than before. That is how it will be in our age of automation. Jobs in manufacturing will dwindle, but more job openings will emerge in what might loosely be described as the leisure sector.

As these disruptions continue to impact the labour market, there will undoubtedly be an increase in the number of the *precariat* - those workers without jobs. Many jobs will never return, which is why education and training are such vital elements in building a new, technologically advanced economy with jobs for humans and machines. That is already happening: caring jobs, jobs in artisanal crafts and foods, jobs in information technology and jobs in sales are all on the rise. Robots are not "eating" all of our jobs and they won't in the future either. But they will make a big difference to the types of jobs we will have, creating more leisure time and realising Keynes's long dormant prediction. The products made by robots will be cheaper and thus more affordable, even if wages of the general population do not increase quickly. When automation is ubiquitous and cheap, it is human experience that becomes valuable, especially to the sellers of goods and services. Market-creating opportunities are always with us; enabling technologies are generally characterised by lower cost as volumes grow.

Innovation will release humans from jobs that are menial and repetitive, which is just as well in a world with an ageing population. The number of people over 65 will surpass that of children by the year 2047 for the first time ever, according to the UN, with the total approaching two billion. This longevity phenomenon will vastly expand the market for life sciences, which we cover in one of our chapters, creating huge employment opportunities in the sector.

The *longevity economy* is in itself an increasingly powerful force, and the consumption levels of the 60-plus is expected to reach

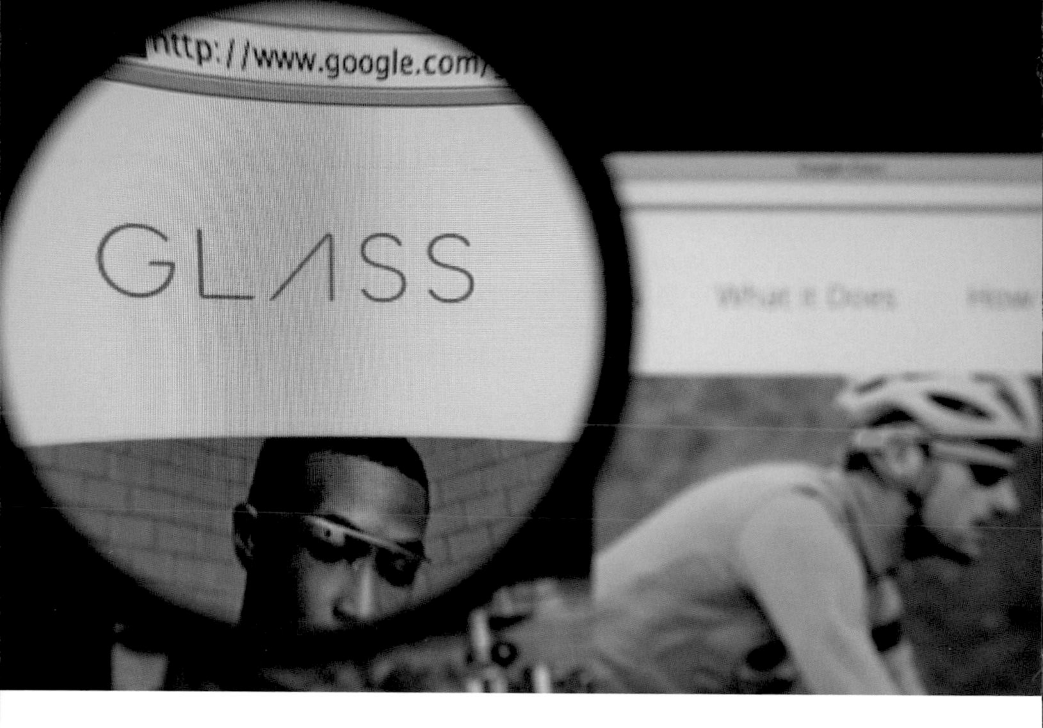

$15 trillion worldwide by 2020, equivalent to one whole US economy[2].

We believe the best investment returns are to be made in innovation, although one of the challenges will be to find a way to bypass the oligarchy comprising the likes of Google, Facebook and Amazon. One way to do that is to study and emulate what Google does. It is, after all, among the best connected and possibly the smartest company on the planet. One thing Google does is to hire great people who are given the creative freedom to visualise the future. Google imagines what key products might look like five to 10 years ahead and reverse engineers them to create a path to the future.

In Google's famous *X Labs,* based near the company's headquarters in Mountain View, California, some of its most innovative products have emerged, such as *Google Glass*, driverless cars, contact lenses monitoring glucose for diabetics, products linked to the *internet of things*, internet service from balloons, and voice recognition systems.

---

[2] *Source: Euromonitor*

All of these products have, according to Google, "science fiction sounding solutions" which have the capacity to improve existing technologies by ten times (hence the "X" in X Labs stands for 10 in Roman numerals).

To begin with, Google doesn't even consider making money from a new technology; after all it already has vast cash flow from its advertising business, so it can afford to be patient. The view of the company is that profits follow good products, and it is an exemplar followed in all of its businesses, not just in its X Labs. Google is also developing industrial robots, has moored some mysterious barges in San Francisco Bay, and is developing a health bioinformatics business called **Calico.**

Of course, some of the projects under development that look a little nutty to the outside world end up being just that. For example, Google has abandoned its efforts to develop hoverboards, jetpacks and teleportation machines. But failure is applauded within the company and viewed as a sign of progress, i.e. vision requires an ability to accept defeat and move on. What Google is looking for are global markets of an infinite scale, and that is what we as investors should also be looking for.

In this book, we believe such opportunities are to be found in the life sciences, new forms of transport and energy, revolutionary payment systems, companion and service robots, and in the internet of things. If we as investors are to match or improve on Google's ability to invest in the future, we must aspire to think like Google. Imagine that there are no limits to technological progress, that every barrier can be overcome, and that we live in a golden age of unprecedented change – change that we need to embrace despite all the uncertainties that comes with it.

The world economy is being expanded hugely by the digital revolution. Digital products now make up the fastest growing component of global trade. Such virtual products are not constrained by delivery times, production schedules, and transportation; they can be ubiquitous and reproduced perfectly in unlimited quantities at very low or no incremental cost.

This digital revolution is changing almost every aspect of the global economy, making labour less important as an input to manufacturing, and increasingly to services as well. The ultimate destination of products will become where they are manufactured. So-called *re-shoring*, which has already commenced in the US and some other developed nations, will become increasingly prevalent.

Three-dimensional printing, robots, and rising labour costs in emerging markets are all contributing factors that will move production closer to the consumer. This will also have the effect of making companies more efficient, reducing inventories and delivery times as goods will not have to spend weeks on container ships being transported from cheap labour countries to their final destinations in the developed world. This *proximity effect* will become more influential as time goes on. The developing world's old model where rural dwellers migrate to the cities to find work in manufacturing (where the output is largely sold to the developed world) is being broken. Indeed, even Foxconn, the largest manufacturer in China, expects in due course to replace many of its one million workers with up to one million robots.

Overall, our three principal takes on the future are that: it's coming to us faster than most people realise; secondly, it will be better than the past, but disruptive in almost every aspect of our lives; and thirdly, if we are to make good returns from our investments in a world of abundant capital and lower average returns, we will need to think and act more nimbly.

We have pored over countless articles in newspapers, magazines, journals and the internet, and met with many companies and innovators as part of our research for *Fast Forward.* We hope that this book will guide and inspire our readers in their quest for higher returns in the coming years.

Jim and Al

October 2014

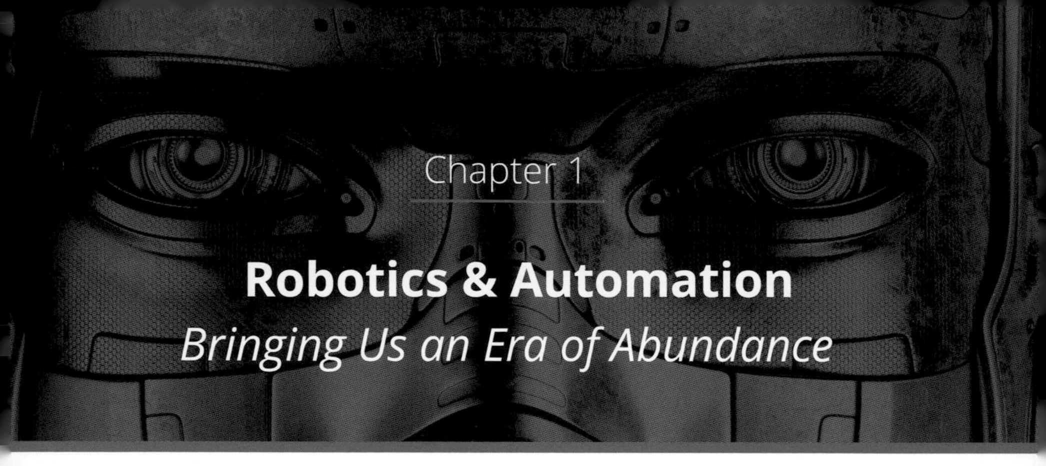

Chapter 1

Robotics & Automation

Bringing Us an Era of Abundance

Robots have always captured mankind's imagination and all of us have watched sci-fi movies featuring robots in all shapes and sizes. Sometimes these robots play good guys; other times they are out to destroy humanity. But in recent years, robots have started to step out of the big screen and into the real world, and whether we like it or not, the day of co-existing alongside robots is less than a decade away.

Since writing a section on robotics in our last book[1] published in 2012, we have been impressed by just how much media attention this sector has been receiving. Undoubtedly, robots have made it to the mainstream media; the number of books, newspaper and magazine articles on this subject has been growing at an exponential rate. Many articles adopt a scaremongering, attention grabbing tactic, warning us about how robots are going to steal jobs and leave us with nothing to do.

What is a Robot?

Although there is no single definition of what a robot is, it is generally accepted to be a machine that is capable of performing a complex series of *mechanical* tasks. So a computer performing numerical calculations wouldn't qualify as a robot, but if that computer had an attachment that it could control to say, pour a glass of water, then that would make it a robot.

An **android** is a robot that resembles a human in its physical form.

---

[1] *Cracking the Code: Understand and Profit from the Biotech Revolution That Will Transform Our Lives and Generate Fortunes*

"We tend to overestimate the effect of a technology in the short run and underestimate the effect in the long run." *Roy Amara, an American futurologist.*

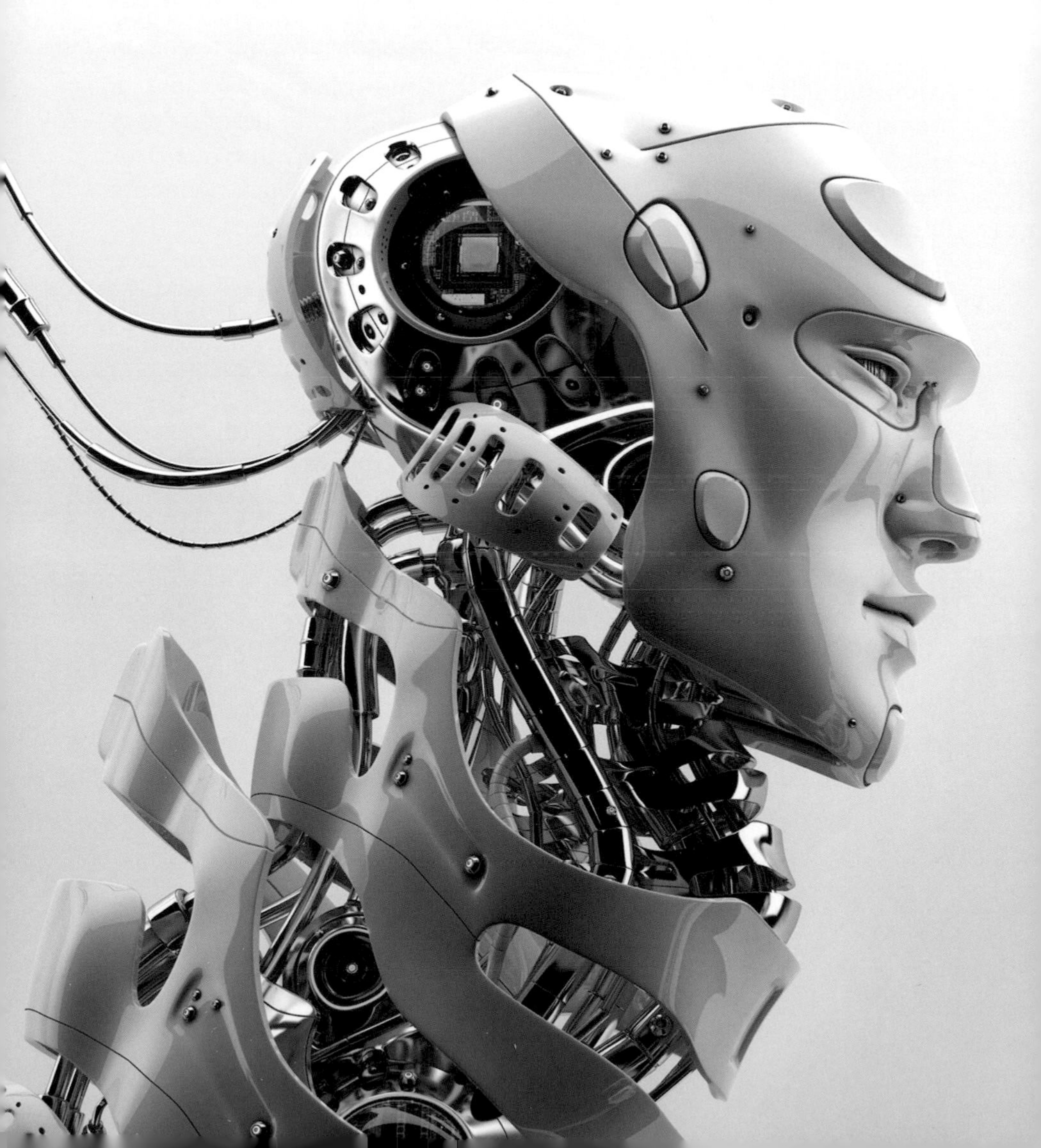

Even Hollywood has jumped on the robot bandwagon by releasing a remake of the 1987 classic film *Robocop,* modernised to reflect advances in robotics since then. These include Artificial Intelligence (AI) and of course Computer Generated Imagery (CGI), developed since the original was made.

Our conviction remains that we are on the cusp of a robotic revolution that will fundamentally reshape the way we live and work. Robots are evolving rapidly, becoming more sophisticated and adaptable to their environments, while at the same time getting cheaper to produce, which is making them an undoubtedly attractive alternative to human workers. After all, robots don't strike, don't have sick days or tea breaks, and generally, don't make mistakes.

Robots come in all shapes and sizes; the smallest type is known as a nano-robot or *nanobot* (a nanometre is one billionth of a metre, about the width of a DNA helix, or a virus.) Such nanobots are still in the early experimental stages of development. One idea to employ these mini-ro-

Figure 1: Early Industrial Robots (1983). KUKA IR160/60, 601/60.
Source: Mixabest for Wikimedia Commons

bots is to inject nanobots into our bloodstream in huge quantities where they could be pre-programmed to locate and destroy anything harmful in our bodies, such as cancer cells or viruses. They might also be deployed to locate particular cells or parts of the body and to deliver their "payloads" in a highly targeted manner to maximise a drug's effectiveness.

At the other end of the robot spectrum, we have the towering industrial robots that can perform nimble and precise manoeuvres at remarkable speed. These types of robots are already widely deployed in large scale manufacturing and are for instance, ubiquitous in the car industry.

Robots have been working for us behind the scenes for decades now and we have enjoyed the benefits of their labour. Readers **will have seen photographs or** videos of industrial robot arms working harmoniously at assembly lines. However, robots are no longer confined to assembly lines, factories and foundries and they are now programmed to be less timid in the company of humans. The science of haptics, or touch sensitivity is rapidly being introduced to robots, making them much more sensitive to their environments.

In fact, many homes already have robots working in them. A few years ago, a company called **iRobot (NASDAQ:IRBT)**, founded in 1990 by MIT roboticists, began selling a series of robots for the home to help perform some basic domestic chores. The most popular of these is called **the** *Roomba*®, a small, low-profile vacuum cleaner that moves around the home autonomously and returns to its base to charge when it has completed its task. For a few hundred dollars, people can choose to delegate their vacuuming to a robot and free up some precious spare time.

Figure 2: iRobot's Roomba 780 vacuum cleaning robot.
Source: www.irobot.co.uk

So popular is the Roomba that over 10 million units have been sold since it was first introduced.

We are still very much in the early stages of the robot revolution, but it is underway now at a fast pace. The key enabler, computer processing power, continues to double every 18 months according to *Moore's Law* and we believe that by 2020, people will be welcoming sophisticated domestic helper robots into their homes and offices. These helper robots will perform a multitude of tasks, from the mundane (but very useful) such as locating misplaced car/house keys, to more sophisticated ones, such as monitoring the health of a home's occupants (including pets). These robots are already debuting in Japan and the United States, as these two countries are clear world leaders in the field of robotics.

In this chapter we will explore how we expect robots to appear in our lives and we identify the companies that in our view seem to have the upper hand in commercialising their products.

Already, robots are being assigned tasks that are too dangerous for humans. These include being sent into a radiation contaminated area, or into a burning building, or even into a war zone to spy behind enemy lines, deliver supplies to troops and even retrieve injured soldiers in hostile territory or to defuse bombs.

We can also expect to see domestic helper robots appear in millions of homes in advanced economies. The robots will be able to do the tasks quicker, more cheaply and more reliably. Being robots, their lot is to accept any job assigned to them, no matter how mundane, repetitive or demanding it is, unlike their truculent human counterparts. Robots are also being designed to do things that humans cannot do with the same level of precision and consistency, such as surgeon-bots performing complex minimally invasive procedures quickly, efficiently and without fatigue. Robots will become the norm in the transportation industry – a driverless car is technically a robot. Transportation stands to undergo major upheaval in the coming years; all types of transportation will be affected. We have dedicated a separate chapter to transportation as the disruptive effect of robotics here will change society.

Finally, the introduction of robots as companions and pets is already a reality but these pet-bots will become more sophisticated and useful to their owners. They may appear a bit gimmicky, and the early versions may have been just that, but pet-bots address a serious condition that many people, especially the elderly experience: loneliness. **Although not a disease in itself**, loneliness has a number of knock-on health risks, such as anxiety and depression.

One of the leading robotics companies in Europe is called **Kuka AG**, listed in Germany, under the symbol KU2. Established over 40 years ago, Kuka is the world's biggest player in the field of industrial robots and in automotive robotics. With 7,800 employees, it has a market capitalisation of around €1.6 billion. Kuka manufactures a multitude of industrial robots, from the "Robocoaster" for amusement parks to a robot that can perform repeated tasks to an accuracy of 0.05mm – that is some precision! Kuka's sales growth has been steady (5.8 per cent per annum over the past decade) and, although the company is not cheap – its stock price trades at a price-to-earnings ratio of around 30 – it is a solid company that is well-positioned to capitalise on the growth in industrial automation.

In Japan, there is a similar robot to Baxter made by **Kawada**

Company Spotlight:
Fanuc Corp (Tokyo Stock Exchange: 6954)

Company website:
http://www.fanuc.co.jp

Founded in 1956, this Japan-based company specialises in factory automation machinery with an extensive range of industrial robots. With over JPY 750 billion (approximately USD 7.5 billion) in cash, very little debt on its balance sheet, annual sales are around JPY 450 billion (USD 4.5 billion) and a net profit margin of 25%, it is worth looking at Fanuc as it will continue to benefit from the increase in industrial automation, where it is a clear leader.

Its market capitalisation is around JPY 4.3 trillion (USD 40 billion)

Company Spotlight: Rethink Robotics (Privately Held)

Company website: http://www.rethinkrobotics.com/

The company was established in 2008 in Boston. One of its founders is a former MIT Robotics Professor, Rodney Brooks. Professor Brooks, who is an Australian, also co-founded iRobot Corporation, a company mentioned earlier. Rethink is currently privately held, with one of its investors being Amazon's Jeff Bezos.

Its flagship product is called *Baxter,* an affordable $25,000 robot designed to be safe enough to work alongside humans in production lines that can be taught new tasks simply through demonstration rather than programming. There is no steep learning curve with human co-workers once Baxter is introduced at a production facility. Being more affordable than conventional industrial robots, there is no high up-front capital expenditure and production down-time is minimal. Baxter is a so-called "chimeric" device, and could ultimately be used in many different ways, such as aiding wheelchair-bound people, conducting physical examinations, and even tending to plants and vegetables.

It is worth following Rethink Robotics – they will probably seek to list on NASDAQ in the next few years, in the same way that iRobot Corporation did in 2005. If Baxter proves to be a hit, it would be a company worth investing in (unless of course Google decides that it likes is too and buys yet another robotics company!)

Industries, Inc., a long-established construction company that created a Robotics Division in 1999. Its robot is called *Nextage.* Like Baxter, it is designed to work alongside humans. It can be taught new tasks without the need to know how to program and it is equipped with sensors to ensure that it cannot accidentally hurt a human co-worker. Unfortunately, in order to invest in Kawada Robotics, one has to buy shares in the entire group, and construction, its main business, is not an industry undergoing exponential growth. It is worth keeping tabs on Kawada in case the company decides to spin off its robotics division.

Figure 3: Rethink Robotics' Baxter, designed for the modern factory.
Source: Rethink Robotics

Another robot worth a mention, but still in the research lab is called *Twendy-One*, a Japanese robot being developed by **Waseda University's Sugano Laboratory.** Its developers describe Twendy-One as a "human symbiotic robot" with a purpose of supporting human daily activities against labour shortages in aging societies. Twendy-One is being developed more for the home than the workplace, helping wheelchair-bound individuals in and out of bed, retrieving household items and even accessing the fridge and preparing meals. A robotic nurse and care giver is exactly what Japan is in desperate need of to look after its elderly. However, little more information is known about Twendy-One and it is too early to tell when it will become available commercially.

There is also **JIBO, an Indiegogo** funded robot that is being designed to be a part of the family. JIBO is expected to ship in 2015, and will perform simple functions such as taking phone calls, providing voice reminders and connecting all the various electronic gadgets of a household. JIBO is also designed to convey emotional states, and its programming is tuned to human presence. It learns to recognise people who come into a room and to adapt to their specific **needs.**

In early 2014, we learnt that **Dyson,** the company known for **its innovative household appli-**

ances, such as vacuum cleaners and fans, is funding a robotics lab at Imperial College, London. Clearly the company has a good track record in household appliances, but making the transition from a vacuum cleaner to a domestic robot is orders of magnitude more complex. We shall just have to wait and see what they come out with.

Cornell University researchers have used crowdsourcing to help "teach" a robot called *Tell Me Dave* how to chat and understand relatively complex orders, such as "boil the water." Dave is currently getting it right about two thirds of the time; this is because humans can convey the same instruction in a variety of ways, including using non-verbal cues like pointing. Robots have yet to learn this skill, and are also limited by "novelty," i.e. they don't understand new instructions that they haven't been taught. The Cornell researchers are using inverse semantics to get around these issues; the robot is programmed to try and find the right words to match its environment. These semantics were collected from people who provided many different types of messages for different scenarios.

Robotics Cluster

The Massachusetts Institute of Technology (MIT) is a world leading institution in the field of robotics. Located in Cambridge, Massachusetts (just across the river from Boston), it has been a driving force behind the emergence of a cluster of robotics companies, such as Rethink Robotics and iRobot Corporation, mentioned earlier. Two more examples are Kiva Systems, which was acquired by Amazon in 2012 and Boston Dynamics, which was acquired by Google in late 2013 (making it the eighth robotics company acquired by Google since it began its buying spree in this sector.)

Evidently, the smart people at Amazon and Google see the inevitability of the rise of the robots and have decided to embrace it to support their business growth and to reduce the risk of being eclipsed by a new technology. In the case of Amazon, of course its vast distribution facilities lend themselves to robotization, particularly in "picking" goods for dispatch.

The other cluster of robotics companies in the United States is Silicon Valley on the west coast. As the world's technology centre, robotics and automation is simply an application of technology. Additionally, Silicon Valley and the Bay area is where many technology investors and venture capital firms are based, providing vital funds that allow business plans to become operating companies.

That brings us back to Google, which is headquartered in Mountain View, Silicon Valley. At the time of writing, the company had purchased nine robotics companies. To absorb and coordinate the activities of these companies within its huge organisation, Google has set up a dedicated robotics division. We wonder whether the management at Google recognised the symbolism when in December 2013, it appointed the former head of its *Android* division, Andy Rubin to run this new robotics group.

That said, two key people be**hind** *Google Brain*, the artificial intelligence and machine learning project at Google, have left to start a new company called **Scaled Inference.** Google Brain is used to power services such as Android's speech recognition system and photo searches. The new company wants to build an AI technology that could be used by anyone to build machine learning, artificial intelligence technology similar to what is used internally by companies such as Google, making it available to anyone as a cloud service.

Privately-held British AI company, **DeepMind Technologies** was Google's ninth robotics company purchase for $400 million. DeepMind specialises in machine learning and systems neuroscience, so it looks like it will give its robotics division an AI slant, and no doubt the technology will also be used to further enhance its famed, hegemonic and cash-generating search engine.

Will Robots Threaten Our Jobs?

In early 2014, Andrew McAfee and Erik Brynjolfsson, both at MIT's Sloan School of Management, published a book called *The Second Machine Age*[2] in which they refer to a second industrial revolution. This second revolution will be a digital one that will

Company Spotlight: Google Inc. (NASDAQ: GOOG)

Company website: http://www.google.com

Founded in 1998 by the now iconic former Stanford University students, Larry Page and Sergey Brin, Google listed on NASDAQ in 2004.

Although Google started off as a search engine company, it has become so much more. Google has invested a great deal of time and vast capital into robotics and automation, that it has in effect become the global leader in this field. Google has such deep pockets, that it can just keep buying any new breakthrough technologies that its management believes would complement its existing portfolio, while at the same time allowing the existing robotics companies under the Google group to pursue their passions with access to the smartest minds and virtually unlimited funds.

Then of course there is Google's autonomous vehicle (driverless cars) programme; these cars have already clocked up millions of accident-free hours during testing on roads in California alongside traditional, human-driven cars. We are likely to see these autonomous cars on sale in just a few years.

Google is one of the most highly valued companies in the world (around $400 billion at the time of writing this book). The company will likely be successful with its autonomous vehicle technology, as well as with its robotics division. Even though it is hard to imagine more upside from a company with already such a high market capitalisation, it would be unwise to exclude Google given its extensive research and development efforts in robotics and automation. It may even end up spinning off some of its more successful new technologies into separate companies if the company starts to look like an unmanageable behemoth.

augment our minds in the same way that the first industrial revolution was a mechanical one that augmented our muscles. Messrs McAfee and Brynjolfsson are optimistic about robots joining the work force, and they believe that massive productivity gains will eventually materialise, even if so far they have not been keeping up with the rate of technological **innovations.**

The authors explain this by pointing out that it took 30 years from the start of the industrial revolution before a surge in productivity was observed, and they believe it will be the same this time around with the digital revolution. Why? The reason they give is that big steps in productivity gains can only happen after the current generation of managers retire or are replaced. These old guard managers typically adopt new technologies to support their current way of doing things, hence we only see incremental increases in productivity. It is only when the new generation of workers reach management level that they will be able to build and redesign factories, service offerings and processes in the full context of the modern digital world without the drag of the legacy systems. A plausible argument, but we will have to wait another decade or so to see if it proves to be the case. Until then, there is definite evidence in manufacturing across the world that the robots are starting to replace human jobs. Let's use a really big example:

Hon Hai Precision Industry Company Ltd, better known by its trading name **Foxconn,** manufactures well-known electronics products such as Apple's *iPad,* Amazon's *Kindle,* Sony's *PlayStation 3,* and Nintendo's *Wii.*

Globally, Foxconn employs 1.2 million people, making it the world's third largest private employer after Walmart and McDonald's[3]. Most of Foxconn's employees are based in China, and in recent years Foxconn has been feeling the squeeze on its margins as its labour costs have soared alongside an appreciating Renminbi against the US dollar.

Consequently, Foxconn started introducing robots into its factories, and at the company's 2013 annual shareholders' meeting, its founder Terry Gou announced "We have over 1 million workers. In the future we will add 1 million robotic workers." Already, it is reported that Foxconn has over 20,000 robots in its facilities in China.

---

[2] *Andrew McAfee and Erik Brynjolfsson, (2014) The Second Machine Age: Work, Progress, and Prosperity in a Time of Brilliant Technologies, W. W. Norton & Company*

[3] *Source: http://www.bbc.co.uk/news/magazine-17429786*

More robots means labour costs have a smaller impact on the bottom line, so companies thinking about where to locate their new factories will be less concerned about having access to low-cost labour and more focused on where its customers are based. Proximity to customers means lower transportation costs, shorter lead times, no currency exchange exposure and no tariffs or quotas to worry about. The United States is the single largest consumer market in the world. China is the single largest manufacturing country in the world, having built its economy on exporting products made using cheap labour.

Now China's labour is not so cheap and robots are becoming more prevalent in factories, a manufacturer would rightly conclude that its new production facilities should be based in the United States. In fact, Foxconn is in talks with several states in America to do just that so that it can better service its best customer, Apple.

This should be viewed as a warning to China's export-based, low-cost manufacturing economic model as it is clearly no longer viable and so its economy must reinvent itself in the coming decade. A failure to do so would put China's domestic economy at serious risk of stagnating.

As fast-learning, affordable robots become more prevalent, factories using human workers will go out of business, in the same way most companies that didn't manufacture in China in the 1990s and 2000s either started to do so or went out of business. A facility equipped with the next generation of robot workers will be able to start production almost right away. The factory owner or manager need only source the raw materials and upload the production software to the robot workers. The days of recruiting, training, re-tooling and supervising workers in manufacturing are numbered. In the coming years, the profits and investment opportunities lie in the robot makers and the software developers.

To highlight the reality of the threat that robots pose to China's workforce, the International Federation of Robotics reported that in 2013 China was the world's biggest buyer of industrial robots, buying a total of 36,500, or 20 per cent of those bought globally. No doubt this trend will continue towards the end of the decade.

When considering which types of jobs could be assigned to robots as they continue to acquire more AI, the first two considerations would be performance and cost: could a robot do the job and if so, what would the payback period be? Already when it comes to jobs requiring high precision and long hours, robots have the upper hand, hence their extensive use in manufacturing.

But this robotization will not just threaten manufacturing jobs; given a long enough time horizon, all jobs could potentially be performed by robots. According to a study by Oxford University in 2013, 47 per cent of US jobs are at risk of being replaced by robots[4], and no doubt other industrialised nations will have a similar figure.

In order to keep humans employed and relevant for the years ahead, we need to develop the skills that we do better than robots, such as those that are more creative in nature. Jobs requiring creative thinking will be the last ones to be replaced by robots. Governments around the world need to act quickly and put more emphasis on computer science and robotics as part of the school curriculum from an early age. Subjects taught by rote learning should be kept to a minimum as we can never compete with robots on this front – and that goes for computer coding as well. There is a view that coding is an important thing to learn but in our view this too will be a roboticized task. Far more important will be the inculcation of creative and intuitive thinking and the recognition that robots will take over almost everything mechanizable in the decades ahead.

2014 has already become a milestone year in the world of AI: for the first time ever, a computer programme has passed the *Turing test.*

The concept of the test was first posited in a 1950 paper written by British mathematics genius, Alan Turing. Turing was famous for his instrumental role as a

[4] *Carl Benedikt Frey and Michael A. Osborne, The Future Of Employment: How Susceptible Are Jobs To Computerisation? (2013) Oxford University.*

code breaker at Bletchley Park during World War II. His eponymous test is an assessment of AI that renders it indistinguishable from communication with a human, in a verbal or written manner. To pass the test, at least 30 per cent of the judges must be fooled by a computer programme. In June 2014, 33 per cent of the panel of judges where fooled into thinking that a chatbot they were communicating with was a 13 year old boy from Odessa, Ukraine. We are still a few years away from a computer programme being able to fool all the judges over a telephone, but we should not underestimate the significance of this achievement.

Other Applications of Robotics

Earlier we qualified a robot as being defined as a machine that performs one or more mechanical tasks automatically. The software is the "brains" behind the robot, and this brainpower, or AI is limited by computer processing power; more processing power translates to greater AI. Computer processing power has been doubling every 18 to 24 months, the formula known as Moore's Law after Gordon Moore who first described this in a paper her wrote in 1965. It still holds true some 50 years later. To give some idea of how this exponential growth translates in microprocessors, in the year 2000, an **Intel** *Pentium* chip of the time contained around 40 million transistors. By 2014, the equivalent chip had around 4 billion transistors, a one hundred-fold increase.

Renowned futurist Ray Kurzweil and now Google's Director of Engineering calculates that by 2020, computer processing power will reach the level of a human brain[5] at some levels. Greater AI means that we'll be able to assign robots more sophisticated and useful tasks, such as understanding a question that is asked in natural speech and responding promptly in natural speech; or it may be a robot that performs high speed, high precision medical procedures.

The next generation of microprocessors are already in the pipeline, one of which is the *True North chip,* being developed by IBM in conjunction with the Pentagon. This chip contains 5.4 billion transistors as well as one million individually programmable "neurons" and 256 million individually programmable "synapses" – this is beginning to approximate the architecture of our own brains. Furthermore, the chip is the size of a postage stamp and consumes a mere 70 milliwatts of power. True North, along with Watson, has broken the so-called Neumann bottleneck between processor and memory, but unlike Watson the chip doesn't consume vast amounts of energy. Without a doubt, this will help the proliferation of super-intelligent robots. And for this reason, we are confident that there will be an untold number of robot applications in the not too distant future. We discuss some of these applications in the remainder of this chapter.

Food & Beverage

As the cost of more sophisticated robots falls, their deployment will increase. One such threatened sector is food and beverage.

Currently more of a gimmick, but serving as a glimpse of what's in store, bar tender robots are already in bars serving drinks to customers. One such robot, named Carl, works at Roberts Bar and Lounge in Ilmenau, Germany.

Another example in this sector is Applebee's, the American-based restaurant chain with

Figure 4: Figure 4: Robot "Carl" serving drinks to customers at Roberts Bar and Lounge in Ilmenau, Germany. **Source:** Reuters

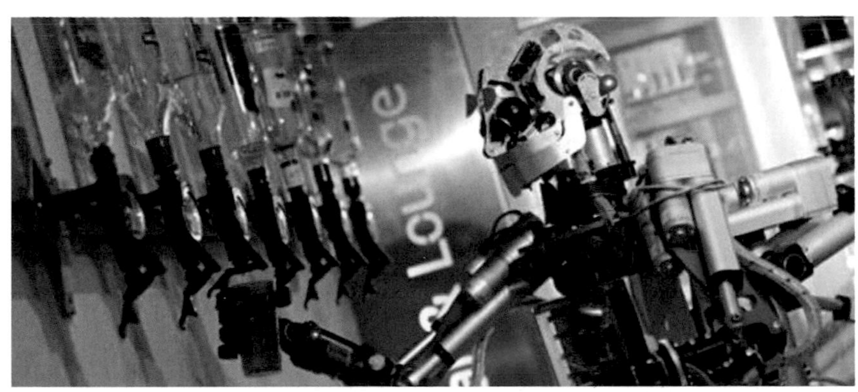

[5] *Kurzweil, Ray (2006) The Singularity is Near, Penguin Books*

over 2,000 outlets worldwide. In December 2013, the company announced that it will have tablets installed at every table by the end of 2014, allowing customers to order from the touchscreen, as well as pay the bill when they are ready to go by swiping their credit card. It is then only a matter of time before robots are implemented to deliver the orders to the tables and clear up between customers. Other chains will certainly follow suit. Why for instance would McDonald's, famed for its automation, employ ANY people in its stores by 2025?

Medicine

Clearly some of the most valuable applications of robotics are the ones that improve the health and longevity of human life. It is estimated that there are 7,000 diseases that affect humans, yet currently only about 500 of them have a medicine. That leaves 6,500 diseases without a treatment, so clearly there is a lot of work to be done, for one robot in particular.

In 2008, the National Institute of Health (NIH) Chemical Genomics Centre in Maryland installed a robot arm, similar to those used in the auto industry, in one of its laboratories. This robot arm works ceaselessly 24 hours a day testing drug compounds against samples of known diseases. It can accomplish in one week what a human would take 12 years to do manually, according to Dr Chris Austin of the Chemical Genomics Centre. The robot tests some 450,000 FDA-approved compounds against various diseased cells or proteins at seven dosage levels.

However, a more intelligent robot would be one that is more intuitive in identifying drug candidates. Some of our readers may remember IBM's *Watson* from our last book, the supercomputer that gained fame in 2011 when it won at the game show

Jeopardy against two if its all-time champions. Three years after its victory, Watson has become even smarter and faster, gaining a 240 per cent improvement in system performance, and it can now operate from a single Linux-based cloud server.

By moving Watson to the cloud, IBM believes it will attract developers to write apps for it. Some of the first customers to sign up to developing apps include **Welltok** (a personal wellness service provider, URL: http://www.welltok.com/), **Fluid** (a digital commerce consultancy, URL: http://www.fluid.com/) and **MD Buyline** (a medical equipment advisory company, URL: http://www.mdbuyline.com/). All of these companies were privately held at the time of writing, but it is worth checking up on them once in a while to see if they have gone public and, more importantly, whether they have made any breakthroughs with Watson's algorithms.

Another area of medicine that is making great progress with robotics is surgery. Robotic surgeons have been around since the 1990s, albeit it in a more basic form.

The *da Vinci Surgical System* by **Intuitive Surgical (NASDAQ:ISRG)** has all the makings of a robotic surgeon, but for the time being the mechanical probes are still controlled manually by a

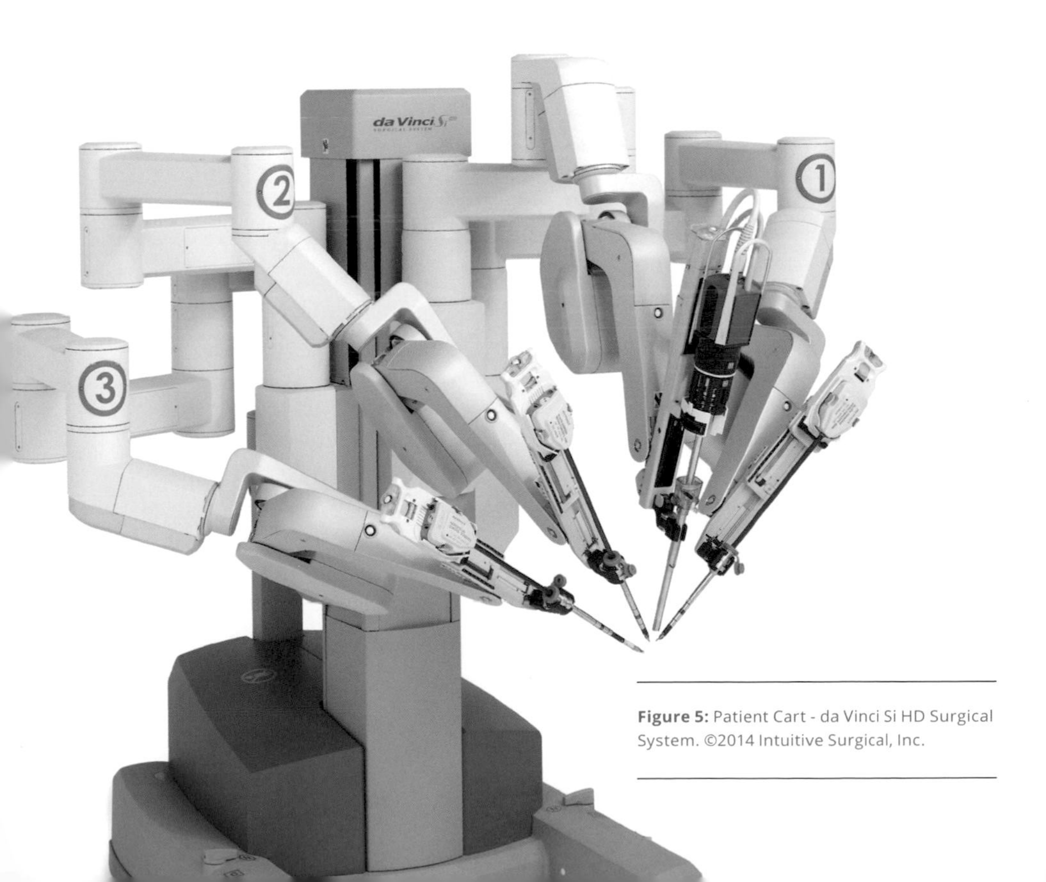

Figure 5: Patient Cart - da Vinci Si HD Surgical System. ©2014 Intuitive Surgical, Inc.

human surgeon at a console looking at a high resolution screen. The logical next evolutionary step for this company is to install AI into its hardware, paving the way for fully automated surgical procedures.

Already Intuitive Surgical has some basic automated features and the company probably has versions with greater automation in the pipeline. The company is the world's leading supplier of robotic-assisted surgical systems; in 2013 there were 523,000 surgeries performed using the da Vinci Surgical System and that number is growing as more hospitals purchase them for their operating theatres.

In the coming decade, it is likely that Intuitive Surgical will develop software to complement the hardware for various surgical procedures, establishing itself as a leader in minimally invasive automated surgery.

Also specialising in robotic surgery is Mountain View, California-based **Hansen Medical (NASDAQ:HNSN).** Hansen is a pioneer in intravascular robotics, allowing surgeons to place mapping catheters in hard-to-reach anatomical locations, such as the heart. Its share price is down over 95 per cent from its 2007 highs due to weak earnings, but its technology is sound and it could be a takeover target for Intuitive Surgical or another company in this space looking to gain market share in robotic surgery.

A company called **Xenex** launched the first version of its cleaning robot in 2010, designed to sanitise all areas of a hospital. The robots have been so effective that they are now used in 250 hospitals across the US. One major hospital reported a halving of C. difficile cases directly as a result of the Xenex robot. The robots clean by using a patented pulse xenon UV disinfection system that is 25,000 times more powerful than sunlight. Xenex is based in San Antonio, Texas and is currently privately held, but we expect it to list on NASDAQ in due course.

Another medical application of robots is the use of nanobots, a topic that gets a lot of people excited. The word nano stems from the System of Units (SI) for one billionth, so nanobots would be small enough to inject into our bloodstream using a needle and syringe. To give an idea of just how small they need to be, a red blood cell is about 7,000 nanometres.

The theory behind nanobots is to have billions of them in our bodies programmed to protect our health by say, destroying viruses, bacteria and cancer cells. They would effectively be a man-made type of white blood cell.

Nanobots could also be designed to repair damaged human cells, keeping us in optimal health. Not only would this mark the end of some human diseases, it would also render at least part of the existing drug-based pharmaceutical industry obsolete – that would be a disruptive technology indeed!

Having said that, we are not convinced that nanobots with this sort of capability will be around by 2020, our time horizon for this book – it will probably take another decade, possibly two. What is likely by 2020 are less sophisticated, first generation nanobots that can be injected into our bloodstream with a specific mission, such as dissolving clots in our bloodstream before they pose a serious threat, and identifying and "scrubbing" plaque from our arteries, restoring them to a healthy state that is clear from any build-up in the arterial walls, or even mopping up LDLs (the so-called "bad cholesterol") from our bloodstream before it can become plaque.

No doubt this will become a reality one day, but it is too early at this stage to identify any serious contenders. In the more immediate future, we will have remote monitoring of patients with serious conditions.

Remote Monitoring Devices

The remote monitoring of patients who are fitted with a medical device is likely to become a big business in future years. For instance, patients with chronic conditions such as heart disease and diabetes can now be monitored by their medical carers remotely, for instance pacemakers or insulin pumps that transmit real-time patient data to a centralised monitoring system. At the end of 2013, about three million such devices were in use worldwide, and a Swedish consulting firm, Berg Insight

Figure 6: The FDA-approved and DARPA-funded DEKA Arm System. **Image Source:** DARPA

estimates that this figure will rise to over 19 million by 2018, although we believe this forecast is too conservative. Patients with sleep disorders, blood coagulation problems, and wearers of diabetic boots (we write more about treating diabetic foot ulcers in Chapter 2) will be remotely monitored to ensure compliance and will flag alerts should any problems arise. Those who adhere to medical instructions and use pacemakers have been found to have half the mortality rates of those who do not.

Prosthesis

Prosthetic limbs are a fast emerging field in medical robotics. Although they have been around for thousands of years in one form or another, prosthetics of today are far more sophisticated.

One such example is the **DEKA Arm System.** In May 2014, the FDA approved the first ever pros-

[6] *DARPA stands for the Defence Advanced Research Projects Agency, an agency of the United States Department of Defence responsible for the development of new technologies for use by the military.*

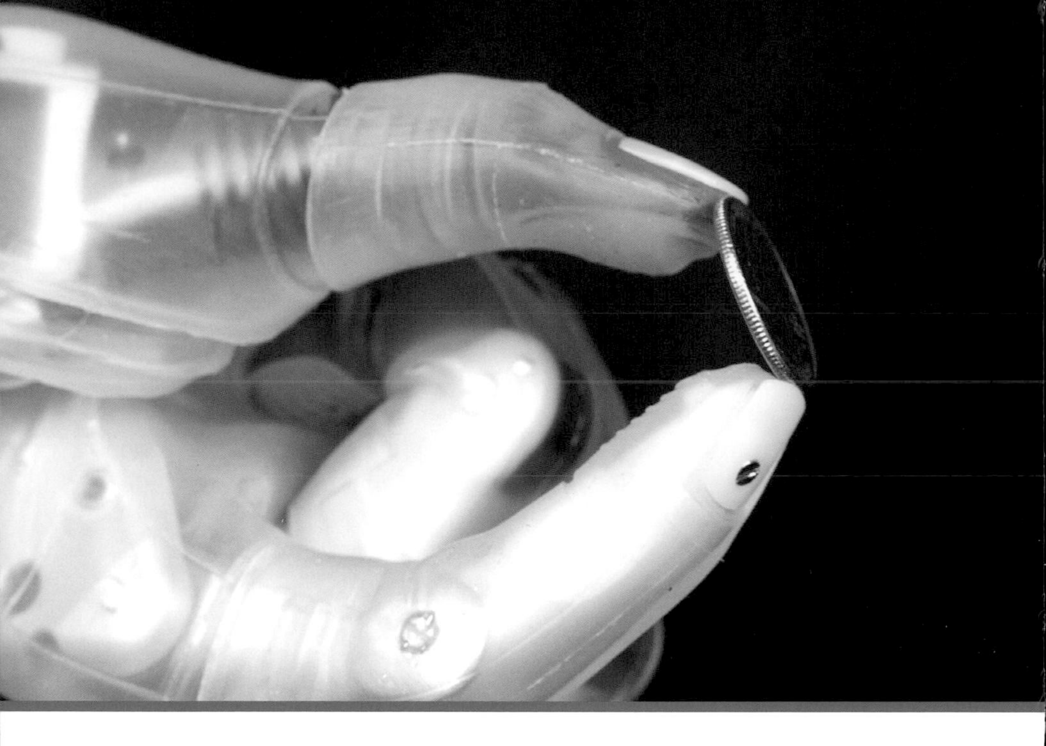

thetic arm that is able to translate the body's own electrical signals to control the prosthesis and perform complex tasks. In 2006, DARPA[6] launched the "Revolutionizing Prosthetics" programme to provide better quality prosthetics for amputees in the military, particularly those injured in the line of duty in Iraq and Afghanistan.

The DEKA system allows amputees to simultaneously control multiple joints using a variety of input devices. Having a similar size to a natural arm as well as a similar weight, it has six user-selectable grips.

The DEKA system establishes the foundation of the technology from which more advanced versions will be developed in the years to come, and it is likely that this technology will eventually merge with regenerative medicine allowing new muscles and nerves to be grown in place of injured or damaged ones.

Another company specialising in prosthetic hands is **Touch Bionics,** founded in 2003 and headquartered near Edinburgh in Scotland. Its *i-Limb* motorised hand has already been fitted to thousands of patients, mostly in the US and the UK. Company sales in 2013 were £20 million (around $33 million) and Touch Bionics is preparing for a stock market listing in the second half of 2014 at a valuation of around £50 million[7], so readers should follow this company's developments through its website (http://www.touchbionics.com).

Also in this space is a relatively new and small company called **Rex Bionics.** Already listed on London's AIM Exchange, Rex specialises in robotic exoskeletons. These are designed to enable wheelchair-bound individuals to stand and walk autonomously without the aid of crutches or a walking frame. Although Rex's walking systems are still very bulky, they do work and these early models will in time get smaller and cheaper.

[7] *Sunday Times, Bionic Boost – Robotics Pioneer to go Public, John Collingridge and Matthew Goodman, 3 August 2014.*

Farm-bots (Agribotics)

Picking fruit and vegetables is a labour-intensive and demanding job. The pickers often work for low wages, and in the US, almost three-quarters of hired farm workers are immigrants. But farming is an industry that is increasingly difficult for farmers to earn a decent living from. Only 200 years ago, 90 per cent of America's workforce was in farming; today it is only 2 per cent. This is the direct result of automation; now that automation is about to be taken to a whole different level.

With each passing season, farmers in developed nations are finding it increasingly difficult to attract pickers. In addition, they are under increasing pressure to cut costs to remain competitive, and so some farmers have started to employ robots to help with the planting and picking process.

In California, there is a robot nicknamed *Cesar,* a so-called *LettuceBot,* which can thin a field of lettuce in the same time it takes 20 human workers to do it by hand.

In Japan a strawberry picking robot has been developed, which is fitted with a 3D camera so that it can analyse the berries and determine which ones are ripe for picking. Currently, it can pick a strawberry every eight seconds, but unlike humans, it can pick strawberries around the clock. No doubt every subsequent generation of robotic pickers will get faster and cheaper.

For farming livestock, there is a robot known as *Rover,* which can herd cows from the field to the dairy for milking, currently being tested at Sydney University. And once Rover has done its job, it can hand it over to **Lely's** *Astronaut A4*, an entirely automated milking robot. The A4 *milkbot* **is** able to scan each cow's collar, which allows it to retrieve the cow's full history of feeding habits and milk production – even the pulsation rate of milking for each cow is remembered to produce the most milk. Each milkbot can milk around 60 cows per day, three times a day. This is a seriously "smart" robot but it comes at a price – around $200,000. But it needs no holidays, or breaks and won't quit to find another job.

These are just a few examples of farm-bots that are replacing human labour; no doubt many more types will be deployed in farms across the world in the coming years.

In Harm's Way

Unlike humans, robots don't need to breathe; they can withstand much higher and lower temperatures than their organic creators; and they can tolerate higher levels of radiation without coming to any harm. Needless to say, they are also more dispensable than humans. For **these reasons and others relat**ing to health and safety, robots are being put in harm's way to do work that is too dangerous for humans. Such applications are numerous, and we name some of them to give you an idea of the many ways in which robots are and will be deployed.

Military Robots

Soldier robots could be sent into battle to fight instead of humans. There has been much controversy over the use of aerial drones by the US military in re-

cent years, but the nature of warfare is evolving and aerial drones only represent a taste of what is to come. Military personnel will increasingly be assigned roles that do not involve them being in harm's way. Ground robots will be deployed in war zones as standard procedure, although these may need a large degree of human input and supervision in the early days. But with each subsequent upgrade, military robots will become smarter, more autonomous, and better networked, requiring human input only when unusual situations arise.

Today, DARPA is working with Boston Dynamics (now owned by Google) to beef up its *BigDog* four-legged robot that can follow troops around in any terrain, carrying 200 kg of payload. The military is often the source of great technological innovations and DARPA has been driving the industry in this regard.

One such initiative to promote innovation in robotics is DARPA's annual Robotics Challenge Trials, where teams from around the world come together to compete. The top eight teams each receive up to one million dollars in DARPA funding to improve the robot for the following year and the ultimate winner receives a two million dollar prize. The winner of the latest challenge at the time of writing was robot by a Tokyo-based company called **Schaft Inc.,** and no prizes for guessing who bought this company in December 2013 (that's right, Google).

Reconnaissance and spying is another area that is ideal for robots – it need no longer be a

high risk, life-on-the-line type assignment for government agents and the military. Robots could be purpose built for their task, so for example a listening and video device could be designed to look like a house fly or another small, discreet insect; it could fly to its target and start transmitting video and audio signals back to base.

Reconnaissance robots are already on the market today, albeit in a more basic form. *Recon Scout* is a robot made by an American, privately-held company called **ReconRobotics.** They are known as tactical micro robots and are in use by the military, which uses them to assess the threat inside a building or unsecured area before attempting to go in without knowing the situation. They are remote controlled and can be thrown into an opening of a building, onto a roof top, or even around corners where trouble may be lurking. The Recon scout then beams back real-time video to someone sitting well out of harm's way to review the situation before deciding on the best course of action.

Disaster Zones

Shortly after the Fukushima Daiichi nuclear disaster in 2011, the Japanese realised that a robot would have made a huge difference in the ability of Tokyo Electric Power Company (TEPCO) to contain the radiation spill, which even to this day continues to leak unknown quantities of radiation. DARPA and robotics companies from around the world are redoubling their efforts to create a robot that could be deployed in both natural and man-made disasters, from typhoon struck areas to coal mines where explosions are not uncommon and result in miners being trapped deep underground.

Robot Asimo by Honda and robot *Atlas* by Boston Dynamics (owned by Google and maker of the BigDog robot) are probably the two most advanced robots around today, but Atlas is bigger, stronger and more rugged than the child-size Asimo. In the coming years, we will probably end up seeing Asimo in the home and Atlas out in the field, performing more dangerous and physically demanding tasks. Such tasks would include rescuing civilians trapped inside collapsed or burning buildings. Being designed to be virtually impermeable to heat, cold, radiation and toxic gases, robots like Atlas will become invaluable in disaster recovery and in search and rescue.

In a Home Near You

In our book *Cracking the Code,* we introduced a cute, affordable 58 centimetre humanoid robot called *Nao,* made by a French company, **Aldebaran.** In 2012, Aldebaran was acquired by Japanese telco giant **SoftBank Corporation** (TYO:9984) for $100 million. Incidentally, SoftBank also owns 80 per cent of US telco **Sprint Nextel Corporation.**

SoftBank's founder and CEO, Masayoshi Son, bought Aldebaran no doubt because he realised that his firm had to catch up in the increasingly important robotics sector. Building on

Figure 7: Honda's Asimo (left) versus Boston Dynamics' Atlas – who is the most advanced robot of them all? **Asimo image source:** Vanillase for Wikimedia Commons. Atlas image source: DARPA for Wikimedia Commons

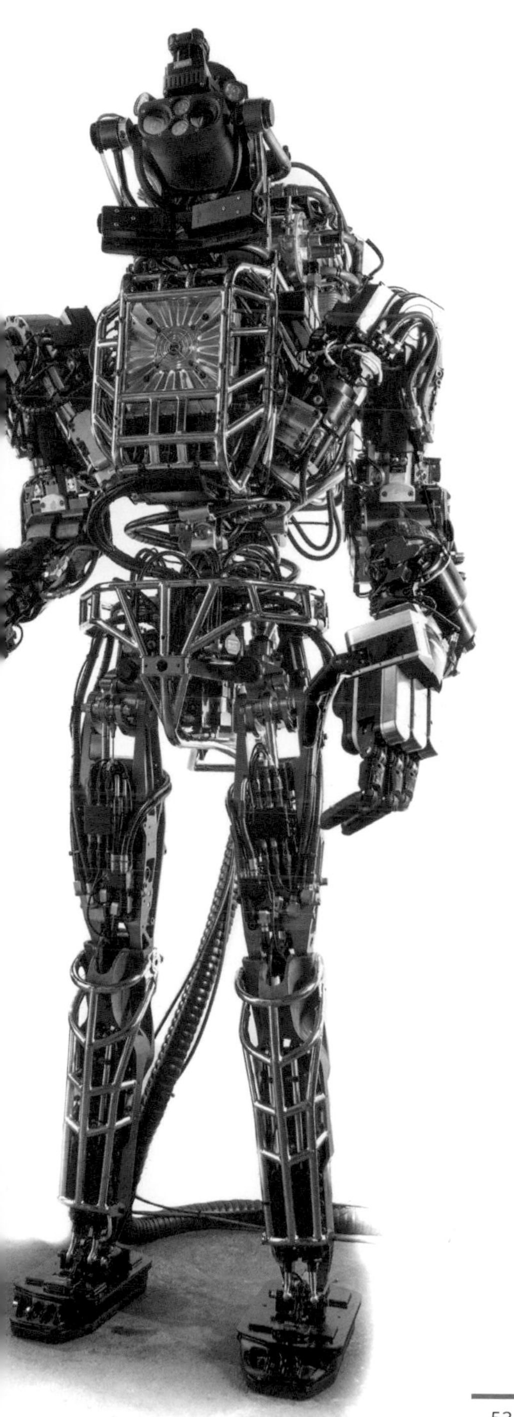

Aldebaran's technology know-how from Nao, SoftBank announced in June 2014 that it had developed a human-like robot named *Pepper* **that it was introducing into its retail outlets in Japan.** Standing at 120 centimetres, Pepper is a little taller than Nao, and it uses wheels instead of legs which significantly reduces its power consumption and allows it to go for 12 hours between charges, instead of 30 minutes for a legged equivalent.

Pepper has been designed to read facial expressions and understand human emotions, and can express emotions using body language, gestures and voice. It is also programmed to learn and adapt to its environment.

Rolling out Pepper across SoftBank's retail stores is just the start of its longer term plans to have the friendly robot become part of the family. Once people get used to seeing Pepper in the shops, they are more likely to consider one for the home, and Mr Son would like to see Pepper adopted by as many families as possible around the world who would use Pepper to undertake some domestic duties, such as baby sitting.

SoftBank plans to sell Pepper from 2015 for around $2,000, which is a fraction of the price of a robot like Asimo.

Cloud Robotics

Although cloud robotics is a relatively new field within robotics, it will no doubt become increasingly important as robots become more sophisticated. It is believed that the term was coined in 2010 by a research scientist at Google.

The concept behind cloud robotics is very straight-forward: think of what you can do with your personal computer or tablet - they can be employed to

Figure 8: Left: "Pepper," the robot with feelings. Right: "Nao," its predecessor. Both robots by Aldebaran, now part of SoftBank. **Image Source:** Aldebaran

perform a multitude of tasks and access a virtually unlimited range of information. Obviously this information doesn't usually reside on the device itself but is retrieved from the internet. It would be too expensive and bulky to attempt to build a device that had all of the internet's information stored locally. The same goes for building personal robots – to reduce cost, weight and size, in the future engineers will design robots which access the cloud for information as they need it, rather than having the robots pre-installed with information, which also becomes outdated over time. The microprocessors and the batteries are the big ticket items in personal robots, so minimising the usage of these will reduce their cost and thereby make robots more affordable for the home, accelerating adoption rates. Once critical mass in the personal robot market is reached, the size of the entire industry will explode, and that in turn, will further spur innovation and the development of related products and services. It was the same story with the personal computer, the mobile phone and the tablet.

Robot Operating System (ROS)

To accelerate the progress and advances in robotics, a *Robot Operating System (ROS)* **was set** up in 2007 by a number of organisations, one of its founders being Stanford University, and has been under constant development since. ROS is a flexible, open source framework for writing robot software. Writing robot software is challenging enough, so the ROS ecosystem comprises a collection of tools, libraries, and conventions that aim to simplify the task.

This creates a consistent and collaborative platform for programmers to tap into the combined expertise of individuals, laboratories and institutions from around the world.

In addition to ROS, there are a number of other open source projects, such as **OpenCV, MoveIt and Gazebo.** ROS currently integrates seamlessly with all of them, positioning ROS to be the industry standard for robot software development. Whilst not yet a household name, like Android and Linux, ROS will likely be one by the end of the decade.

Helping the Elderly

The world's human population is getting older, which shouldn't come as a surprise to our readers, given that we have mentioned it in all of our previous books. The developed countries account for the bulk of the growth in the elderly around the world.

By 2020 there will be 116 million more people over the age of 65 in the world than there were in 2010 – that means on average, there are almost 32,000 people in the world turning 65 every day!

One of the consequences of an ageing population is a shrinking working age population. In China, this has already started to happen: according to the National Bureau of Statistics of China, the country's working age population fell by 2.44 million in 2013, following a 3.45 million contraction in 2012. Accentuated by the one child policy, this trend is set to continue, with a further decline of 30 million working age people between 2015 and 2025, according to the United Nations.

If robots are going to be stealing many jobs in the coming years, in some ways it is a good thing that many countries will have a shrinking working age population. This will not be the case for pro-immigration countries such as the United Kingdom and the United States, as a steady flow of young migrants regularly tops up the workforce. This is unfortunately not the case for Japan.

Discounting city states such as Monaco, Japan is the world's "oldest" country in the sense that over 65s make up a higher percentage of its population than any other country; the figure currently stands at 25 per cent, and is projected to increase to 33 per cent by 2035. In 1950, only 5 per cent of Japan's population was over 65. Needless to say, Japan has a falling population; in 2013 it stood at 126.4 million, a decrease of 244,000 from the 2012 figure. By around 2045, Japan's population is expected to drop to 100 million. It is not easy to grow an economy with a shrinking work force and a growing number of retirees, most of whom depend on the state to support and to care for them in old age.

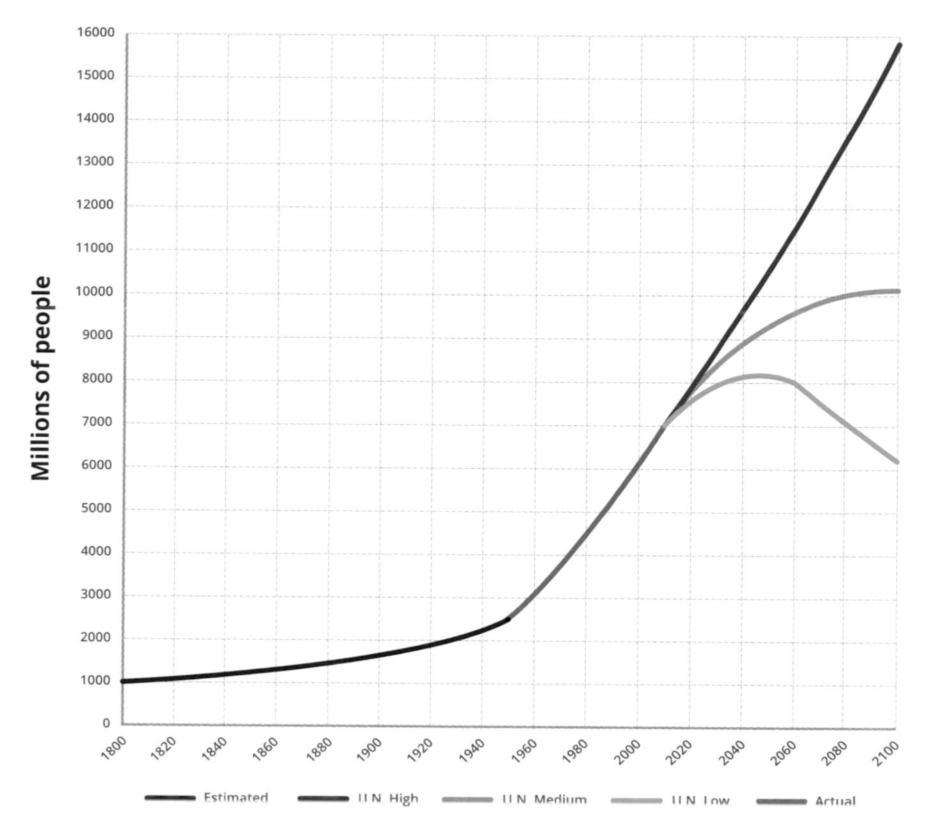

Figure 9: United Nations' projections global human population growth to the end of the twenty-first century. **Source:** United Nations

Japan has been aware of its rapidly ageing population problem for many years – tracking births and deaths is a relatively easy thing to do. So why then has Japan not taken any steps to alleviate this very foreseeable situation, especially when the country's birth rate stands at around 1.4 births per woman, well short of the 2.1 figure necessary to maintain a constant population? It is a natural phenomenon for nations to experience a fall in the birth rate as they become more prosperous, but why is Japan's birth rate much lower than the other developed countries of the world?

The answer lies in the country's strict immigration policy and xenophobic tendencies, which has meant that there has been no influx of migrants to offset its low birth rate. Clearly it is too late to make any difference even if Japan were to open its borders to young foreigners tomorrow.

Luckily for Japan, it has a highly advanced robotics industry and it is hoped that the next generation of robots will come into service in the home and at work to make up for the lack of working age people. Earlier we discussed some of the robot candidates that may help Japan overcome its demographic challenges, the likes of Pepper, Asimo and Twendy-One, and there will also be more sophisticated industrial robots in manufacturing and assembly lines. Such robots, if successful, would also be a huge export business for Japan, but it is too early in the game to tell whether Japan will be able to stay ahead of the key players in the US and Europe.

Nursing & Domestic Helper Robots

Anyone who has visited a nursing home will know that it can be a very challenging working environment for the staff. The work can be physically and mentally demanding, yet staff salaries are among the lowest of any industry. Consequently, staff turnover is high.

By our estimates, nursing and domestic helper robots will be in use by 2020, most likely in Japan first. The main advantage of having a robot that can look after an elderly person in need of care is that it can be done at home. People prefer to stay in their own homes, and the only reason most people move (or are moved) to a nursing home is if they live alone and their mobility becomes limited or if their mental faculties start to fail. If robots can help address these shortcomings, there would be less of a reason to move the elderly into a nursing home, save for exceptional cases. This would take some of the pressure off nursing homes, which would otherwise become increasingly congested as the population ages further.

As a compliment to robot nurses, Honda also makes what it refers to as "walk assist, mobility devices." Still in trials, this is an exoskeleton that attaches to the legs and supports the bodyweight of the wearer. It offers some independent mobility to people who would normally feel too frail to walk around. After all, staying active and getting regular fresh air and sunlight is good for the health.

Therapeutic & Pet Robots

We wrote about therapeutic and pet robots in our last book so we'll mention them only briefly here. They may sound like a gimmick but a pilot study on elderly patients, especially those suffering from dementia was recently published by the *Journal of Gerontological Nursing* and concluded that such robots had *"a positive, clinically meaningful influence on quality of life, increased levels of pleasure and also reduced displays of anxiety."*[8]

Paro is the name of the leading therapeutic robot. It takes the form of a cute harp seal pup and is equipped with sensors that detect and respond to light, touch, sound and pressure. Paro was designed by Japan's National Institute of Advanced Industrial Science and Technology, also referred to as AIST.

As therapeutic robots become smarter, they will be assigned to patients on a full-time basis as nurses and carers, but for the time being they serve to calm and comfort.

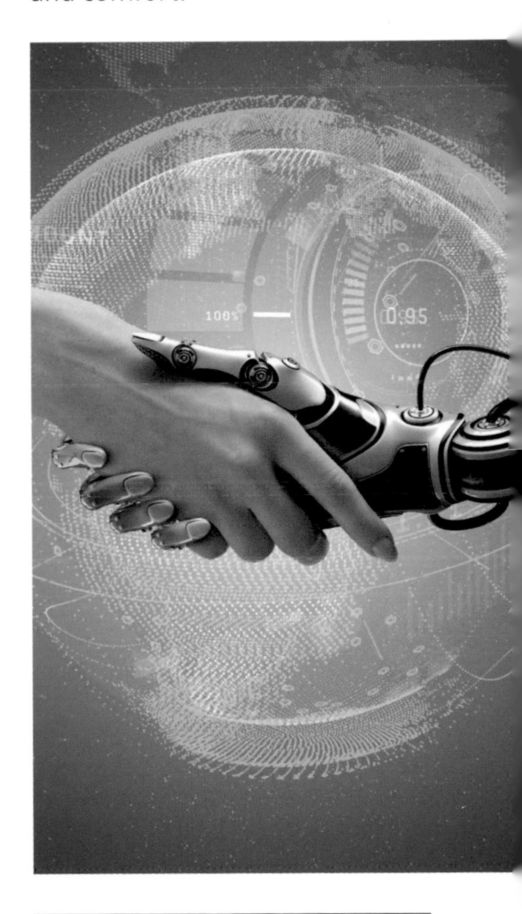

[8] *Journal of Gerontological Nursing, May 2013 - Volume 39 · Issue 5: 46-53*

Swarm Robotics

Inspired by insects, fish and birds in nature, scientists have been working on ways to utilise swarming behaviour in the application of robotics. So-called swarmbots are typically small and simple robots, cooperating and interacting in large numbers to achieve a common goal. The goal is usually a task or problem that is beyond the capability of any individual swarmbot. Swarming behaviour is achieved by using algorithms and the swarm may number just a few or as many as one thousand, which is the number of swarmbots researchers at Harvard University have been able to control[9]. Swarming is of practical interest because its approach is robust and exhibits many levels of redundancy (if one swarmbot is damaged, another one can easily step in and replace it).

The concept of man-made swarms is not new and was the subject of bestselling author Michael Crichton in his 2002 book called *Prey*, but once again it is thanks to faster computer processing power that we are now seeing significant progress in swarmbot development. There are many potential applications of swarmbots, some of which we can expect to see in just a few years, others may take another decade to perfect. Such applications may include clean-up operations of oil and toxic spills, search and rescue after a natural disaster or a collapsed building, as well as a number of military uses, such as sabotage and espionage. There is also the potential of designing nano-swarmbots to perform tasks invisible to the human eye, for example to identify and destroy a specific strain of virus, or to remove pollutants from the air. We can also expect to see swarmbots that will be able to self-assemble or be used to assemble specific objects or structures.

Investing in Robotics

We have discussed many aspects of robotics and some of the leading players in the sector. It is still early days to identify the clear winners and the best investment approach as always is to build a basket of companies to diversify the risk. One approach to do this is through an ETF.

In November 2013, a company called ROBO-STOX, based in Dallas, Texas launched a Global Robotics and Automation Index ETF on NASDAQ, making it the first ETF dedicated to this sector. No doubt others will appear in due course. The ETF trades under the ticker ROBO and at the time of writing, the fund size was around $100 million.

There is an annual management fee of 0.95 per cent and no other fees that we could find in the prospectus.

The fund comprised investments in some 80 companies; amongst its top holdings were **Kuka, Krones, HIWIN, Fanuc, Intuitive Surgical** and **iRobot,** most of which we have covered in this chapter.

For a more complete and updated list of the ETF's holdings, readers should visit the company's website: http://www.robostoxetfs.com

[9] *http://news.harvard.edu/gazette/story/2014/08/the-1000-robot-swarm*

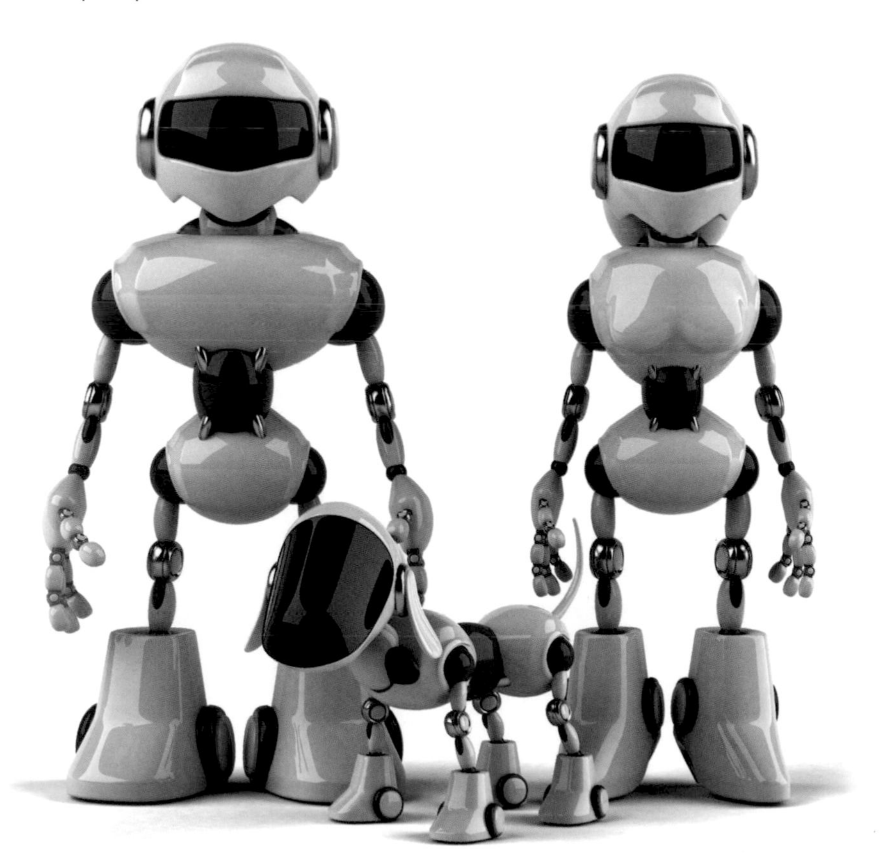

Life Extension
Enhancing Lives and Portfolios

In 2012 we published C*racking the Code*, a book that foretold an accelerated pace of medical technologies and predicted an unprecedented extension of average human lifespan. Although the book took a 10 to 20 year view, some amazing breakthroughs have already been made and some of the advances currently underway are revolutionary and life-changing. In this chapter we highlight some of the most important ones, as well as those where we see an opportunity for significant investment profits.

The goal of *"wellderly"* long life, one that we highlighted in the previous book, is well in sight. This contrasts with the commonly held and still current view that old age (previously defined as anything over 70), is a condition marked by illness and general decline. However, we are convinced that this *"illderly"* state could become a thing of the past for many older people in ten or so years.

This may seem to be a mighty mountain to climb, at least to those not versed in the discovery process that is underway in centres of medical excellence. Granted there remains no cure or effective treatment for diseases such as Alzheimer's or Parkinson's, but there is a significant body of research that suggests we are within ten years of effective therapies for some generally age-related degenerative conditions.

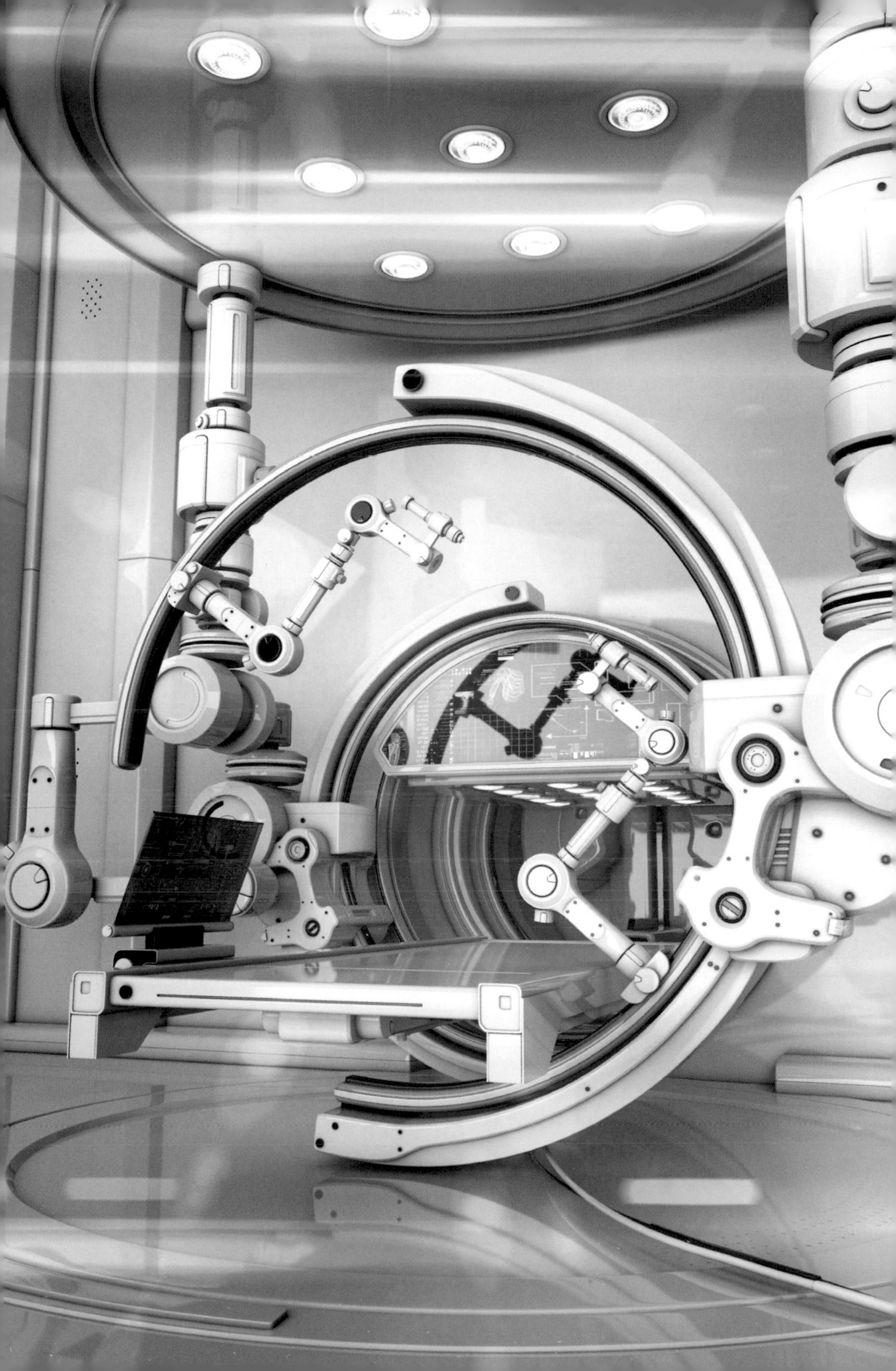

In addition, although cancer can and does strike at any age, it is a disease largely associated with ageing. In this chapter, we are going to explain some of the advances in cancer therapy that might make it possible to largely eradicate deaths from cancer within a relatively short period.

Life expectancy continues rise, but not yet at the pace we expect over the next decade or so. In the UK, for example, life expectancy at birth is 82.6 years for a girl and 78.7 for a boy, about six years longer for girls and eight years longer for boys since the 1980s. But we believe that life expectancy will dramatically increase from the current statistics – the goal of taking human life expectancy to over 120 as an *average* is within reach. It is certainly not fanciful to say that the first person to live over 150 is alive today. Turning 100 will become routine, and working till 80 or beyond will become the norm. This will be the result of incremental gains in fighting disease, improved lifestyle management, and innovative developments in medicine such as the use of stem cells to replace body parts, as well as genetic engineering and advances in neuroscience.

Of course there are already a lot more old people in the world as a whole. For example, in the UK in 1917, there were just 17 centenarians; today that number is estimated to be 13,000, with a further 500,000 people in their nineties. By 2060, there are expected to be at least 500,000 centenarians living in the UK alone – and most of them will have "outlived" disease and will simply die of frailty.

Living longer will further skew the fundamental shift in demographics that is underway almost everywhere in the world. It is a fact that most populations are ageing and that fertility rates are declining, in some countries dangerously so. Sooner rather than later this will lead to a "topping out" of world population numbers, probably at around 9 billion in the year 2050, and thereafter a gentle decline.

The universal norm will be for people to have fewer children as they realise just how long they themselves are going to live. This is the standard consequence of extended lifespans. People reproduce less for a variety of reasons, and not least because their progeny are likely to survive to old age. The profiles of most societies will be forever altered as a result.

The great worry that demographers have is that the preponderance of older people will lead to an unsupportable burden of care on those who are younger. This concern is founded on the notion that old people will be in a state of physical and mental decline that will require intensive or possibly, round-the-clock care. We are going to demonstrate that as a result of innovation, this is unfounded. Until the very last years of a person's life, it is likely that a healthy life will be the usual scenario for people aged between 75 and 110 years or so.

There is a reason why the healthcare sector stocks, in particular *biopharma*, have been best performers since we published *Cracking the Code*, and that is because these are arguably the most important industries in the world. They have the capacity to change the entire dynamic of human existence and indeed we believe that they are doing so.

Without ploughing too much over old ground, all of these advances – some as yet whimsical, admittedly – are founded on the two key achievements of recent times, one occurring approximately fifty years apart from the other. The first of course, was the unveiling of the structure of DNA, and the second was the sequencing of the human genome.

As we explained in *Cracking the Code*, these two milestones have provided us with the human body's blueprints, which when combined with the exponential growth of computer processing power, allows us to decipher the language of these blueprints.

At the end of this book we provide an appendix showing how the various portfolios we recommended to our readers in our last book have performed. The original tips have performed very well overall, but this is partly because the sector has been in a raging bull market and our readers got in early (we hope). These markets are highly volatile however, and indeed capricious.

Strong stomachs and staying power are needed to be successful. The trend towards larger companies swallowing smaller ones to gain access to new drug pipelines is only just beginning (the so far failed bid by **Pfizer** for **Astra Zeneca**) and this will tend to put a floor under stock prices in the sector.

This journey is only just beginning, and as we outline some of the developments that we have identified as being key to the biosciences sector in the next few years.

A Quick Recap

Before we discuss how we see things developing in the next ten or so years, let's first do a brief recap of the various industry accomplishments and developments since *Cracking the Code's* release.

Hepatitis C

There is now a cure for *Hepatitis C.* Admittedly it costs over $80,000 per patient to get the medicine but those who have the disease (and there are believed to be 350 million people worldwide with the condition) can now be entirely rid of it.

Stem Cells

Stem cells are ever closer to being used in therapeutic contexts. Both so-called induced *pluripotent stem cells* and *mesenchymal cells* are being actively researched in therapies for cardiovascular, spinal, organ regrowth and orthopaedic use. It will not be long before they are in widespread use. *Windpipes* have been grown and implanted using scaffolds seeded with *autologous* (from the patient's own body) stem cells. Heart attack victims are being treated in trials with stem cells to regrow functional heart tissue, and people with knee problems are being similarly treated.

Small Interfering RNA

SiRNA is ever closer to being useful in man, and our favourite companies pioneering this work, **Arrowhead Research** and **Alnylam**, have been using this technology in human trials with, so far, impressive results. *SiRNA* is just one example of where genes, or the proteins that they express, are being manipulated or engineered to change disease within the body. Other examples, which we will talk about in this chapter, include *zinc finger nucleases, CRISPRS, micro RNAs*, genetic selection prior to conception, and *antisense* technologies.

Obesity

So-called lifestyle diseases have become the largest cause of death in the world. Lifestyle diseases usually develop as a result of one or more of the following: being obese or sedentary, smoking, consuming excessive alcohol or taking drugs.

Obesity is now so prevalent that more people die from it than from starvation. In the developing world, such as Latin America and China, obesity-related diabetes (type II) is forecast to grow fivefold between now and 2030.

That said, three new drugs have been or are about to be approved by the FDA for obesity, and gastric band surgery has been refined and is being used extensively. Food manufacturers are being pressured to reduce sugar and sodium content. Even activity levels are actually increasing in the developed world. There is also more education and a better understanding of the dangers of obesity, all of which are contributing to a small, but distinct reduction in obesity levels in the key regions affected, namely Europe and the US. And since obesity is directly linked to other diseases, most notably diabetes, cardiovascular disease and chronic kidney disease, these, while at epidemic levels, should begin to abate, at least in the developed world.

Unfortunately, the reverse is true in the developing world, especially in Latin America and China. One quarter of Chinese are now overweight with 60 million obese. As a result, a health disaster is unfolding. Heart disease now accounts for one third of deaths in China and over 12 per cent of Chinese are diabetic, up from 1 per cent in 1984.

Cardiovascular Disease

Once the West's most lethal killer, the threat of cardiovascular disease is abating, as the use of statins, ace inhibitors, beta blockers and low-dose aspirin therapy has become ubiquitous.

Cancer

Aspirin's role as a wonder drug has been recently enhanced. In 2010, researchers published an observational study in *The Journal of Clinical Oncology* showing that women with breast cancer who took aspirin at least once a week were 50 per cent less likely to die of breast cancer. Further, it has been observed in long term studies that those who took aspirin for at least ten years halved their risk of pancreatic cancer. The anti-cancer protective effect of aspirin outweighs the risks; for every seventeen lives saved through the use of low-dose aspirin, two people died from a stroke or internal bleeding.

But perhaps the most impressive advance of the last few years, one which will revolutionise the treatment of cancer, is the emerging science of *immunotherapy,* which will, over the next ten years become the dominant factor in oncology.

Cancer is well and truly on the run for the first time, and while some cancers remain intractable with poor prognoses, this will not be the case for much longer.

Cancers such as lung, liver and pancreatic, which until now have been major and near-certain causes of death, are on the way to being defeated. In just a few years from now, people with these conditions will be treated with positive outcomes and will live much longer lives post-diagnosis. *Biomarkers* (aids in diagnosis) will more accurately describe the disease to doctors who will then be able to "personalise" treatment for patients. For instance, **Gensignia,** an Italian company likely to list shortly in London, has developed a test for non-small cell lung cancer that picks up the disease two years before other tests and allows for early and effective surgical intervention. For liver cancer for instance, researchers at UCL in London recently discovered a link between the use of ***chloroquine*** a malaria pill, and a substantial reduction in liver cancer disease.

Sadly, however, while death rates for most cancers have fallen in recent years, it has been four decades since any fall in mortality has been observed in patients with cancer of the pan-

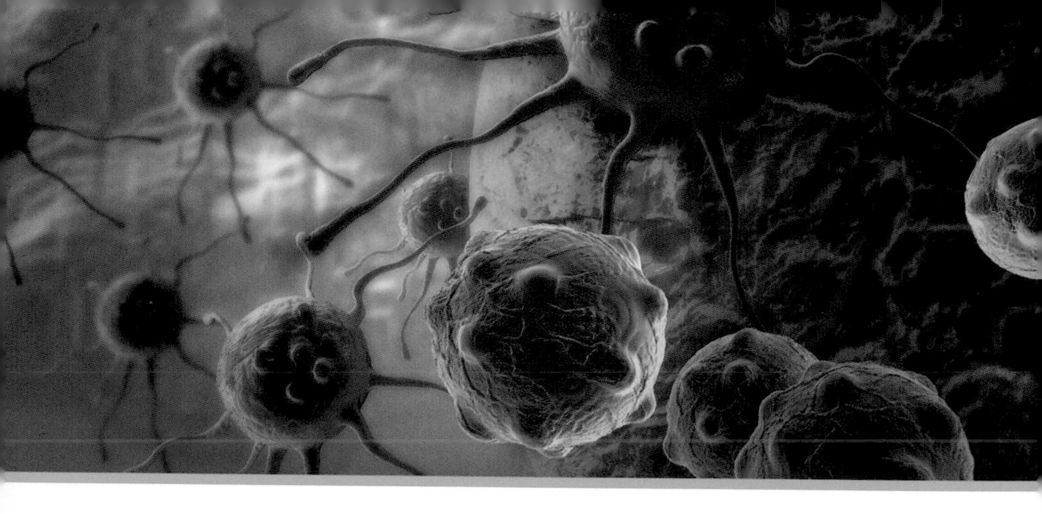

creas. Only about 6 per cent of these patients will survive for five years or more.

But new biomarkers (identifiers of disease), including one for *CA19-0*, as well as for three other blood markers which have not yet been disclosed, have been developed at **MD Anderson Cancer Centre** in Houston. This test has an overall 91 per cent accuracy, which means that this lethal disease could be detectable earlier, before metastasis occurs. As a result, surgery and new forms of treatment should have a better chance of succeeding. The main issue with cancer of the pancreas at the moment is that by the time it is detected, it is usually too advanced to treat effectively.

One of these new treatments for example, might come from **Merrimack Pharmaceuticals Inc.** This company has so far had disappointing results since listing in 2012. That could be about to change after announcing positive data from its Phase 3 trial of MM-398, a *nano-liposomal encapsulation of irinotecan* – for metastatic pancreatic cancer, with a 1.9 month improvement in overall survival. This doesn't sound like much, but it's the start of the long road towards a cure.

In addition, immunotherapy is being trialled in pancreatic cancer. **Newlink Genetics** is testing *Hyperacute Pancreas (algenpantucel-T)* in post-surgery pancreatic cancer patients. Hyperacute therapies consist of human cancer cell lines modified to express *alpha-gal*, which are designed to stimulate an immune response that can "teach" the body's own defences to attack tumour cells.

Immunotherapy, while exciting, is not the only game in town as far as cancer goes. In prostate cancer, **Medivation's** drug *Xtandi*, which we wrote about extensively in *Cracking the Code* is fast becoming the treatment of choice in so-called *castration-resistant prostatic cancer*, and is markedly improving survival chances for patients. Another drug, *Kryopolis*, is now an established medicine for *multiple myeloma*, and its creator **Onyx** has been bought out by **Amgen.**

Allied to all of these advances is the rapid development of personalised medicine, facilitated by the advent of cheap and accurate genomic or partial-genome sequencing. The latter is much more likely to be in widespread use, as whole genome sequencing still suffers from inaccuracies that make it suspect in a clinical setting.

However, in a matter of just a few years, almost every clinical setting in the developed world will employ some form of sequencing on a regular basis. This will enable not just the identification of the correct treatment options for the multifarious types of cancers that exist in man, but will also be used in the treatment of many other diseases as well as the identification of genetic disorders prior to conception.

Orphan Diseases

Orphan diseases, typically resulting from genetic mutations or defects, are one by one being addressed, partly by the use of accurate diagnosis using sequencing techniques. Modern sequencing machines are a bit like computers; ever smaller and more powerful, they are also tumbling in price; the thousand dollar genome is almost here. More importantly, the ability to "read" the information that is being sequenced is improving through the development of *bioinformatics.*

Big Trends Driving Industry

Underlying all these advances are three global industry trends, which we will call "medical bioscience."

1. Demographics and the ageing of the population;

2. The urgent need to address *intractable diseases*, particularly those associated with ageing; and

3. The rapid development of technologies resulting from the *Kurzweillian* notion of the convergence of computing power and scientific discovery.

Indeed, *synthetic life* is one step closer, with the creation of a form of yeast that has an artificial *chromosome* artificially made in a research lab. In addition, *microbes* with expanded genetic codes are being made in the **Scripps Institute** in California, comprising six letters instead of the normal four (A, T, C, G). The extra two letters have been incorporated into living *E. coli* bacteria.

These cells took them into their genome naturally, making matching pairs that face each other on either side of the DNA double helix – the first time this has ever been done. Ultimately, the idea is to build semi-synthetic cells that operate two separate genetic codes in parallel. The original genetic software would keep the cells alive, while a parallel synthetic or semi-synthetic genetic code would cause the cells to act as nano-factories, producing useful materials, for instance in making miniature versions of electrical components such as batteries or molecular level drugs.

There are amazing new drug delivery systems which, for the first time, allow doctors to deliver drugs directly and safely to exactly the desired area, for instance, to cancerous tumours. One particularly exciting discovery has been made by an 18-year old Polish researcher who has developed a way of using gold nano-particles embedded in nanotubes, used as stitches to deliver **doxyrubicin**, a chemotherapy drug to specific tumour sites post-operatively.

There is such a plethora of discovery underway that it would be impossible for us, or anyone else, to cover every angle. Suffice it to say that the cumulative effect of this mountain of innovation makes us absolutely confident in our main thesis: We are all going to live longer, healthier and better lives (as long as we don't mess it up with wars and conflict, that is!)

For the remainder of this chapter, we focus on the areas which are of greatest interest to us and the ones that we believe have the best investment opportunities. Let's start with the area where the greatest evident strides are being made, and that is in cancer.

Cancer

For most patients, although certainly not all, cancer is now a long term condition rather than an acute disease. People are living much longer in most developed nations after being diagnosed with cancer, according to official figures. In the UK, mortality from cancer has fallen by at least 10 per cent over the past ten years or so.

In 2014, almost 9 in 10 women diagnosed with breast cancer will live for at least five years after diagnosis, compared to about half in the early 1970s. Melanoma and bowel cancer rates are on a similar trajectory.

In the case of UK males, the "age-standardised mortality rate" for cancer fell by 11 per cent from 229 per 100,000 in the period 2001-03, to 204 in 2008-10. For women, the rate dropped from 160 to 149, i.e. by 7 per cent. The smaller improvement in the female population is partly due to fewer women giving up smoking than men. (The standardisation of mortality rates takes into account the fact that the population is ageing and that there will be an increase naturally in the number of cancers as a result.)

Until very recently, the standard of care for cancer patients has been described as "poison, burn or slash." This referred to the three main options of treating cancer: chemotherapy, radiotherapy, and surgery.

These three options have between them improved survival rates (defined as living five years beyond diagnosis) considerably. Today, out of all cancer patients, including those for whom survival rates are low, the survival rate is around 75 per cent.

No longer is cancer necessarily a sentence of death. Improvements in chemotherapies, the introduction of biologic drugs such as **Avastin** and **Herceptin,** better diagnosis and differentiations of cancers, as well as superior surgical techniques have improved the chances for patients.

These gradual improvements in technology are about to be surpassed by something much, much more significant – immunotherapy.

Immunotherapeutic approaches leverage the patient's own immune system to eliminate or slow the growth and spread of cells that form tumours. There are several types of immunotherapy in use or in development, but it is clear that using or encouraging the body's own immune system to fight cancers is going to have a game-changing impact in the near future.

The growth of immunotherapy is directly related to making tumours visible to our own immune system, thereby precipitating more durable responses than those elicited by conventional chemotherapies. In fact, immunotherapeutic responses thus far, while by no means universal, have sometimes demonstrated astonishing shrinkages in tumours and hitherto unattained longevity in cancer patients.

In conventional chemotherapy, or indeed even with newer *Tyrosine Kinase inhibitors*, patient responses can often be encouragingly good to begin with, only for the tumours to then rapidly redevelop. These quite often take the form of secondary tumours around the body, so-called metastases.

In contrast to conventional chemotherapies, patient tolerability and safety profiles have become increasingly improved in immunotherapy and durability of responses appear to be much longer.

The use of immunotherapy is not new. In the 1850s, German scientists observed tumours shrinking if they became infected. These were very sporadic reactions, however, and more often than not the patients died of the infection and not of the cancer.

However, the general idea of inducing fevers or disease to cure cancer gained hold, and since then, numerous attempts have been made to refine treatment involving infection and/or inducement of the body's own immune system.

In the 1980s and 1990s, there was considerable excitement around the development of biologic drugs for cancer. **Interferon alpha2b** and **Proleukin (IL2)** were sometimes used but had limited impact given their high toxicity and limited patient response, and even then only in highly selective tumour types.

In the late 1980s, French researchers discovered a new protein receptor on the surface of T cells, and named it *cytotoxic T-lymphocyte antigen 4*, or *CTLA-4. T-lymphocyte T* cells belong to a family of white blood cells known as *lymphocytes*, and are very important in immunity. They are different to other *lymphocytes*, such as *B-cells* and *natural killer cells (NK cells)*, and are marked by the presence of a *T cell receptor (TCR)* on cell surfaces. Subsequently, an American researcher named James Allison found that *CTLA-4* acted as a "brake" on T cells, preventing them from activating a full immune response in the way they were designed to do.

The idea of inhibiting this blocking receptor (the CTLA-4 molecule) and thereby allowing the immune system to do its job of destroying cancer was born. It was a small biopharma company, **Medarex**, which advanced the idea of an antibody which would work against CTLA-4 and started trials in advanced melanoma. Subsequently bought by **Bristol-Myers Squibb**, the Medarex drug was the first true cancer immunotherapy, but it certainly won't be the last.

This drug became **Ipilumab**, which is a fully humanised monoclonal antibody, and it is known commercially as **Yervoy.** It has been shown to prolong life quite significantly in end-stage melanoma patients (by an average of 11 months versus six months with prior standard of care).

Yervoy is a so-called *checkpoint inhibitor*, because it prevents T cell inhibition. As an early immunotherapy, it is by no means perfect, and certainly works better in combination with other therapies. It is also potentially toxic, as the immune response it creates can get out of control and lead to a fatal proliferation of T cells. But Yervoy represents an amazing first product in what will undoubtedly be one of the most exciting fields in medicine in the coming decades.

From the same small company also grew the idea of P*D-1 inhibitors*, a class of antibody in the same family as CTL4-A inhibitors. Just as with Yervoy, these PD-1 inhibitors work to change the way that cancer cells are detected by the immune system; PD-1 or programmed death is a checkpoint molecule that inhibits T cell reactions, and many antibodies are in development currently to unblock its actions.

In the same genre of compounds are the *PDL-1 (Programmed Death Ligand)* drugs, also in development. It appears that its *up-regulation* may allow cancers to evade the body's own immune system. PDL-1 on the tumour cell surface seems to inhibit anti-tumour *CD8+* T cells that would otherwise attack the tumorous cells. Recently, Merck's **Keytruda (pembrolizumab)** was approved for the treatment of malignant melanoma by the FDA, the first PD-1 inhibitor to be approved in the US.

In addition to near-stage immunotherapies, there are also several highly effective and interesting new compounds either approved or about to be approved for cancer treatment. Among the most interesting of these are the two key drugs being developed by **Incyte** and **Novartis**. One is the approved (under orphan status) **JAKAFI**, an inhibitor of the *JAK* pathway, and now being administered to pancreatic cancer victims. This drug is also being trialled in the treatment of intermediate or high-risk *myelofibrosis*, a type of bone marrow cancer, as well as in *lymphomas.*

Additionally, there are the *PARP inhibitors,* which are a family of drugs that inhibit *poly ADP ribose polymerase or PARP)* enzymes. Bristol-Myers Squibb has a highly promising selection of such drugs in development, with its **BMN 673** displaying particular promise across a broad range of tumours, particularly those that are short of oxygen, so-called hypoxic tumours. Such PARP inhibitors used in combination with *anti-angiogenic* (vascular endothelial growth factors) *VEGF* inhibitors (such as **AstraZeneca's cediranib)** appear to have amazing results in ovarian cancer, which is a disease with a notably high rate of relapse. A combination of these two is being fast tracked for FDA approval.

Incyte also has a highly promising late-stage small molecule compound in development for melanoma and breast cancers, a so-called *IDO pathway inhibitor.* IDO inhibitors seem to have low adverse event incidence, and might work with checkpoint inhibitors such as CTLA-4 and PD-1. IDO inhibitors stop tumorous cells from depleting *tryptophan* by employing stimuli such as *interferon gamma.* This inhibition allows immune cells to work better, and we advise readers to watch out for news on IDO inhibitors over the next couple of years.

Pfizer has **palbocicilib**, a *CDK4/6 inhibitor*, under extensive trialling in a wide variety of diseases including breast cancer, solid tumours, non-small cell lung cancer, multiple myeloma, Non-Hodgkin Lymphoma, mantle cell lymphoma, and liposarcoma. A Phase 2 trial in first-line *ER+, HER2* negative breast cancer (60 per cent of all metastatic breast cancer is *ER+/HER2* negative) has recently been completed and should be out in 2014. Palbocicilib is projected by some analysts to be one of the biggest selling drugs by the turn of this decade, with sales between five and 10 billion dollars. That is, of course, provided it receives FDA approval.

Ceritinib, an *ALK inhibitor* in development by Novartis has similarly large potential; it is twenty times more potent than its nearest competitor, **crizotinib (Xalkori)**, which was recently launched by Pfizer for non-small cell lung cancer, and which itself will likely be a multi–billion dollar drug.

In addition, already on the market is the **Pharmacyclics/Johnson & Johnson** drug **ibrutinib** marketed in the US under the name **Imbruvica.** This is a drug targeting *B-cell malignancies* and it was approved by the FDA in November 2013 for the treatment of *mantle cell lymphoma* and in February 2014 for the treatment of *chronic lymphocytic leukaemia (CLL).* It is an oral, selective inhibitor of the enzyme *Bruton's Tyrosine Kinase (BTK).* It is likely to be approved for several more blood cancers, including multiple myeloma and thus far, evidence from trials is highly positive. This makes Pharmacyclics one of our favourite large companies as a long term investment.

The development and trialling of second generation immunotherapies is now well underway. Targeted antibodies designed to attack cancer-related antigens can and do work sometimes quite effectively but often there is a big problem. This is because the environment in which a tumour operates is often *immunosuppressive*, rendering the antibody effect ineffective.

So, the idea has emerged of using so-called *chimeric molecules* to act in combination with checkpoint inhibitors and other immunotherapies to improve clinical outcomes. This can take the form of attaching an immune stimulating *cytokine (such as Interleukin 2*, a modulator of immune response), to an antibody. The aim is to target cytokine activity to specific tumours, which would then be destructive of cancer cells without the serious adverse events of less targeted cytokines. The use of chimeric molecules is discussed in greater detail below, because it represents the single most exciting aspect of immunotherapy for the near future.

In a very short space of time, there have emerged several key strands to what is known as *T cell immunotherapy.* The clear front runners in this field are drugs involved in *checkpoint inhibition* and *T cell vaccine or adaptive therapies.*

These include Bristol-Myers Squibb's Yervoy, already on the market as discussed, but also the same company's **nivolumab,** which is likely to be approved for *non-small cell lung cancer (NSCLC)* sometime in 2014.

As a result of this impressive portfolio and pipeline, Bristol-Myers Squibb is our favourite stock in immunotherapies. Its checkpoint inhibitors will likely have combined peak sales approaching 10 billion dollars, within this decade. **Roche** is also a contender, even though it may have cannibalisation problems with Avastin in due course. Novartis has a good immunotherapy pipeline as well.

The PD1/PDL-1 compounds from these companies and others will have broad application beyond just melanoma, renal carcinoma and *NSCLC.* Roche has an anti PDL-1 compound in development for renal and lung cancer, and while it is 18 months behind nivolumab, it appears to have fewer side effects and application in all of these disease categories.

Other leaders in the *checkpoint field* include AstraZeneca, which through its **Medimmune** subsidiary has established a number of promising partnerships.

All of these new drugs will be used generally in combination therapies (as indeed will most immunotherapies), and all represent potentially huge advances in the treatment of the diseases to which they are relevant.

The types of combinations which these drugs will be used in include existing cancer treatments (chemotherapy, Tyrone Kinase Inhibitors, radiotherapy, and monoclonal antibodies). In addition, they are likely to be used together with other types of immunotherapy (such as other types of *checkpoint therapy*) as well as with cancer vaccines, or with adoptive T cell therapy, including perhaps with CAR-T treatment.

A promising example of this is the use of *anti-CD47 antibodies*, which block the protein *CD-47* from signalling the immune system not to attack cancer tumours. This is very interesting because *CD47* is present on all known cancer cells. After the cancer cells have been engulfed by macrophages (the clean-up system of the body) the immune system's CD8+ T cells become mobilized against the cancer. This results in an individualised response to almost any form of cancer.

When this immunotherapy technique was tested on human tumours transplanted into mice, it stopped the spread of cancer 90 per cent of the time and often eliminated all signs of the cancer. This is preclinical stuff, however, and Phase 1 human trials are only just beginning, the result of **Stanford University** research efforts.

In addition to the checkpoint inhibitors, there is great excitement around a new development in immunotherapy which is the so-called *adoptive T cell technology* or *adoptive cell transfer (ACT).* Briefly mentioned earlier, those using CAR-T technology appear to be the most potent amongst the different types of ACT.

This approach to immunotherapy involves engineering patients' own immune cells to recognize and attack their tumours. Although CAR-T has been confined to small clinical trials so far, treatments using these engineered immune cells have generated some remarkable responses in patients with advanced cancer.

In several current Phase 1 trials using CAR-T in patients with *Acute Lymphoblast Leukaemia (ALL)*, for example, there was a complete response in almost all patients, with several of these patients remaining in total remission for long periods.

The way this technology works is that T cells are collected from the patient's own blood or tumour. After collection, the T cells are genetically engineered to produce specific receptors on their surface named *chimeric antigen receptors (CARs).* CARs are proteins that enable the engineered T cells to recognize a specific protein (antigen) on tumour cells. These engineered CAR-T cells are then grown in the laboratory in their billions. These altered T cells are encoded with *anti-CD19 receptors*, which allow these cells to specifically target and kill CD19+ cancerous B cells.

The resulting CAR-T cells (called CART-19 or CTL019) are re-infused back into patients where they expand many times and go on to destroy the cancerous B-cells to which they are guided by their engineered receptors. The development of this potent CAR-T cell treatment, an area in which Novartis is the clear leader, is even more exciting than that of the checkpoint class.

Kite Pharma Inc. (which recently went public in the US) has an anti CD19 chimeric antigen receptor. Its lead candidate for a blood disorder called *diffuse large B-cell lymphoma* is in Phase 2 trials. British companies **Adaptimmune** and **Immunocore** (both privately held) are also a key participants in CAR-T research, and have developed alliances with several major pharma companies.

If we take B-cell malignancies alone (and CAR-T is likely to have significant effects in solid tumours as well), then the potential market is huge. There are 37,000 deaths from B-cell malignancies every year in the US and a conservative estimate for the value of therapies in this area is about 10 billion dollars a year. Although **ibrutinib** has efficacy in some of these cancers, and there is the (very expensive) option of bone marrow transplant for some patients, there is little that can be done for refractory B-cell malignancies, which is why CAR-T is such a hopeful development.

Some analysts expect that the total market for immunotherapeutic approaches in cancer treatment will exceed 50 billion dollars by 2025, driven by novel agent combination therapies, longer treatment times (because patients will live longer) and the emergence of predictive biomarkers. Bristol-Myers Squibb, Roche and Novartis look well positioned in this important nascent market.

AstraZeneca is developing an experimental treatment called **Medi4736** that *"showed durable clinical activity and tolerability across a range of tumour types"* in Phase 2 trials, supporting its decision in 2014 to accelerate it into a pivotal Phase 3 study. AstraZeneca put Medi4736 at the heart of its defence against Pfizer's aborted approach, forecasting that the drug could generate peak annual sales of up to $6.5 billion.

There is also a great deal of research going on in the field of *epigenetics;* this is where the DNA is not mutated, but genes are switched on or off, typically by a lifestyle trigger, such as stress, diet and smoking. This on/off gene switching can happen by the addition or subtraction of a methyl group (a carbon atom bound to three hydrogen atoms, a process known as epigenetic methylation.) Researchers at **Baylor College** in Texas have been working on mouse models to demonstrate that using a "magnet" to promote a protein called *p16*, tumour growth is suppressed and the mice do not acquire cancers. Still early stage research, but exciting.

Additionally, there is considerable research underway in using cancer angiotensin blockers such as **Bevacizumab** (Avastin) along with **Losartan** (generic) – also an angiotensin blocker but one used in cardiac disease – to reduce the *cellular matrix* around tumours. The most intractable cancers tend to have a high ratio of non-cancer cells, including *fibroblasts* and *collagen*, compressing on blood vessels, creating a hypoxic environment in which cancer drugs cannot reach the target tumour(s) due to the inability of blood vessels to carry them. This research is ongoing and we are watching it closely.

But the most exciting approach to curing cancer will be *vaccine-based,* which we think is only a decade or so away. People who are at high risk of cancer because of familial traits or lifestyle could be prophylactically vaccinated against them. This would work by elevating levels of known antibodies to known antigens in at-risk populations. We are looking out for new investments in this area, one of which is **Viammune,** a private company in early stage trials for *triple negative breast cancer,* which has a high recurrence rate.

In summary, we like Bristol-Myers Squibb, Roche, AstraZeneca and Novartis among the big players. Among the medium-sized companies, we like Pharmacyclics, Incyte, and Immunogen (a strong beneficiary of royalties from **Kadcyla**, licensed to Roche). Among the smaller companies, we are looking at private businesses which are likely to go public in the near future.

Adaptimmune and Immunocore in the UK have good partnerships to develop cancer immunotherapies.

Lifestyle Diseases

The second major therapeutic category in which we are seeing strong innovation is in the non-cancer lifestyle diseases. These include obesity, diabetes, *Chronic Kidney Disease (CKD)* and so-called *NASH* (non-alcoholic steatohepatitis, or fatty liver disease,) as well as in Hepatitis B and C.

Obesity rates have doubled over the past 30 years, and globally 1.4 billion people are overweight, and 500 million are obese according to the **World Health Organisation (WHO).** By 2030, 50 to 60 per cent of the population in many countries are likely to be classified as obese. The prevalence of overweight and obese individuals is highest in the Americas (62 per cent overweight in both sexes, and 26 per cent obese) and lowest in South-East Asia (14 per cent overweight in both sexes, and 3 per cent obese).

In Europe, the Eastern Mediterranean countries and the Americas, over 50 per cent of women are overweight. In all three regions, approximately half of these overweight women are obese (23 per cent, 24 per cent and 29 per cent respectively.)

Demographic changes are also playing a role, with the ageing of the population in many countries tending to put many overweight adults into the obese category and to push many of those who are already obese into "severely obese" territory.

Obesity is the fifth leading global risk for death, accounting for at least 2.8 million deaths a year worldwide. This means that a large proportion of healthcare spending is a direct or indirect consequence of obesity, with total healthcare costs estimated at more than 40 per cent higher for obese patients than for normal-weight patients. The annual cost of obesity-related illness in the US alone is estimated to be $190 billion, or over 20 per cent of the country's annual medical spending.

A gradual shift to high-calorie fast food diets, combined with a lack of physical activity are the major drivers of the obesity trend. The key ingredient of many soft drinks is high-fructose corn syrup, the intake of which has increased significantly over the past four decades. At the same time US fast food sales have grown by more than 50 per cent in the past ten years or so.

There is some good news, at least in the US: recent evidence[1] suggests that the obesity epidemic there may have peaked. According to the survey, the percentage of obese adults remained at 35 per cent for the second straight time implying no changes in weight over the past ten years or so amongst the broad US population. Education, stricter food labelling and lower fat content in foodstuffs are probably the main reasons, and there has also been a marginal pickup in physical activity levels.

Nonetheless, the extensive prevalence of obesity globally will result in a significant increase in certain disease categories. Principal amongst these are diabetes, kidney diseases, NASH, hypertension, sleep disorders, gout, depression, and some forms of cancers associated with obesity.

Before we move on to those co-morbidities of obesity, let's briefly review the progress made to date in tackling this disease, which we will divide into two parts, the rich world (where progress has been made,) and the developing world (where the situation is deteriorating.)

In developed nations, calorie consumption seems to be falling (not by much; a reduction of 70 calories a day per person since 2000,) but it is a move in the right direction. Additionally, two new drugs (**Belviq** and **Qsymia**) have now been approved for obesity in the US, and they will also gain approval in Europe before too long. A third drug, which we think will be a blockbuster, **Contrave** (a combination of **bupropion** and **naltrexone**), is likely to be approved before the end of 2014 and this will be a positive for its producer, Orexigen, one of our suggested investments.

---

[1] *2009/10 National Health and Nutrition Examination Survey.*

Although sales today are relatively small, by 2018 obesity drugs should be a multi-billion dollar industry in the US.

SRI Labs, the company responsible for the technology behind Apple's *Siri*, has developed image recognition systems for food, allowing consumers to get an estimate of the calorific content of a meal by simply taking a photo of it. There is also an app called *Meal Snap* that does the same thing, but in a less advanced way than SRI's version.

Gastric band or *bariatric surgery* has been refined and is being employed to good effect (150,000 patients a year in the US alone.) The danger of hydrogenated fats has been well advertised, as has the need to reduce sugar consumption, but still the average Briton eats 238 teaspoons equivalent of sugar a week! Despite this and the continued growth of the fast food industry, the war on obesity is slowly being won, literally inch by inch.

Sports are being played slightly more frequently, fruit and vegetable consumption is increasing, and sodium and sugar content in processed foods is being reduced. This is all gradualist stuff, but it is important, because the side effects of being obese are truly dreadful.

Diabetes

The number one of these *effects is type 2 diabetes*, by far the more prevalent type of diabetes although not exclusively obesity-related. That said the vast majority of new patients being diagnosed with the disease are overweight to a significant degree. In the developed world they also tend to be disproportionally from ethnic minority groups and from low income families.

According to the **American Diabetes Association**, approximately 26 million US citizens are diagnosed as diabetics and type 2 diabetes accounts for around 90 per cent of these cases. The number of diabetics in the US has nearly tripled since 1980, with similar growth rates in many other parts of the world too. There are 1.4 million type 2 diabetics in the UK. Diabetes is in many ways the single biggest threat to well-being in the developed world as well as in China and Latin America. The disease is characterized by high blood glucose levels (hyperglycemia) as a result of the body being unable to produce enough insulin and/or not being able to respond to insulin properly (insulin resistance.)

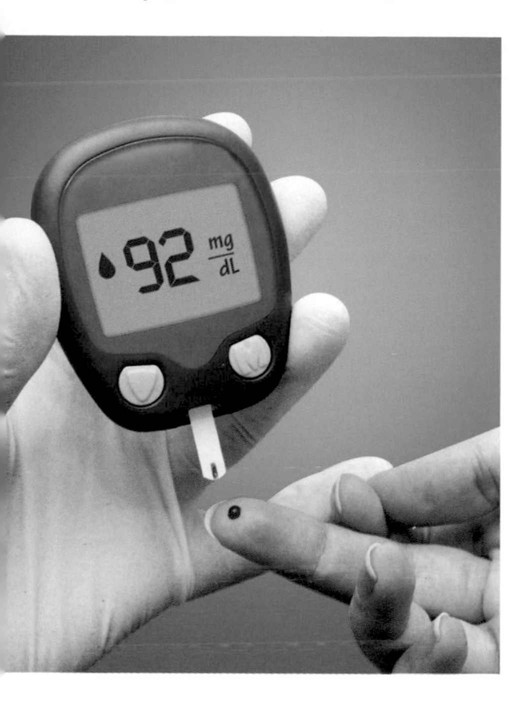

Left untreated it leads to elevated glucose levels, which often leads to serious health issues such as nerve and kidney damage, blindness, cardiovascular disease, and possible amputations from foot ulcers. Almost all of our readers will know someone with diabetes and recognise the disease as an appalling blight.

Newer treatments on the market for diabetes include long-lasting insulin, incorporating new methods of delivery, new categories of oral and injectable medicine for diabetes, including *GLP-1-agonists* such as **Bydureon** and **Byetta** by **Eli Lilly.** Also, **Farxiga (dapaglifozin)** by AstraZeneca has been recently approved. It is a *sodium-glucose co-transporter 2 inhibitor (SGLT2)* and works by preventing the kidney from reabsorbing glucose, increasing excretion of glucose and reducing blood sugar levels.

These drugs and others are undoubtedly leading to an improvement in most diabetes-related complications, and the statistics support this: between 1990 and 2010, heart attacks in diabetics declined by two thirds, and stroke and amputations by about half. In addition, scientists at the **Salk Institute** in California have discovered that injecting a protein FGF1 into type 2 diabetes patients has a reversal effect on the disease without hypoglycaemic effects, one that lasts for up to two days.

So the drugs are good and getting better, but better still would be to gain a deeper understanding of how diabetes, in particular type 2, takes hold in the first place and why some people are more susceptible to it than others.

It has been found recently[2] that people with just one copy (as opposed to two) of the *SLC30A8* gene have a two-thirds lower risk of developing type 2 diabetes. This fact was discovered by **Decode Genetics** of Iceland. SLC30A8 encodes a protein called *ZnT8*, which is needed to allow zinc to enter the beta cells of the pancreas and for subsequent production of insulin molecules. Original research showed this mutant single copy gene to be more common in Finland than elsewhere, but further research found another anti-diabetes protective gene that had the same effect in different Scandinavian populations. This is very early stage research, but it throws open the possibility of using genetic engineering (see later section of this chapter) to improve outcomes in type 2 diabetes.

[2] *Nature Genetics, March 2014 edition.*

In *type 1 diabetes, islet transplantation* is becoming more common, with insulin producing islets being transplanted from cadavers into patients. There are risks associated with this approach and anti-rejection drugs are required to be taken, but for those who receive the transplant, the quality of life is generally improved.

In addition, experimental *gene therapy* has cured mice of diabetes in ground-breaking research at **Baylor College** in Houston in the US. This was done by inducing liver cells to become beta cells (such as those found in the pancreas,) then to introduce the beta cells (using a viral vector) into the liver, thereby producing insulin from the livers of the "cured" mice. To paraphrase Robert Burns, there is quite a difference betwixt mice and men, but this shows that by using cell induction and genetic engineering, it might be possible to reignite the body's production of insulin, which would pave the way to a complete cure to the disease.

Other progress of note in diabetes includes the development of new compression and pulse shoes to promote the healing of diabetic foot ulcers (a very common problem among diabetics.) An ulcer that fails to heal can often lead to lower limb amputation, which carries a high risk of mortality in subsequent years. **The Diabetic Boot Company** is behind this pulse boot, which has plans of going public in the UK in 2014. We are investors in the business.

Insulet Corporation (NASDAQ:PODD) has developed an innovative pump to deliver continuous insulin to patients with type 1 or type 2 diabetes. We like this company and think its market potential is very large.

Biokier, a private US-based company has an interesting proposal to mimic gastric bypass surgery (which seems to reverse diabetes, albeit with complications.) This is to use *L-Glutamine* to mediate changes in the micro biome of the gut in order to stimulate more *glp-1* production in response to meals, thereby improving the post-prandial needs of diabetic patients. Indeed, the gut micro biome is increasingly being recognised as an "organ" in its own right.

Mannkind Corporation, (NASDAQ:MNKD) a US-listed company, has secured FDA approval of its **AFREZZA** inhaled spray for the delivery of insulin, and it might succeed in the market. The benefits of this in terms of control and convenience are obvious over injection, though many are sceptical about this form of delivery.

In terms of larger, longer term investments in the diabetes field, we prefer **Novo Nordisk** and **Sanofi,** both leaders in the *DPP4 inhibitors* and *GLP agonist fields,* as well as in modern insulin. While neither company's stock is cheap, they should perform in the long term because whatever happens in genetic engineering or in lifestyle moderation, it won't be enough to reverse an explosion in diabetes numbers worldwide in the near and medium term.

Chronic Kidney Disease (CKD)

Another co-morbidity of obesity is *chronic kidney disease (CKD)* which is characterised by progressive loss in kidney function over a period of years. People with high blood pressure, diabetes or familial history are most at risk of the disease. High levels of *creatinine* is the key signal indicating a low *Glomerular Filtration Rate (GFR)* and as a result a decreased capability of the kidneys to excrete waste products. The disease is ranked in stages 1 to 5, with 5 being end stage renal disease requiring a kidney transplant or dialysis for life.

CKD is the cause of many deaths worldwide; an estimated 735,000 in 2010 a near doubling from 1990, and there is no effective treatment of the disease in its later stages. Indeed, the disease often has the side effects of anaemia and bone disease. An estimated 10 per cent of adults in the US have the disease of varying levels of seriousness[3], with a very high relative incidence in African Americans who do not respond to anti-hypertensive drugs, such as beta blockers, as well as Caucasians do.

In our previous book, we thought quite highly of **Reata's** CKD candidate drug, **Bardoxolone,** but alas it failed to attain FDA approval in 2013. We were very impressed by this compound and by the management and funding of the company, but it was sadly not to be. Bardoxolone is an *Anti-oxidation Inflammation Modulator (AIM),* and as such a potent activator of the transcription factor *Nrf2*. Nrf2 seems to produce anti-oxidant and anti-inflammatory gene responses, while suppressing pro-inflammatory enzymes. Nrf2 suppression is implicated in many inflammatory diseases, including *Chronic Obstructive Pulmonary Disease (COPD),* Alzheimer's and some cancers.

Reata is now redeveloping Bardoxolone for cardiac use, but its failure in CKD means that there is little currently available to treat late stage renal failure patients who would otherwise have benefitted from Bardoxolone. Fortunately for us and for our readers, Reata was not a public company and so no money was lost. The saga of this drug is illustrative of the difficulty in predicting outcomes in drug trials with any certainty. In fact about 25 per cent of Phase 3 trials do fail, despite the millions spent on them up to that point. The class of *AIM* drugs however is of great interest to us and readers should keep an eye out for developments in this area.

Companies with interesting CKD candidates include **Akebia,** which has a drug in Phase 2b trials for a *Hypoxia Inducible Factor (HIF)* compound inhibiting *Prolyl Hydroxylase (PH).* The idea of inhibiting PH is to boost natural production of *ErythroPOietin (EPO)* and to raise haemoglobin levels in *CKD* patients. Trials have been encouraging and we regard Akebia as an interesting albeit a speculative investment.

La Jolla Pharmaceutical Company (NASDAQ:LJPC) is also worth looking at. Its CKD drug, **Galectin-3** had positive Phase 2 results with a good improvement in the GFR compared to a placebo.

Non-Alcoholic Steatohepatitis (NASH)

One further consequence of obesity is the increasing prevalence of *Non-Alcoholic Steatohepatitis (NASH),* an increasingly common and often undetected liver disease. The major signal for NASH is excess fat in the liver, along with inflammation and damage, which could lead to cirrhosis. If cirrhosis develops, there are few treatment options and a liver transplant is the only current treatment for advanced cirrhosis with liver failure. NASH is the next major cause of cirrhosis in the developed world after *hepatitis C* (which is now curable) and *alcoholic liver disease.*

NASH has exploded in prevalence in recent decades and affects 2 to 8 per cent of Americans. An additional 10 to 20 per cent of the US population have fat in their liver, but no inflammation or liver damage, and therefore do not have NASH.

In the last couple of years, two companies have made progress in addressing NASH; one is **Intercept Pharmaceuticals (NASDAQ:ICPT)** which has been an incredible success, with a multi-billion market valuation. Its lead compound, **obeticholic acid (OCA)** is a bile acid analogue and first-in-class agonist of the *farnesoid X receptor (FXR).* FXR is a nuclear receptor which regulates bile acid build up in the liver and thereby reduces toxicity.

---

[3] *Source: Centres for Disease Control & Prevention (CDC). http://www.cdc.gov*

The liver is vital as it performs functions that are critical to survival, including the regulation of bile acid metabolism. Bile acids are detergent-like emulsifying agents released from the gallbladder into the intestine as food is ingested, and enable the absorption of dietary cholesterol and other nutrients. Bile acids are mediated through dedicated receptors of which the most important is the FXR receptor. The up regulation of FXR appears to induce anti-fibrotic, anti-inflammatory and other mechanisms that are necessary for the normal regeneration of the liver.

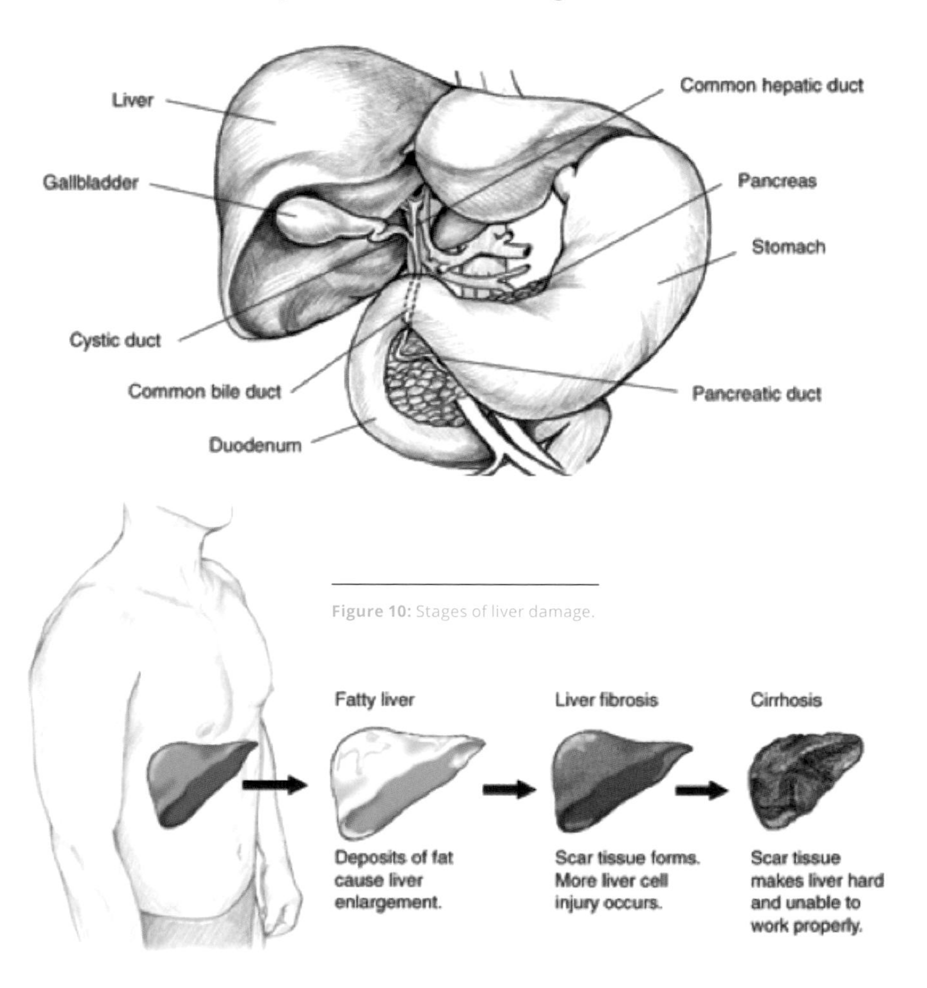

Figure 10: Stages of liver damage.

So good has the effect of OCA been in trial patient populations that the latest trial was stopped because of efficacy. Almost half of NASH patients treated had remarkable responses to OCA and it is also believed (and indeed some trials are underway) that OCA or similar FXR mediators could be useful in other liver or kidney diseases, as well as in biliary disease.

There is, however, a potential hitch with OCA, and that is it appears to raise *lipid (cholesterol)* levels in patients treated, which could signal some cardio risk. This makes us wary of investing in Intercept, especially as its valuation is so elevated.

There is another company, which we have visited, and which we like as an investment for NASH treatment. This is a company called **Genfit,** from Lille, France. Genfit's drug, **GFT505** is based on an agonist of *PPAR alpha* and *delta* nuclear receptors which increase fatty acid oxidation and also appear to increase HDL (good) cholesterol and reduce LDL (bad) cholesterol.

The drug also appears to increase *insulin sensitivity,* and indeed to reverse established NASH. There will be a readout of its Phase 2b studies in 2014, and we are optimistic on this compound. Further, in February 2014, the FDA granted Fast Track designation to GFT505 in NASH. Although Genfit is about eighteen months behind Intercept, we think its drug has a cleaner safety profile and potentially equal or greater efficacy. Plus, its market value is a fraction of Intercept's.

Overall the market potential for NASH drugs is huge. Estimates range from 3 to 5 billion dollars per year, with a forecast of 165 million addressable patients by 2020.

Viruses, Bacteria and Other Nasties

The most remarkable development in the area of *viral disease* since our last book was published has come from one of our favourite large cap companies, **Gilead.** Already the leader in *HIV* medications, its acquisition of **Pharmasset** in 2011 for $11 billion has proved to be a masterstroke.

The drug that has emerged from that acquisition, **Sovaldi, (sofosbuvir)** for *hepatitis C* is both effective and controversial. It is also likely to be one of the biggest blockbusters of all time, with annual sales in 2014 alone estimated at $10 billion.

But, first let's rewind. What is *hepatitis* and what is the remarkable science that is emerging or has recently emerged in the hepatitis space. *Hepatitis* is the acute inflammation of the liver and is divided into several types, *A, B, C and D* (there is also *E* and *G* but they are less important). *Hepatitis D* can only survive in the presence of *Hepatitis B.* The condition can be self-healing or it can go on to cause fibrosis, cancer or cirrhosis. It is often characterised by jaundice, anorexia, or fatigue. It is normally caused by hepatitis viruses, but can also be brought on by excessive drinking, environmental pollutants, as well as by autoimmune diseases.

Hepatitis A and B can be prevented by vaccinations and immunity conferred by these in both A and B through vaccination is between 95 and 100 per cent. However, hepatitis B is still widely prevalent, particularly in Asia and parts of Europe, and there is a residual large carrier population in the US. Worldwide, there are estimated to be 300 million carriers of hepatitis B, 1.2 million of which are in the US.

There is no effective vaccine for *hepatitis C*, which also has a large carrier population, numbering 2.9 to 3.7 million people in the US, and about 350 million worldwide.

Sovaldi is a therapy based on an inhibitor of the *RNA polymerase* that the hepatitis C virus uses to replicate its *RNA*, and is taken either with *ribavirin* or with *pegylated interferon*, depending on the *genotype* of the carrier. A 12-week course of Sovaldi costs $84,000 and a 24-week course costs $168,000. These costs have raised concerns, including from US Congress, adding to questions about the price burden of medicines in general.

Our own view is that some price erosion will occur, but it will be generally *de minimis*. It is a lot cheaper to cure a hepatitis C sufferer than to have him/her go on to develop liver failure, and Sovaldi represents in almost all cases a genuine cure for the disease. There are other hepatitis C drugs in close chase to Sovaldi, from the likes of Roche and **Idenix**, but our opinion is that Gilead will dominate this market for years to come, as indeed they have in the *HIV/AIDS* space. The only caveat is that hepatitis C is a disease of poorer people in general, and it is not certain whether insurance companies will cover all of the treatment costs.

As far as hepatitis B is concerned, where the method of transmission is in some ways similar to that of hepatitis C (blood transfusion, shared needles, sexual contact and mother to infant transmission), there is currently no fool-proof cure. Interferon is sometimes used but has very nasty side-effects and is not necessarily curative.

One company that could change all that is **Arrowhead Research,** one of our favourite picks in our last book. The company has developed a platform technology for hepatic disease, based on *short interfering RNAs (siRNA),* and its first novel drug in development is *ARC-520* for hepatitis B.

Arrowhead is aiming to achieve a functional cure, represented by an absence of hepatitis B (so-called immune clearant state). The siRNA in ARC-520 intervene at the *mRNA (messenger RNA) level* and in mouse models of hepatitis B infection, a single co-injection of Arrowhead's *polyconjugate delivery vehicle* with its siRNA targeting the hepatitis B virus resulted in a massive knockdown of the virus's RNA proteins and viral DNA with long duration of effect. Essentially what we are saying here is that if ARC-520 works, only one treatment could cure hepatitis B. Arrowhead is currently mid-way through its Phase 2 trials in patients in Asia. Its siRNA platform will no doubt extend to other diseases, and like **Alnylam**, despite large rises in its share price, remains one of our favourite long term picks.

In addition, it is worth noting that the incidence of *cervical cancers,* which are mostly related to the *human papilloma virus (HPV)* are beginning to decline rapidly in areas where anti-HPV vaccinations have been widely administered (**Gardisil** by GlaxoSmithKline is the most well-known of these).

Such vaccinations have mostly been given to young girls but increasingly boys are being inoculated as well. More than 170 million doses have been administered worldwide without serious adverse reactions.

In the United States, infections from HPV *types 16 and 18*, which cause 70 per cent of cervical cancer, have dropped by half. Young women in Australia and Denmark, where the vaccines were introduced early, have had sharp declines in precancerous lesions.

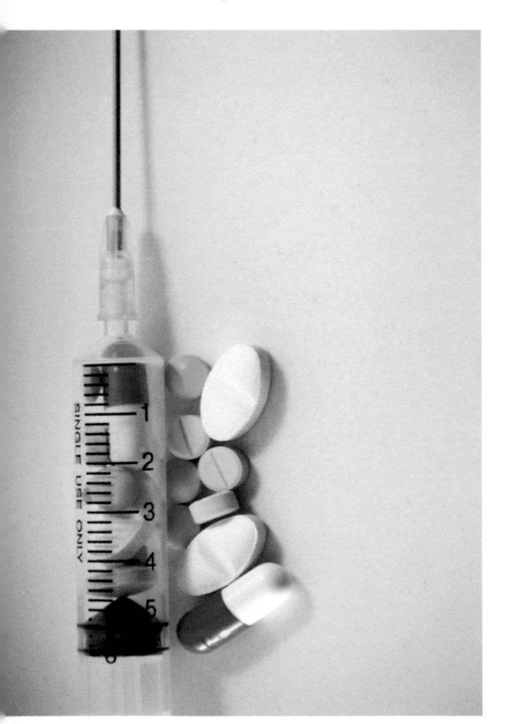

This is a great example of virus-induced cancer being prevented by successful vaccination.

C. difficile, TB and Other Antibiotic Resistant Diseases

In the last few years, rising levels of antibiotic resistance have been well heralded in press reports. Overuse of antibiotics in humans and in animal husbandry has caused bacteria to develop resistance to many established antibiotic therapies. The drug industry, until relatively recently, tended to underinvest in antibiotic research, as most antibiotics are generic and low margin. Only when it became apparent that it was becoming increasingly difficult to treat some diseases, particularly hospital acquired superbugs such as *C. difficile* and *MRSA (Methicillin-resistant Staphylococcus aureus*) did the industry start to pick up its research efforts. The absence of anti-infectives that work well in those diseases, as well as for instance in tuberculosis (TB), which is once again rearing its ugly head, is a cause for concern. The good news is that innovation is at last reappearing in the industry.

The drug of choice, **vancomycin,** for both C. difficile and *MRSA* is encountering new potent strains of resistance, most recently in Brazil, where the *vanA* cluster of resistant strains is becoming a matter of serious concern. As a result, research is being ramped up across the board.

A key example is the work being done in *C. difficile*, a Gram-positive spore forming bacteria which tends to cause severe diarrhoea after antibiotics have wiped out the gut flora. *C. difficile* infections are therefore a condition directly caused by overuse of antibiotics, and can lead to colitis and so-called *toxic megacolon*, which can cause premature death.

Such deaths number about 14,000 a year in the US, out of an estimated 250,000 cases. The disease starts when the gut has been overwhelmed by a *broad spectrum antibiotic*, and C. difficile then takes over. Drugs such as vancomycin or metronidazole have until now been the standard of care. More recently **DIFICID (fidaxomicin)** from **Cubist** has been used, but the problem with all of these is disease recurrence, particularly in already weakened patients.

It is estimated that 20 per cent of patients relapse with vancomycin, and a smaller but still significant number with fidaxomicin. Selective eradication of C. difficile with minimal disruption to the myriad types of bacteria which make up the normal, healthy gut flora is what fidaxomicin aims for, but there may be better compounds out there.

Summit Plc's novel antibiotic **SMT 19969** is being developed as a treatment for initial C. difficile infection and the prevention of its recurrence. It combines excellent potency with super-specific selectivity for C. difficile meaning that it does not disrupt the healthy gut bacteria. The development of SMT 19969 is being supported by the **Wellcome Trust** following the award to Summit in 2012 of a prestigious Translational Research Award worth up to £4 million. Summit is one of our favourite each-way bets in biotech, as it also has an interesting programme in *Duchene Muscular Dystrophy,* which we will write more on later.

Incidence of TB is once again on the rise, even in the developed world, where London has become the capital with the highest number of cases. A disease that was sent into retreat with the introduction of antibiotics in the 1940s, TB has started to develop antibiotic resistance and is starting to pose a serious threat. Risk factors for TB include HIV, addiction, being an immigrant and homelessness.

In response to this TB upsurge, about 10 compounds are at various stages of development around the world. Amongst them is one from the **École Polytechnique Fédérale de Lausanne** in Switzerland which appears to be extremely powerful. The drug, **PBTZ169** attacks the TB bacteria, called *Mycobacterium tuberculosis (M. tuberculosis)* through the cell wall that protects it from other antibiotics. This compound literally bursts the cell open, destroying the bacteria. The drug appears to work best when combined with two pre-existing TB drugs, **bedaquiline** and **pyrazinamide**, which reduces the chance of mutation by the TB into a resistant form.

Malaria

The *malaria* parasite is amongst the most resistant in the world, and efforts to combat the disease over the centuries have so far yielded little compared to progress made against other diseases. Malaria, meaning "bad air" in Italian, is preventable and treatable, but still every year about 1.2 million people die as a result of being infected by it. Huge efforts have been made to deal with the problem, including large scale studies in rendering mosquitos infertile and thereby unable to reproduce, as well as educating people in affected regions, particularly in Sub-Saharan Africa, on how to minimise the risk of contracting malaria.

In the 1990s, Chinese research yielded **artemisinin**, which in combination with other therapies had exceptionally high efficacy in treating malaria. This drug was based on ancient Chinese herbal medicine. However, in the past two years artemisinin-resistant strains of malaria have evolved and have become evident in the Mekong Delta in Cambodia. Other herbal remedies are being trialled, with some success, but so far to no avail.

So science is now turning to genetics to try and solve this conundrum. A recent article in **Nature Chemistry Magazine** showed that blocking the activity of the *NMT enzyme* in the most common malaria parasite *Plasmodium falciparum* prevents mice from showing symptoms and extends lifespans. This is very early stage stuff though and no products will emerge from this for several years, if at all.

Malaria vaccines continue to be researched intensively, but as yet none has proved more than 50 per cent effective. A new vaccine is being trialled at the moment, which focuses on the few minutes the parasite spends in the bloodstream before moving to the liver to hide. We expect that the use of genetic engineering will eventually be the key to curing and preventing this disease that has claimed more human lives than anything else in the history of mankind. Every year there are more than 100 million malaria cases in African children under five, Africa accounting for about 90 per cent of the world's cases of malaria. Easing this plague would have enormous human, social and economic benefits.

Bacteriophage

An alternative approach to antibiotics and a potential way of overcoming the bacterial resistance problem perplexing medical practitioners around the world is the use of bacteriophage, a technology last used extensively in the Soviet Union.

Bacteriophages are literally "devourers of bacteria" and are highly targeted viruses that infect only specific bacteria. Since bacteriophages multiply their numbers many times in the presence of their specific bacterial host, initial dosing levels can be extremely low – one billionth or less of the amount required for conventional antibiotics to be effective. A dose of about one thousandth of a billionth of a gram of bacteriophage has been found to be effective against infection. According to **Ampliphi Biosciences Corporation**, a company currently researching the application of bacteriophages, the potential for unwanted side effects appears to be very limited.

We like the potential of Ampliphi, which is based in Richmond, Virginia, and we are investors in the company. Its shares trade on the OTC Bulletin Board under the symbol APHB.

Bacteriophages are abundant and only attack bacteria, not human cells, and they evolve to combat resistance in their host bacteria. Lytic bacteriophages, currently under development, re-programme the infected cells they are designed to attack and once introduced, they "ampliphy" by the billions, overwhelming the infection. They stop replicating when the target bacteria are all destroyed.

Ampliphi Biosciences is initially developing bacteriophages to address *Pseudomonas aeruginosa* infections, which are a common soil organism that infect burns, wounds, and body cavities. It is the principal issue for patients with *cystic fibrosis*, and leads to damage in the lungs often resulting in respiratory failure.

Genetic Engineering

Genetic engineering is the alteration of an organism's genome by biotechnology. It has a relatively recent history, but its use is accelerating fast and it offers huge potential for mankind. Genetic engineering can now be performed on many different types of organism.

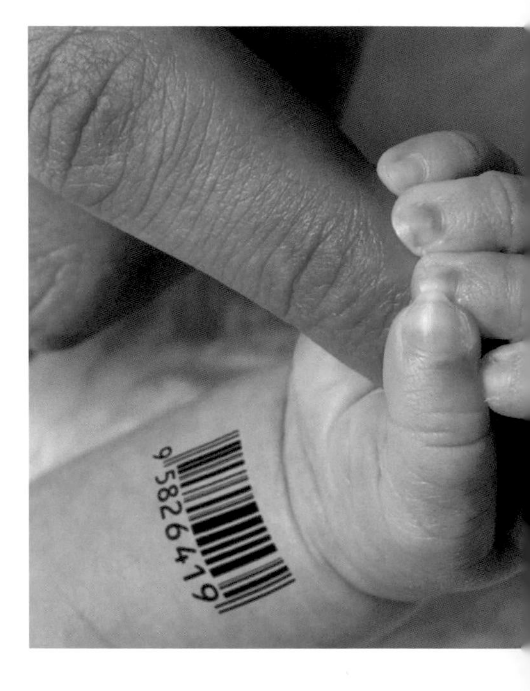

Genetic engineering occurs in several ways: *Genes* (of which humans have about 20,000 to 30,000) can be "knocked out" or removed using *nucleases*. Additionally, an altered DNA might be inserted into the host genome by using *molecular cloning* methods to generate a DNA sequence outside of the body.

These techniques, widely used in industry and research already, are being updated by much more sophisticated techniques which are being rapidly developed. Genes can now be specifically altered using *recombinant* techniques to change an *in situ* gene (using methods such as *CRISPR*, which we discuss below). These methods can be used to add genes, introduce mutations, delete specific genes, or to remove or to "skip" *exons* (exons are nucleotide sequences encoded by genes that remain present after parts of the gene have been removed by splicing.)

Genetic engineering techniques have already been applied to many industries including agriculture, industrial processes, and medicine. For instance, enzymes used in laundry powders and drugs such as insulin and human growth hormone are now manufactured in *Genetically Modified (GM)* cells, and GM crops have been widely commercialized for decades, not without controversy.

The first *Genetically Modified Organisms (GMOs)* were simple bacteria when the science first took off in the 1970s. Genetically engineered mice followed a decade later; insulin producing bacteria were commercialized in 1982 and GM food came along in 1994.

In medicine, genetic engineering is being used to mass-produce insulin, human growth hormone, folates for treating infertility, albumin, and haemophilia factors. In addition, vaccines which lack infectious sequences are now manufactured routinely. Mouse and hamster cells are fused together to create *monoclonal antibodies* for biologic drugs.

The obvious forward move from these developments is the genetic reengineering of human cells by replacing defective human genes with new functional copies. This can occur either in tissue which is already in the body *(somatic)* or in *germ line* tissue (tissue which is part of reproduction and can be handed down to descendants).

Gene therapy has so far been used with some success to treat several diseases, including *X-linked SCID (boy-in-bubble syndrome), chronic lymphocytic leukaemia (CLL),* as well as symptoms of *Parkinson's disease.*

In 2012, a gene therapy called **Glybera** (by **UniQure**) for treating *lipoprotein lipase deficiency (LPLD),* which leads to severe pancreatitis, became the first gene therapy treatment to be approved for wider clinical use anywhere in the world, although to date the company, or its commercial partner has not sold a single dose of Glybera.

Another gene therapy company that shows promise is **Bluebird Bio Inc (NASDAQ: BLUE).** It recently unveiled good results in replacing defective genes in two patients with *beta-thalassemia,* a disease that prevents oxygen-carrying haemoglobin from functioning properly. This leads to chronic anaemia and lifelong blood transfusions. Bluebird's therapy, known as **LentiGlobin,** replaces the defective gene with one that is fully functional.

Glybera and LentiGlobin are of course just the beginning of this field's true potential, and genetic engineering is finally approaching the point where its application will be clinically universal. This raises ethical issues about how far humans should be allowed to go towards achieving genetic perfection or to be able to engineer specific physical traits (such as eye and hair colour).

The biotechnology industry was born in 1973, when Herbert Boyer and Stanley Cohen inserted DNA that they had engineered in the lab into bacteria. Boyer went on to co-found **Genentech**, which went on to use *E. coli* modified with a human gene to manufacture diabetic insulin. In all the early examples of genetic engineering, however, researchers were limited to techniques that inserted the foreign DNA into cells at random. This understandably led to multiple failures and errors.

However, in the early 2000s, researchers developed *zinc finger nucleases (ZFNs).* These are synthetic proteins which are engineered to cut DNA at specific spots without the hit and miss of previous techniques. One end of the protein can be designed to recognize a particular DNA sequence; the other end cuts DNA. When a cell then naturally repairs those cuts, it can patch its genome by copying from supplied foreign DNA. Later, synthetic nucleases called *TALENs (transcription activator-like effector nucleases)* provided an alternative and possibly an easier way to target specific DNA.

But each of these methods relies on custom-making new proteins for each specific DNA target, and they are therefore relatively labour-intensive and technically complex.

Now, as a result of very recent research, *CRISPRs (clustered regularly interspaced short palindromic repeats)* have emerged, which use *guide RNAs* to target and alter more genes than the previous methods of ZFNs and TALENs.

CRISPRs are clusters of short DNA sequences that read similarly forward and backward, and are found in many types of bacteria. These sequences form part of the bacterial defence system. When viruses attack, bacteria can incorporate sequences of viral DNA into their own genetic material, sandwiching them between the short DNA segments.

The next time the bacteria come across that particular virus, they use the DNA in these clusters to make RNAs that recognize the matching viral sequences. A protein attached to one of these RNAs then cuts up the viral DNA, destroying the virus.

CRISPRs simplify the process of modifying a genome by replacing, deleting, or adding DNA. As a result, we are near to be point where genetic therapies will be widely available. In 2012, Emmanuelle Charpentier, a microbiologist at the Helmholtz Centre for Infection Research, and Jennifer Doudna, from the University of California at Berkeley, showed they could use a single RNA allied to a cutting protein, the enzyme *Cas9*, to slice any desired sequence of DNA in test tubes. The following year, two geneticists separately demonstrated that the CRISPR/Cas9 system could be used for gene editing in the cells of animals, including humans.

One good example of a disease which might be treatable with genetic engineering through *CRISPRs* is *sickle cell anaemia,* which results from just one base pair out of three billion in a body being defective.

CRISPR will in the future be used to rewrite specific bits of DNA to repair this single mutation. The **Georgia Institute of Technology** has already used CRISPR to correct sickle-cell mutations in human cells grown in a dish. In the near future, after harvesting hematopoietic stem cells from the bone marrow of a sickle-cell patient, scientists could use CRISPR to correct the defective gene.

Then the genetically altered stem cells would be returned to the patient, and start producing healthy red blood cells to replace sickle cells.

There are now large libraries of CRISPRs, each targeting a different human gene, and all of them are open-source and available to researchers.

CRISPRs really are amazing as they open up the possibility of rewriting genes to fight disease and may possibly even be able to stop or slow down the process of ageing. Investment opportunities are sure to emerge in this area.

Editing Options

	1 Zinc finger nucleases	2 TALENs	3 CRISPR
What is it?	A protein consisting of a DNA-cutting enzyme and a DNA-grabbing region that can be tailored to recognize different genes.	Also a protein containing a DNA-cutting enzyme and a DNA-grabbing region that can be programmed to recognize different genes, but it is easier to design than zinc finger nucleases.	A DNA-cutting protein guided by an RNA molecule that is able to find the specific gene of interest.
Pros and cons	It was the first programmable genome-editing tool, but it relies on proteins that can be difficult to engineer for new gene targets. Potentially dangerous off-target cuts are also possible.	Though simpler and cheaper to design than zinc finger nucleases, TALEN proteins can still be difficult to produce and deliver. Off-target cuts are a problem.	This technique is affordable and easy to use, and it works for high-throughput, multi-gene experiments. Like the other tools, it can make off-target cuts.

Already of course, patent disputes have started between the original collaborators on the technology.

ZFN technology is more cumbersome than that of CRISPR but still viable in some areas. Zinc Fingers are small proteins characterised by *zinc ions*, and their name results from their finger-like structures. There are a number of types of zinc fingers, each with a different three-dimensional architecture. Their use is closer to commercialisation in terms of treating disease than CRISPRs and TALENs.

Sangamo Biosciences (NASDAQ:SGMO) is one of our favourite companies in this space, though still speculative. The company is using ZFN genome editing technology in trials to engineer in HIV patients a naturally occurring mutation in the T cell (immunity system) genome.

This appears to provide resistance to HIV infection. ZFN-modified T cells have been well tolerated when re-infused and treatment in the trials has resulted in decreased viral loads in a number of patients who were taken off their antiretroviral therapy, including one whose viral load became undetectable. Although not yet a proven cure for *AIDS*, this approach offers considerable promise and Sangamo is a platform company with many other potential strings to its bow.

Therapeutics: Antisense and RNAi Finally Come to Market

After years of disappointing results in the form of poor efficacy, high toxicity and the lack of an effective delivery method, *RNAi* and *antisense* are starting to make a comeback. **Kynamro,** a drug by **ISIS (NASDAQ:ISIS)** for hereditary heart disease was launched in 2011, and Alnylam's (NASDAQ:ALNY) siRNA drug **patisiran** for *amyloidosis* was launched the following year.

Amyloidosis is referred to as an "orphan disease" (one that affects a small percentage of the population), and patisiran is paving the way for other siRNA drugs that will be approved over the next few years, including potentially Arrowhead's ARC-520 drug for hepatitis B that we mentioned earlier.

In the case of patisiran there are two common types of amyloidosis: *familial amyloid cardiomyopathy (FAC),* which affects more than 40,000 patients worldwide; and *familial amyloid polyneuropathy (FAP),* which affects about 10,000 patients worldwide. Longevity for both types is severely affected, with many sufferers succumbing to heart failure in the absence of effective treatment. Patisiran is the only option in this respect, and is the first widely available siRNA drug, but it certainly won't be the last.

In the case of ISIS, it has become the established leader in antisense and it has a highly promising platform validated by the launch of Kynamro. This drug (**mipomersen sodium**) is an *oligonucleotide inhibitor* of *apolipoprotein B-100* used as an adjunct to lipid-lowering medications (such as statins) and diet to reduce *low density lipoprotein levels* ("bad cholesterol") in patients with *homozygous familial hypercholesterolemia (HoFH).* This disease leads to early death due to aggressive cardiac plaque build-up.

Antisense works as follows: when the sequence of a gene causes a disease, antisense technology now makes it possible to synthesize a strand of *RNA* that will bind to the disease causing gene's *messenger RNA (mRNA),* thereby inactivating it. This occurs because antisense adds another strand to the mRNA which renders it unreadable, as mRNA has to be single stranded to work. This is the method that ISIS uses in its HoFH drug Kynamro.

A further way that antisense therapy works is by modifying the exon content of an mRNA. This approach is used for example by **Sarepta Therapeutics (NASDAQ:SRPT)** in its *exon skipping* trial therapy for D**uchene Muscular Dystrophy,** which we cover in more detail later.

Another drug developed by ISIS, and now under licence to privately-held **Atlantic Pharmaceuticals** is **Alicaforsen,** which is an antisense drug that targets *intercellular adhesion molecule 1 (ICAM-1).* ICAM-1 is over-expressed in a wide variety of inflammatory disorders, including *ulcerative colitis* (UC) and *pouchitis* (an inflammation of the pouch created in UC patients who have had a colectomy).

Regenerative Medicine: Stem Cells and Sequencing

In the 1970s and 1980s, early work began on engineering human tissues to "grow" replacement organs for transplanting into patients. This effort has accelerated in recent years, and many readers will be familiar with the successes in this area. Replacement body parts are now a reality and in the next decade or so, further progress is extremely likely.

As previously mentioned, some basic organs (such as windpipes) are already being grown outside the body, and synthetic liver tissue especially for research is being used in the development of drugs for malaria and hepatic (liver) conditions. Recently, the unprecedented survival (600 days) of pig hearts in four baboons has given hope that denatured animal organs *(xenotransplantation)* could overcome the global shortage of organs for transplant. Previously the impediment to this was the rejection risk by the host body, but genetic engineering to disguise the transplanted organ's source from the human immune system is very close, as are methods to prevent clotting in the transplanted organs.

"Human-on-a-chip" systems where up to ten different human tissue types are grown outside of the body is being developed in the US, in a large scale research effort funded by the **Department of Defence.**

Tissue engineers are also developing humanized tissue lines that promote wound healing. This occurs by setting healthy tissue composed of *endothelial cells* (which respond to injury by the secretion of *wound promoting proteins)* on implantable *"scaffolds"* next to diseased tissue. Uses for such techniques are likely to include burns, damage caused by smoke inhalation, surgical interventions, and cardiac disease.

But the primary goal of *regenerative* medicine is to be able to regrow or repair organs that are diseased or not functioning well in-situ; or to be able to grow complex organs outside the body and transplant them into the patient.

The main issue confronting scientists in the development of such complex synthetic organs is the connectivity of the organs. The need for an effective *vasculature* (blood vessel system) is the principal obstacle to getting artificial organs into human bodies. Research in this area is focused on inducing blood vessels by growing cells which develop into vasculature on patterned surfaces, some of which are created by 3D printers.

All of this development in the field of artificial organs depends on cell technology, and specifically the use of *stem cells*. Since writing extensively about stem cells in *Cracking the Code*, they have become ubiquitous. **Cellular Dynamics (NASDAQ:ICEL)** has developed multiple lines of *induced pluripotent stem cells,* which are now widely used in research.

Mesoblast (ASX:MSB), a company listed in Australia, uses *highly purified mesenchymal precursor cells (MPCs)* and *expanded hematopoietic stem cells (HSCs)* in its multi-pronged approach to regenerative medicine. Mesoblast's principal focus is on cardiovascular and neurological programmes with its partner, the Israeli company **Teva Pharmaceuticals** (which also has a US ADR listing NYSE:TEVA). MPCs are being used in a Phase 3 trial currently underway in congestive heart disease. MPCs appear to interact with damaged heart tissue to induce new blood formation and regeneration of heart muscle. During the Phase 2 trials, over a three year period none of the patients suffering from heart failure went on to have a heart attack, unlike 30 per cent of those who were not administered the MPCs.

In addition, Mesoblast is conducting trials with MPCs for degenerative spinal disc disease; early stage results have been very impressive, as were trials using MPCs in immune mediated inflammatory conditions, such as *Crohn's disease, diabetes and rheumatoid arthritis.* Mesoblast is well capitalised and fairly far advanced in its programmes, most notably in heart failure. Expected readouts of the Phase 3 trials are expected in 2015/16, and if the concept is validated, it would make Mesoblast one of the largest pharma companies in history, so it is worth looking at as a speculative buy.

Another company, this time private, but no doubt at some stage slated to go public, is **Silver Creek Pharmaceuticals,** based in San Francisco. This company is developing protein therapeutics to regenerate functional heart tissue in post heart attack victims. The company is close to its first human trials, and based on the results from studies in mice it is a very exciting technology. There are 800,000 deaths a year in the US due to heart failure, half of them as a direct result of a heart attack.

In the UK, there is a company called **Reneuron Plc (LON:RENE)** that is engaged in two trials of its *autologous* (meaning the patient's own) stem cell therapy. Alongside a Phase 2 trial of **REN001** in stroke disability, the company is in Phase 1 development of the same cells, designated **REN009**, in the treatment of critical limb ischemia, in order to avoid amputation. Despite its mention, Reneuron would not be one of our picks. However, the use of stem cells in therapeutic contexts is absolutely going to happen; the avoidance of introducing stem cells that may turn "rogue" or cancerous is now well understood, and the technological improvements in this area are wondrous.

Almost certainly, stem cells will provide the key role in the growth and implantation of complex organs. Our guess is that externally grown lungs which are fully functioning, and partly functioning livers and hearts will be available within ten years.

Diseases of Ageing

The conversion of *"illderiness"* to *"wellderliness"* is one of the key goals of medical researchers today. It is all very well for people to live much longer lives as the risks of death from cardiac disease, lifestyle diseases and cancers are reduced over time; but if the latter years of these now very old people are characterised by pitiful degeneration, then the prolongation of life may be unfortunate rather than serendipitous. In September 2014, **Calico** (a division of Google) entered into a joint venture with **AbbVie** to work on diseases of ageing, looking for ways to extend and improve human life, with each party initially investing $250 million.

This JV is headed up by Art Levinson, formerly of Genentech, and will establish a research and development facility in the San Francisco Bay area.

The key diseases that are specific to ageing and are intractable and widespread are *Alzheimer's disease* and other forms of *dementia, osteoporosis, arthritis,* and *Parkinson's disease.*

Alzheimer's Disease

Currently, there are five approved drugs for Alzheimer's in the US. All are compounds which treat the symptoms of the disease, temporarily helping memory and thinking problems in about half of patients. But so far there is nothing available to address the underlying causes of Alzheimer's.

This may be about to change. Many of the new drugs in development have as their endpoints the modification of the disease itself, achieved by altering one or more of the many brain changes that Alzheimer's causes. This is with a view to at least slowing the progression of the disease in a marked way. Alzheimer's was implicated in 500,000 deaths in in the US in 2010. This means that in a single year, Alzheimer's is responsible for almost as many deaths as AIDS in its entire US history (about 600,000 deaths since 1982). In addition, it is now increasingly believed that Alzheimer's as a term might cover multiple strands of similar, but not identical, disease.

The good news is that over the past two decades or so, Alzheimer's has become much better understood and methods such as the *ApoE4* and *ApoE3* gene markings (indicating a higher chance of getting the disease) and *PET scans* (which give a reasonable diagnosis of disease presence) have been developed. Drugs such as **solanezumab** and **pioglitazone** have been developed (although not yet in use), offering some modicum of disease slowing.

It is clear that ageing, amyloid accumulation and calcium dysregulation are key factors in Alzheimer's and that the disease can result from a number of causes, including a variety of genetic mutations. There is also increasing evidence to suggest that Alzheimer's is linked to epigenetics (lifestyle and environmental conditions) as well as diabetes. About 17 genes subject to *methylation* as a result of epigenetic effects have thus far been identified, with the most notable being *ANK1*, coding for *ankyrin1,* vital to keeping the outer membrane of brain cells intact and it is also linked to type 2 diabetes. The good news is that methylation is reversible with the right drugs, so this seems to be a positive discovery.

One recent discovery published in **Neuron,** a medical journal, is that mice with mutations of the *presenilin gene* have memory defects associated with Alzheimer's but no plaques. Instead, they have loss of *synaptic spines* which are critical connections between neurons. Presenilin mutations lead to lower levels of a calcium sensor, *STIM2*, and ultimately to less activity of the enzyme *CaMKII,* critical for maintaining *mushroom spines,* which are required for normal brain function.

Notwithstanding the *presenilin mutated* mice, a major feature of most patients with Alzheimer's is the presence of *beta-amyloid plaques,* and researchers now know that this protein is generated from a parent compound *amyloid precursor protein (APP).* This is activated by two enzymes, *beta-secretase* and *gamma-secretase.* Having understood this key fact, companies are engaged in developing ways to: block these enzymes; stop the clumping of *beta-amyloid*; and clear the brain of beta-amyloid plaques.

Another key component of Alzheimer's, *tau protein tangling,* is also the target of further drug research. Attempting to stop *tau* molecules from twisting into tangles, which has the effect of upsetting the normal vital cell transport system of the brain, is the goal of these programmes. There is also research being done on how insulin is processed in the brain and its effect on Alzheimer's. This is because there appears to be a causal link between *insulin resistance* and Alzheimer's.

Further research is being done on what is the basis of familial (inherited) Alzheimer's when it occurs. There is an extended family of 5,000 people in Antioquia, Colombia who have an exceptionally high predisposition to Alzheimer's.

Administering anti-beta-amyloid drugs to some of these people who carry the Alzheimer's causing gene, but don't yet exhibit symptoms is currently underway to see if prophylactic treatment will be effective at keeping the disease at bay in later life.

The identification of such at-risk individuals who are pre-symptomatic is a key part of what small British private company **Cytox** is working on. It has developed a blood test using the *mTOR* pathway to identify at-risk patients. One can imagine that a drug such as Eli Lilly's **solanezumab** which failed in Phase 3 trials in Alzheimer's patients (possibly because the disease was too far advanced) will be administered to pre-symptomatic individuals, having been identified by a test such as that from Cytox.

Although there have been 10 failures in Phase 3 trials for drugs targeting beta-amyloid or the tau protein, it could be that these drugs were administered too late to have any enduring beneficial effect. In other words, if those at-risk from Alzheimer's or have it in its early, pre-detectable stages could be identified, then the disease could be more effectively halted or slowed.

However, to underline the difficulties with this disease, Australian company **Prana** recently announced that its experimental drug **PBT2** failed. This drug promised to address Alzheimer's by triggering a chemical balancing act in the brains of Alzheimer's victims at a prodromal or early stage of development. It failed the primary endpoint of reducing amyloid beta plaques and also failed the secondary endpoints of brain activity, cognition and function compared to a placebo.

Among novel drugs targeting Alzheimer's through tau protein tangles, the most promising drug is **LMTX**, currently in Phase 3 clinical trials, by a company called **TauRx**. LMTX is a second-generation *Tau Aggregation Inhibitor (TAI),* acting by reducing levels of aggregated or mis-folded tau proteins, which are associated with the progressive neurodegeneration caused by the disease.

Additionally, although in very early stages it appears that generic *metformin*, widely used as a diabetes drug, may have some effect in slowing Alzheimer's, as it appears that diabetes is implicated in some types of Alzheimer's (as mentioned earlier). There also seems to be some positive correlation between the disease and those who are carriers of the ApoeE3 gene, which is 70 per cent of the population.

Researchers from the **University of Southampton** in the UK are also working on the idea of vaccinating at-risk people in their forties with a variant of amyloid plaques, to create an immune response to the plaques before they develop in later life. We are watching this initiative with great interest.

Parkinson's Disease

Parkinson's is one of the most common neurological disorders, with around one million Americans patients and 10 million others worldwide. The disease is progressive and degenerative, characterised by the death of brain cells. This causes an array of motor and non-motor symptoms, including tremors, rigidity, slow movement and instability. There is no cure for Parkinson's, largely because its causes are not wholly understood.

Parkinson's occurs due to a loss of nerve cells in the brain. The symptoms of Parkinson's emerge when around 70 per cent of cells have been lost, and the brain can no longer produce adequate levels of *dopamine.* The use of a dopamine agonist, **levodopa** is currently the front line treatment for the disease, but the real research effort is being focused on preventing the loss of *dopaminergic neurons.* Initial symptoms are treated with drugs, but these lose potency over a number of years, and the next line of treatment for some patients is a surgical intervention named *deep brain stimulation (DBS),* which was approved in the US in 2002. DBS involves implanting electrodes in the brain to regulate its aberrant impulses, in much the same way a cardiac pacemaker works in heart patients. A current trial funded in the UK is looking at ways of supplementing this treatment by adding a nerve graft from a patient's own *peripheral nerves.*

Peripheral nerves, unlike brain nerves, can regenerate, and the idea is to take nerve tissue from a patient's ankles and to try and get the implanted tissue to release neurotrophic factors to encourage nerve regeneration in the brain. Five patients have been treated thus far and results are expected to be released in 2015.

Recent research in the UK spearheaded by Doctor Richard Wyse has identified **ursodeoxycholic acid (UDCA)** as potential therapy. This drug, used for decades in liver disease appears to improve the function of mitochondria and might be effective in up regulating natural dopamine.

A further drug in late stage development is **IPX066** (a combination of extended release levodopa and **carbidopa**) by **Impax Laboratories (NASDAQ:IPXL)** which is designed to lower the so-called "off time" (the unable to function moments) in patients with advanced Parkinson's. So far it has proved much more effective than levodopa. In addition, psychosis which is a major problem in patients with late stage Parkinson's, is being addressed with new drugs, most notably **pimavanserin**, which blocks serotonin *5-HT2A* receptors in the neocortex. The neocortex is the area of the brain responsible for sensory perceptions, conscious thought and language, and the 5-HT2A receptors are linked to visual hallucinations and delusions. Pimavanserin is being developed by **ACADIA Pharmaceuticals (NASDAQ:ACAD).**

Gene therapy may also prove to be useful as a treatment for Parkinson's and there is also ongoing research into the use of stem cells in Parkinson's patients. *Dopamine-producing* cells that are damaged or gone in people with Parkinson's might be replaced with new, healthy dopamine-producing cells derived from stem cells developed in the laboratory.

More immediately, **LiftLabs**, a private company based in San Francisco, has developed a small device that tracks and compensates for small vibrations and tremors. LiftLabs' *Liftware* technology is similar to that used in image stabilization in high end cameras. The result is that a device such as a spoon remains smooth and level despite the tremors of the user's arm or hand. Food that normally would fly off stays put. A neat and practical idea until medicine catches up.

Rheumatoid Arthritis, Osteoporosis and Multiple Sclerosis

Rheumatoid Arthritis (RA) is an autoimmune disease leading to inflammation of the joints and affecting 0.5 to 1 per cent of adults in the developed world, and it is generally regarded as a disease of ageing. The disease is caused by a complex combination of genetic and environmental factors and multiple genes (over 100 have been shown to be related with the disease).

There is a significant link between RA causing genes and those involved in blood cancers and other immunodeficiency disorders. *TNF inhibitors* such as **Humira** (by **Abbvie**), **Enbrel** (by Pfizer/Amgen), and **Remicade** (by Johnson & Johnson) are the largest class of drugs to treat RA. These suppress responses to tumour necrosis factors (TNF), which form part of the inflammatory response. TNF is involved in clinical problems associated with other autoimmune disorders such as *ankylosing spondylitis, Crohn's disease*, *psoriasis* and *severe asthma*. These drugs are huge blockbusters; for example, sales in Humira will reach about $12 billion in 2014.

Following on from the TNF inhibitors are *JAK pathway inhibitors*, with Pfizer's **Xeljanz** already on the market, with Lilly/Incyte's **baricitinib** and **Vertex's VX-509** in the queue for approval. The treatment paradigm for RA in the future will likely use TNF inhibitors first and then JAK inhibitors subsequently.

RA drugs are amongst the most prescribed and fastest growing segment of the pharmaceutical industry and are highly profitable to the companies that sell them.

Newer therapies for RA under development include using existing drugs for cancer such as *CDK4/6* inhibitors, as researchers have identified a strong correlation between RA, human primary *immunodeficiency disorders* and cancers of the blood.

Osteoporosis is a progressive bone disease that is characterized by a decrease in bone mass and density which can lead to an increased risk of fracture. Osteoporosis results in bone mineral density being reduced as well as the deterioration of the bones' microarchitecture.

The key risk factors for osteoporosis is advanced age, where females are at greater risk. Oestrogen deficiency following menopause or hysterectomy is correlated with a rapid reduction in bone mineral density, while in men, decreasing testosterone levels have a comparable (but less pronounced) effect. About 50 per cent of Americans over 50 have some form of osteoporosis, and of those 80 per cent are women. Last year, 750,000 hip fractures occurred in the US, directly related to osteoporosis. Mortality post fracture increases, so this is a big deal. About half of all patients with osteoporosis will break a bone of some sort following a fall.

Osteoporosis is more prevalent in people of European or Asian ancestry, and there is a hereditable factor of between 25 and 80 per cent involved in the disease. There are over 30 genes implicated in the different types of the disease, but for almost all patients the current standard of care includes *bisphosphonates,* which reduces fracture risk.

The holy grail of drug research in the disease is to find a compound that rebuilds bone and re-strengthens the skeleton, and it looks like this could be close to happening. The experimental drug **romosozumab** from Amgen/UCB stimulates bone production by inhibiting chemical signals that naturally inhibit bone formation. The compound is a humanized monoclonal antibody that targets *sclerostin.* It is currently in Phase 3 trials, having proved highly efficacious in earlier studies.

It is also worth keeping an eye out for another monoclonal antibody from **Novelmed Therapeutics** in the US. In early models, cartilage degeneration and osteophyte formation were reduced by 90 per cent compared to no treatment.

Another autoimmune disease of note is *Multiple Sclerosis (MS)* and whilst there are so-called disease-modifying drugs available that can actually slow down the progression of MS and prevent relapses, there is currently no cure. These drugs, such as **interferon beta 1b**, help suppress the immune system, preventing it attacking the nerves' protective sheaths (called myelin).

Scientists at Bristol University are working on a novel approach that so far has had encouraging results on animals. It is an allergic desensitisation method that stops the immune system from attacking the protective myelin sheaths. By slowly injecting synthesised sheath proteins into the body, they have figured out a way to allow for the body to recognise and accept them. We shall have to wait and see if the results are as promising once they move towards human trials.

Orphan Diseases

A rare disease, also referred to as an orphan disease, is any disease that affects a small percentage of the population. There are estimated to be 7,000 of these diseases, many of them chronic and not necessarily serious. Attention is focussed on those which are life-threatening or life-limiting.

Orphan diseases often occur in early life, and about a third of children with such rare conditions will die before their fifth birthday. One disease, *ribose-5-phosphate isomerase deficiency* has only one known patient, but most orphan diseases have a few thousand identifiable patients globally. Some diseases, such as *cystic fibrosis,* or *sickle cell anaemia* are quite well known and have larger patient populations.

In the US and EU it is easier to get marketing approval for an orphan drug than for others, and there are often other financial incentives, such as extended exclusivity periods, all intended to encourage the development of drugs that might otherwise not attract sufficient research dollars due to the small size of the market. About 30 million people in the US have an orphan disease, and the definition of such a condition is one that affects fewer than 200,000 people. About 95 per cent of rare diseases have no known treatment, but most of these are not significantly life-threatening.

There is a fair amount of research focused on orphan diseases, mainly because if a drug is successful it can enjoy high prices, high margins and long periods of marketing exclusivity. **Alexion's** drug **Soliris**, which addresses a small number of patients in limited indications, has encouraged multiple other companies to engage in orphan research. Alexion has a market capitalisation of close to $30 billion, even though its compound only treats less than 5,000 patients globally.

Soliris is a humanized monoclonal antibody that is a first-in-class terminal complement inhibitor and the first therapy approved for the treatment off PNH, a rare, progressive and life-threatening disease characterized by excessive destruction of red blood cells. Soliris is also the first agent approved for the treatment of another rare condition aHUs, an ultra-rare genetic disease that causes abnormal blood clots to form in small blood vessels throughout the body, leading to kidney failure, damage to other vital organs and premature death. Treatment with Soliris runs to about $450,000 per patient per year – a remarkable amount, which is why orphan diseases can represent such an attractive market.

A more common orphan disease which is the focus of intensive research is *Duchene Muscular Disease (DMD)*, an always fatal disease that affects 500,000 boys worldwide, and one for which there is significant research underway.

The disease is a degenerative neuromuscular disorder and causes progressive muscle loss and premature death. DMD affects approximately one in every 3,500 boys born worldwide. DMD is caused by specific errors in the gene that codes for *dystrophin*, a protein that plays a key structural role in muscle fibre function. Progressive muscle weakness in the lower limbs eventually moves to the arms, neck and other areas, including the lungs and heart. The condition is absolutely fatal, and death occurs before the age of 30.

Several companies pursuing a variety of approaches are involved in DMD. Sarepta is the largest of these. Its lead compound is **Eteplirsen,** which is designed to produce a functional dystrophin protein. It uses novel *phosphorodiamidate morpholino oligomer (PMO)-based chemistry and proprietary exon-skipping technology* to skip *exon 51* of the dystrophin gene, enabling the repair of specific genetic mutations that affect approximately 13 per cent of the total DMD population. Eteplirsen is designed to restore the gene's ability to make a shorter, but still functional form of dystrophin from mRNA. This is not a cure, and has had mixed but still generally positive results in trials. Eteplirsen, along with another exon skipping drug from **Prosensa,** have the ultimate potential to treat nearly half of all patients with DMD, possibly leading to longer lives with improved quality for the boys who suffer from this disease. One of the terrible things about the disease is that the boys remain cogent and brain-normal right to the end, knowing that their bodies will ultimately let them down.

A company called **Summit Plc (LON:SUMM)** is involved in a different approach to the disease. Summit has a drug in Phase 2 trials for the up-regulation for *utrophin,* which is an early-life substitute for dystrophin. We regard Summit to be an excellent investment prospect as it also has a promising new antibiotic in development for C. difficile, excellent management and adequate cash to take it through significant trials.

Orphan diseases are typically the result of *mono-genetic* (single gene) defects, and as such, with the ability of doctors to do more careful screening of patients, employing whole or partial gene sequencing, they should eventually become less prevalent. Because about half of monogenetic diseases are hereditary, would-be parents may choose to have their defective genes "selected" out prior to conception. This is already happening with some diseases in selected countries, but we firmly believe that pre-conception screening will become the norm in the developed world, and ultimately the whole world, over the next 10 to 20 years.

All of these developments are leading to the cumulative and rapid advances in medical science that in turn are going to break the traditional view of human life expectancy. As we said at the outset of this chapter, it is undoubtedly here that we find the greatest disruption occurring. It is also the investment area with the greatest promise.

New Procedure in Cosmetic Surgery

On a lighter note, there is a company we have invested in (currently private) that has developed a procedure to permanently change a person's eye colour. Strōma Medical Corporation is a clinical stage research and development company based in Laguna Beach, California. It has developed and patented a non-invasive procedure to permanently change the colour of the iris from brown to blue in a single treatment. The procedure is not yet commercially available, however once approved it is anticipated to take less than 30 seconds to perform on each eye and will likely cost the patient around $5,000 for the procedure.

Strōma's system treats the iris of the eye with light and heat to photo-disrupt the pigment in the iris. Eye colour is determined by the amount of pigment covering the anterior layer of the iris. Blue colour is produced by the light within the collagen fibres of the iris, so everyone has blue eyes under the brown or green layers. When little or no pigment exists on the anterior iris, light freely enters and exits the tissue and the iris appears blue. Strōma uses an Nd YAG laser, with a map created using a proprietary software algorithm to photo-disrupt and then remove or lessen the density of the pigment located in the anterior iris, making the eye appear blue in colour.

The Internet of Things

The Things Around You Will Astound You

It has been about twenty years since the internet was first introduced into our lives. Remember those big, clunky screens and the tediously slow modem dial-up services? Fast forward two decades and the internet has matured into being the main means of communication, the main form of news dissemination, a major shopping destination, and an important source of entertainment. It has spawned behemoths such as Google, Amazon, Facebook and eBay, all of them revolutionary in their business models. There are few parts of the world remaining that have not been touched by the internet, which probably ranks as the single most important invention of the post war years.

The internet has been the creator of more billionaires than any other single industry in the history of the world, and many of them of tender years. The internet acts as the great leveller of the proverbial playing field. Anyone from anywhere at any age with a computer and a good idea can make it big developing a novel application that addresses an unmet need or improves upon an existing service.

Evolving out of a US Department of Defence system into a university communication project and then exploding onto the world's consciousness in the late 1990s, the internet is the defining invention of our time. The internet's hegemony over global communications has occurred in the blink of an eye: in 1993, it represented only 1 per cent of the information passing through two-way networks,

"The internet has been the creator of more billionaires than any other single industry in the history of the world."

51 per cent by 2000 and more than 97 per cent of telecoms information by 2007. Today, it accounts for pretty much all of it. Cisco's *Visual Networking Index* (VNI) forecasts that by 2016 the total volume of internet traffic will be 1.3 zettabytes – a zettabyte is 10^{21} or one followed by 21 zeros!

The Internet Has Already Enabled So Much Disruption

Despite massive and continuing expansion, the key areas of supercharged growth that we are now familiar with have been largely staked out: social media, shopping, news, search, and to some extent the "sharing economy" are today well covered. In almost every area that could be disrupted, the internet has done it, or is in the process of doing so.

Google dominates search and, as a result, a large part of internet advertising. Alibaba and others like it have become dominant in supply chain business-to-business activity. Amazon, ASOS, Ocado, eBay and many others have begun to seriously eat the lunches of traditional brick and mortar retailers. The likes of Expedia and Hotels.com are taking over the travel agency industry, while companies such as Facebook, Twitter, Snapchat, and LinkedIn have spawned vast and still-growing social media and business communication networks.

In entertainment, Netflix is redefining the TV and movie business, as is YouTube (a Google company). YouTube, along with companies like Spotify, Deezer, Grooveshark and Pandora are eviscerating the traditional record labels, as is Apple's iTunes, though to a lesser extent.

Cloud services such as Dropbox and GoogleDrive are taking off, and internet dating is now an established part of the social scene with such sites and apps as Match.com and Tinder. When it comes to written communication and sending messages, everyone on the internet (which is about half the planet) uses email and messaging apps like WhatsApp, Viber and WeChat.

Furthermore, real estate agents, with their high overheads and high fees are likely to become a thing of the past in the relatively near future. As an example, while in 2014 only around 5.5 per cent of UK house sales were carried out through ultra-cheap, online estate agents, that figure is expected to rise to 70 per cent by 2020.

Many aspects of finance are being transformed, thanks to improved efficiencies made possible by the internet. In fact, there is so much happening in this space that we decided to devote chapter 6 entirely to cover payment processing in more detail. Similarly for media, publishing and education, chapter 8 focuses on how the internet is enabling new entrants with novel ideas and applications to upset the cosy world of the long-established media and publishing giants.

The Internet's Next Wave of Change is Underway

Earlier we mentioned some of the changes that have already taken place since the internet entered our lives, yet as the internet becomes increasingly pervasive, the uncharted future promises to deliver even more disruption than we have experienced over the past two decades.

One particular new growth area is referred to as the "internet of things," which is the theme of this chapter.

The internet of things (IOT) is fast becoming a common term that is being used to describe the connectivity of the things that we use in our daily lives; things such as cars communicating with garage doors, refrigerators communicating with supermarkets, agricultural crops communicating with irrigation systems. As the examples show, the IOT spans all industries.

In this section, we outline some of the key areas in the new internet, and highlight which ones are likely to provide the best returns for investors. We also look at some industries that are just beginning to feel the internet's disruptive force.

The Internet of Things

The IOT, also known as Ubiquitous Computing (ubicomp), everyware, or pervasive computing, is widely discussed but is not yet very apparent to most of us, but this is about to change.

IOT provides objects, people and animals with unique identifiers that transfer data seamlessly and automatically over the internet. This enables things to happen within a predefined set of parameters without manual involvement. Many objects, such as coffee machines are in fact already networked through the power grid and the IOT is simply an addition to existing networks.

The IOT is a broad-sweeping term for a lot of communication. This can take many forms, some of them quite odd-sounding. For example, how about a farm animal with a bio-chip transponder that sends signals to the farmer relating to, for instance the animal's health, weight or some other characteristic? A Dutch company called Spark has developed a chip that does just that; each cow connected to its system transmits 200 megabytes of information annually.

There is also a pacemaker and cardiac monitor that transmit data to the patients' doctor. The *NUVANT Mobile Cardiac Telemetry System* from Corventis (a private US company) continuously measures, records and transmits patient data to physicians treating patients with cardiac arrhythmias.

Then there is the fridge that sends information to a food retailer to tell it to deliver more of a particular item. This one is not quite a reality yet - and some commentators question whether it ever will be, as it would require the food and beverages in the fridge to be "smart" in order to detect remaining quantities. This may sound fanciful but we firmly believe it will happen.

Of course, all these IOT-enabled devices will require vast quantities of cheap chips, and so an investment in a high quality chip manufacturer would be a sensible investment approach. A company such as Intel fits the bill, or London-listed ARM (LON:ARM), known for its power-efficient processors that are used extensively in many tablets and smartphones.

The IOT is made possible by the assignation of a unique identifier, an IP (internet protocol) address to each connected device or item. The limit to the number of assignable IP addresses has been boosted substantially as a result of the introduction of the so-called IPv6, the newest version of the Internet Protocol and fast becoming the new industry standard.

Under IPv4, the address was limited to 4 groups of numbers, each group ranging from 0 to 255. This puts a cap on the number of IP addresses at 256x256x256x256, which works out to be just under 4.3 billion.

With IPv6, the address has been increased to 8 groups of 4 hexadecimal numbers, which is calculated by starting with $(16x16x16x16)^8$ and works out to be 3.4×10^{38} – that's 38 zeros, an unfathomably large number. Under the new system, it is possible to conceive of a kettle or a pen having its own IP address, as there are now enough IP addresses to assign to every single atom on earth and still have enough to spare – one hundred times more, in fact!

Already, smart meters for utilities employ this type of technology, but soon the whole system will be ubiquitous. The IOT was first written about in the 1990s, and has recently become fashionable among investors and corporations. The really attractive thing about the IOT is that it doesn't depend on us humans to provide information – the information is generated automatically, with the capacity to reduce waste and improve productivity.

In 2013, about $1 billion was invested by venture capitalists into IOT companies. Start-ups are everywhere, with products ranging from "wearable" tech to home automation systems. In January 2014, Google bought Nest Labs for $3.2 billion, a company that makes smart thermostats and smoke alarms. Google then augmented its portfolio of IOT companies by purchasing Dropcam for $550 million in June 2014, a home monitoring company.

Nest has made some of its software open source, so that any company is free to integrate its products and services with *Android @Home*, and indeed this has started to happen, with for example, Mercedes and Whirlpool.

Dropcam employs webcams to stream images and video to mobile phones and tablets to allow people to see what is happening in their homes when they are not there, or even if they wish to look in on one room while in another. That in itself isn't particularly revolutionary, but the cameras link to a cloud service which analyses images to look for anomalies and generate alerts. Supposedly, information generated by Google's Nest will be kept private and separate from the Leviathan's huge library of information on almost everyone on the planet – a claim that is difficult to verify so we will have to take the company and its "don't be evil" mantra at its word.

Whatever growth projections are used, the IOT will be huge. Gartner, a tech research firm, believes that 26 billion devices will be online by 2020, whereas Cisco, a provider of hardware and software to the internet's backbone believes that this figure will be more like 50 billion. This rapid expansion is enabled by the cloud, the storage of data remotely from users' devices, as well as "big data."

Big data is the term used to describe data sets that are too large to handle in conventional ways. It has developed as a result of the huge rise in the amount of data being generated every year and stored all over the internet. The world's technological capacity to store information has roughly doubled every 40 months since the 1980s. As of 2012, every day 2.5 exabytes of data were created (2.5×10^{18}). To put into perspective how much data this actually is, 5 exabytes are equivalent to all the words ever spoken by human beings throughout history. Google is using an automated system called *Knowledge Vault* to compile facts, creating the world's largest database of knowledge, with 1.6 billion facts accumulated so far.

Cisco estimates that by 2020, the IOT will potentially be worth $14 trillion, most of that from home automation but with, 27 per cent, or nearly $4 trillion, from manufacturing. This projection, which will take IOT to approximately the size of the US economy in just six years, seems rather fanciful to us and self-serving on the part of Cisco, but nonetheless it shows the direction of travel. IOT is going to be huge.

In home automation, the smart home is thought of as one where security systems, lighting and household appliances are controlled remotely, optimising energy use, "learning" to understand the home occupiers' behaviours and likes, and collecting data to improve home performance (and to provide useful aggregated information to the likes of Google.) Applications of IOT in the home will include, entertainment, plant watering and garden maintenance, pet feeding, the creation of different "mood scenes" with altered lighting, as well as home robotics.

Wine cellars can be linked to the internet to replenish stock or to alert owners when specific wines are ready for drinking. TVs can be watched by two or more people, watching different pictures on the same curved screens (already Samsung has such a model). Intelligent mirrors will remember clothes combinations and alert the owner to what might be suitable to wear. The list is long, with new applications constantly being added.

For industrial applications, the IOT connects entire plants to the internet by using a variety of sensors on the factory floor. Sensors that could, for instance, save energy or alert suppliers to when to send new parts, improving inventory control and lessening the cost of stock.

The IOT market will grow as consumer and industrial applications are introduced that offer greater utility to users, providing data that is valuable to an enterprise or household. As exciting as all of this sounds, it will not be easy to accomplish, and the Harvard Business Review points out that the task ahead for companies that are at the forefront of the IOT market (namely Google, Apple, Samsung in home automation, and Rockwell and Honeywell in manufacturing applications) have their work cut out for them.

Android @Home from Google is already in its ascendance in the IOT home market, with over half of all mobile devices already using its software. Samsung, which along with Google's Nest division is making a big play in IOT, is also a user of Android. Apple is lagging behind, with only 15 per cent of global device users using its iOS. However, Apple has recently unveiled its own competing system for home use called *HomeKit*. Smart Things, a US-based start-up, has sold several thousand units of its home communications hubs, which use open source software and are capable of getting, for instance the washing machine to send a text when its load has finished.

The problem with getting so many eclectic devices from different manufacturers to work together is being addressed by a consortium of 40 companies, and backed by the UK government, with members including IBM, ARM, and BT. This consortium has come up with a network called *HyperCat* that allows different devices to discover and to communicate with each other.

The proliferation of what are in effect tiny computers on everyday objects poses serious security issues. It has for instance been shown that cars or medical devices can be controlled remotely by hackers, so companies are focusing their efforts on ensuring that the IOT does not present a cyber-threat where malicious or illegal acts can be carried out. One suggestion is to embed IOT chips with antivirus software and a "kill switch" as a mechanism of last resort.

According to CB Insights (a venture capital database), in 2013 venture capital firms invested a record $1.4 billion in 239 cyber-security companies in the US alone. These companies ranged from mobile-app security platforms to online authentication systems. One such company is called FireEye, which listed on NASDAQ in the second half of 2013. FireEye merits investors' attention although, with a market capitalisation of around $4 billion at the time of writing, it looks too expensive for our taste.

Google's far sighted leadership has as usual put the company out in front as far as the IOT goes. Microsoft has created its *Kinectv2*, which is an also ran and unlikely to make a big impact. The likely winner in the IOT is likely to be Google, along with any company it happens acquire along the way.

The Sharing Economy

An area that is related to the IOT and made possible by the proliferation of the internet and big data is the "sharing economy" - a concept that appeals to the zeitgeist of the environmentally conscious, nomadic, urban dweller. It basically describes an economy that uses assets in an increasingly shared way; assets such as cars, accommodation, pets, tools, and in fact anything that is not in constant use by its owner. The sharing economy is also sometimes referred to as the peer-to-peer economy, the mesh economy, the collaborative economy or collaborative consumption. It is a socio-economic phenomenon built around the collectivisation (for a fee) of human and physical assets.

It is not, as some have described it "digital socialism" but rather just the opposite and more like digital capitalism. It represents the view that assets can be maximised in terms of return by using the disruptive power of the internet. So although sharing things dates back to the barter economy, it is the internet that has allowed all sorts of sharing to take place, including that of surplus labour – in a very effective way.

There are different iterations or sub-sets of the sharing economy, or as trendier folk generally term it, the "mesh economy." According to the inventor of the term, Lisa Gansky, mesh companies *"create, share and use social media, wireless networks, and data crunched from all available sources to provide people with goods and services at the exact moment they need them, without the burden and expense of owning them outright."*

There are now thousands of such companies, all seeking attention, with only a handful making it big. Some names will be familiar to our readers, such as Airbnb, Zipcar, RelayRides, Sidecar, Flywheel, BlaBlaCar, Waze, eBay, Craigslist, and SnapGoods.

Peer-to-Peer businesses like eBay allow anyone to become a retailer, and other sharing sites allow individuals to act as a taxi service (we cover Uber and Lyft in our next chapter on transportation), car hire firm or small hotel as and when it suits them, or to share information or labour, or even money, with others.

Rachel Botsman, the author of a book on the sharing economy, *What's Mine is Yours,* calculates that the consumer peer-to-peer rental market alone is worth $26 billion in the US. Broader definitions of the sharing economy could include peer-to-peer lending (which we discuss in our chapter on payment processing) or selling power back to a utility by putting solar panels on your roof.

All of these rely on a collaborative consumption model and can take the form of internet marketplaces such as eBay, Craigslist and Airbnb. There are also peer-to-peer lenders, peer-to-peer shared travel experiences (such as Trip Advisor) and, in car sharing, Zipcar or RelayRides or in bus sharing activities, there is Bridj. BlaBla car, a French start up, recently raised $100 million and now has eight million members in 12 countries that use a ride-sharing service between cities. Not all such companies are regarded positively; Monkey Parking in San Francisco, for instance, has developed a rather controversial app that allows its users to sell parking spaces they are about to vacate on the street. There is something dubious about selling a public asset.

Additionally, many companies new and old are involved in "reduce, reuse, recycle, repair" businesses that deal with waste or unwanted goods, with internet characteristics. These markets might be for the swapping or outright gifting of goods. With companies where the goods are free, such as Freecycle and Kashless, there is usually a charitable component of the business model. However, there are plenty of swapping sites where goods are exchanged for other goods, where the sites take a fee. There are a growing number of specialist marketplaces for preowned fashion items, such as Copious, Vestiaire Collective, BuyMyWardrobe and Grand Circle. There are also plenty of sites for bartering, bike sharing, book swapping, carpooling, collaborative workspace sharing, flat sharing, garden sharing, or even, pet sharing. As an example, the UK-based Borrow My Doggy connects people who want to spend time with a dog but don't have one of their own, with people who have a dog that needs more walks.

Many of the thousands of "sharing" sites will sink without a trace, as they are highly dependent on being seeded with plenty of offers to lure users and never succeed in attaining an escape velocity for their business. But some do really take off, as for instance ThredUP has done. This site facilitates kids' clothing swaps. One year after launching, there were 10,000 members exchanging more than 14,000 items per month and now they have an average of 1,000 mothers signing up every day. This is the original hand-me-down concept writ large.

In addition, there is the explosive growth of Zipcar, which has been bought out by Avis. After joining, Zipcar's members can rent different types of cars, trucks and vans by the hour. Zipcar's membership has grown to around 800,000, each of whom pays a monthly fee, plus a time and mileage charge for vehicle usage. Fuel and insurance are included. Originally, members had to drop off their cars where they picked them up, but now point-to-point rental is becoming the norm. There are many imitators, including from the established car rental companies, but Zipcar is by far and away the largest of its kind. It has established links with universities to provide on-campus cars, with businesses to reduce fleet costs, and with a variety of other affiliate organisations.

As with most novel businesses, Zipcar has spawned several variants, some of which have very clever business models. For example, RelayRides, a San Francisco company raised $25 million from amongst others, Google Ventures. This company allows people to rent out their own cars to others on a peer-to-peer platform, for short or long-term rentals. Its most innovative rental plan is available in 2,100+ cities and 300+ airports throughout the US.

RelayRides operates almost like a regular car rental company except that it has the key advantage of not owning the fleet, and it is also able to offer a much wider selection of car models.

In a different, but even more lucrative space, Airbnb has carved out a dominant position in the rental of spare bedrooms or room space globally. Around 40,000 people rent rooms through Airbnb every night. These rooms are rented from a listings range of 600,000 rooms across 30,000 cities in 192 countries. Again, Airbnb is a San Francisco founded firm, started only in 2008, and recently it was valued at $10 billion in a $500 million capital raising. As with Uber and other disruptors of entrenched interests, Airbnb has attracted the ire of the disrupted. Cities claim they are losing out on sales taxes and hoteliers claim that

Airbnb and its rooms are not subject to the same health and safety rules and regulations as they are. Sour grapes aside, this disruptor is here to stay. It will be worth looking at Airbnb when it goes public, depending of course on the valuation.

Although Airbnb has such a head start over everyone else and has listings in 192 countries, one may be tempted to view the company as a very large business. But, it owns no physical assets and uses the internet to disintermediate demand for space. It upends the traditional hotel model, and that surely makes sense for travellers everywhere. Airbnb says that those who rent out their space in San Francisco do so for an average of 58 nights a year, generating $9,300 of income.

Car owners who rent out their vehicles to others using RelayRides make an average of $250 a month; some make more than $1,000. Renters, meanwhile, pay less than they would if they bought the item themselves, or used a traditional provider such as a hotel or car-hire firm. From the point of view of vetting renters, the use of Facebook and other social networks, participants can check each other out and identify friends (or friends of friends) in common, as a form of endorsement.

The "sharing" rental business has become so lucrative that some people have bought cars specifically to rent out through RelayRides, and some take in a steady stream of guests through Airbnb as an alternative to having a roommate or lodger.

Wearables

Wearable technology, wearable devices, or fashion electronics are accessories or clothing (such as watches, wristbands, glasses or jewellery) incorporating electronic technologies.

Many readers will have seen, at least in pictures, the rather odd looking Google Glasses being sported by the (invariably nerdy) early adopters. The past few years have also seen the rise to prominence of wrist-worn sports or activity measuring devices, such as the *Jawbone*, *FitBit* and Nike's *FuelBand*.

Smartwatches are beginning to seep into the mainstream, and

while early versions, such as the crowd-sourced *Pebble*, or the Samsung watch were of limited use, next generation versions are getting better all the time.

Apple is planning to launch its *iWatch* in late 2014, and the company is rumoured to be gearing up to produce three million of them every month. The *iWatch* is likely to have a heart rate monitor, step counting capability and a link to an iPhone to relay messages to its user (perhaps using the voice recognition system, Siri).

There are now 65 million registered users of *My Fitness Pal*, a calorie-counting app that links to a user's mobile phone, and 2.4 billion steps have been taken by users of *Fitbit*, the equivalent to walking from Earth to Saturn – and back.

All of these devices so far share the common characteristics of being somewhat fiddly to use and are of limited utility.

But in the next ten years or so, wearables will have voice control and be permanently connected to the web, making them much more useful. There are of course privacy concerns with many of these devices but they will be similar in nature to those associated with smartphones.

Figure 11: Nike's FuelBand **Source:** Peter Parkes (Flickr: Nike FuelBand) [CC-BY-2.0 (http://creativecommons.org/licenses/by/2.0)], via Wikimedia Commons.

The limitations of wearable devices at the moment are obvious: Google Glass is unsightly; smaller wearables such as watches are fiddly and have limited battery life; and there is only so much information people need about their pulse. In some ways, wearables are a solution in search of a problem.

Overall though, wearable technology in multiple forms that incorporates cameras, voice recognition, directions, etc. is here to stay. Incidentally, there are already "smart shoes" that vibrate to tell the user which way to turn.

With all of the big boys jumping into this nascent market, competition will spur innovation. Many of these devices will be linked to new healthcare software being developed by Apple, Samsung, and Google, to monitor vital body functions, possibly passing the information on to the user's doctor. The remote healthcare monitoring market – particularly for people with conditions that are chronic, such as diabetes – is going to be very large indeed. This will push wearables from being glorified calorie counters to sophisticated health care devices, being able to monitor such things as blood sugar levels and ovulation.

Cisco believes that there will be 177 million wearable devices in use globally in 2018, up from 22 million in 2013, and an increasing percentage of them will be connected to the web. British company ARM, which is a leader in mobile chip design, has recently unveiled a new operating system for IOT and is about to produce a suite of new chips for connected devices. We like ARM as a stock.

An interesting new device is the FreeWavz, which are wireless earphones that independently (i.e. not linked to a smartphone) measures distance and pulse information and delivers it by voice right into the runner's ear, allowing the eyes to stay focused on the road/trail. Being keen runners ourselves, this is the kind of utility we like. It also shows the future path of wearable technology. FreeWavz is Kickstarter-funded, demonstrating that not all new ideas have to come out of the labs of the big boys. That said, Google is likely to announce a new Android version – possibly called Lollipop – that incorporates a heavy focus on smartwatches and smart home devices.

One final example to illustrate the diversity of the functionality we can expect from wearables is by a company called Netatmo, which has come up with an ultraviolet (UV) light sensor, worn on the wrist, designed to notify the wearer when to put on sunscreen or indeed when to stay out of the sun.

Virtual Reality

Another category of wearable devices is the virtual reality headset. Creating a convincing 3D virtual environment requires a great deal of computer processing power, which is why it has taken so long for this technology to develop. But virtual reality is finally approaching the point where processing power is able to deliver on the demands of this technology.

In 2013, a then recently crowd-source funded virtual reality headset company called Oculus, was bought by Facebook for $2 billion. The fact that Facebook was prepared to spend so much on a start-up with one somewhat ungainly looking product, demonstrates the vast market potential of virtual reality in coming years.

Although virtual reality is heavily associated with gaming, its true potential extends way beyond this. For example, teleconferencing is an obvious application, as are virtual tours of ancient monuments and museums. Older virtual reality headsets made users suffer from motion sickness, as the processors and algorithms were not fast enough to match the human brain. Oculus is the first company to successfully counterbalance this effect, which it achieves by using stereoscopic 3D (a wide view field and 360 degree visualisation) to create a virtual reality experience that feels like normal reality.

One of the ways in which the device is able to achieve this realistic environment is by taking high frequency measurements from an accelerometer, a gyroscope and a magnetometer to evaluate and predict motion. The sample rate is an impressive 1,000 times per second.

Virtual reality is sometimes referred to as immersive multimedia, and is an electronically simulated environment that mimics the feeling of actually being in that environment. In addition to sight and sound, virtual reality can also incorporate virtual smell, virtual taste and virtual touch.

The concept of vreality was first popularized in movies such as *Brainstorm* and *The Lawnmower Man* in the 1980s and '90s. For the time being, virtual reality is primarily visual (using stereoscopic displays) although there are systems that allow for sensory sound, and indeed, touch, through what is known as haptic technology. This involves so-called force feedback that is now commonly used in gaming, medicine and in flight simulators. The inevitable improvement in processing power and the development of lighter head-mounted displays (in this respect Google Glass is a forerunner), the incorporation of sensory data gloves, and further miniaturization, will eventually make virtual reality much more accessible and useful to us.

It will be possible to virtually be in a movie, experiencing realistic sounds and physical sensations, possibly even with smell and taste thrown in for good measure. In June 2014, Metaio, an "augmented reality" software company, released what it calls its *6D Holodeck* technology, superimposing virtual environments directly onto the real world. This is ultimately supposed to allow the wearer to experience an enhanced reality through a headset, but for the time being, neither Google Glass nor Oculus's Rift headsets are powerful enough to cope with the software. Sony is working on a virtual reality headset, codenamed project Morpheus that is being designed to work with its PlayStation 4 and PlayStation Vita. No release date has been announced but the reviews so far have been very positive.

The Cloud

Cloud computing or *the cloud* is, in general terms, a way of sharing computer resources, from processing power to applications, over the internet.

The cloud has become a real buzz term in recent years. But the cloud has been around for a lot longer than that; anyone who has ever used a web-based email account has used cloud computing.

Web-based email or webmail typically uses a browser to view and navigate within the email application, but the application itself is hosted at a remote server.

This means that the bulk of the computer processing is done at the server end, so the computer at the client end requires less processing power. This configuration is known as a thin client.

In contrast, if the application is installed locally on the client's device, say Microsoft Outlook, then the bulk of the computer processing is done at the client end when using this application.

This configuration is known as a *thick client* (sometimes also called a *fat client*).

Cloud computing has taken off thanks to the near ubiquity of broadband internet access in the

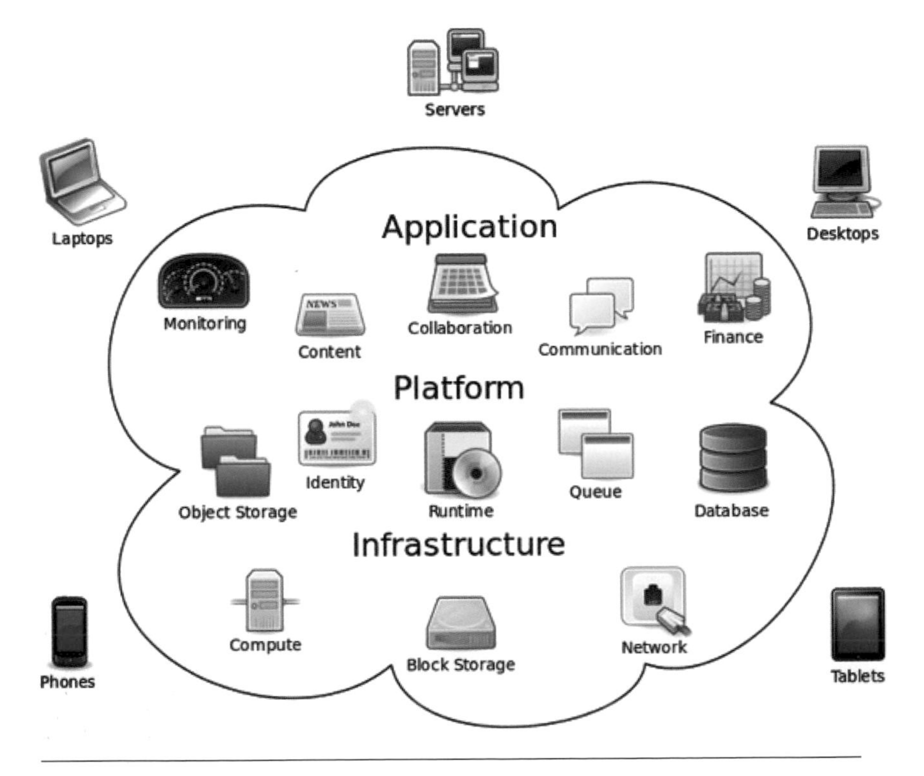

Figure 12: Cloud Computing **Source:** Sam Johnston using OmniGroup's OmniGraffle and Inkscape. Licensed under Creative Commons Attribution-Share Alike 3.0 via Wikimedia Commons.

developed world.

At the application level, the cloud is "software as a service" or SaaS, allowing companies and individuals to pay a monthly or annual license fee (or sometimes no fee at all) for one or more software applications that are hosted at a remote server. This has become a hugely popular way to buy software and the advantages are many, the main ones being: (1) the licensee or user does not have to worry about installing updates and bug fixes to the software, as the licensor ensures that all of its software is constantly updated at its remote servers; (2) the licensee does not have to worry about buying an expensive server, along with additional software and hardware that are required to run the application – all of this is included in the cloud pricing model; (3) the licensee does not have to worry about periodically upgrading the server as this is the responsibility of the licensor; (4) the licensee does not have to worry about backing up data as this will be done automatically on a regular basis at the data centre hosting the software; and (5) it is cheaper for the licensee to pay a low monthly or annual fee than to pay an up-front fee. With lower up-front costs, SaaS allows many IT expenditure items to be moved out of the capital expenditure (CAPEX) budget and over to the operational expenditure (OPEX) budget.

Below this SaaS application level, there is also "platform as a service" or PaaS, which usually includes some development tools for writing applications, as well as a database and webserver. At the bottom layer is the most basic of cloud services, known as "infrastructure as a service" or IaaS. This is mainly hardware, such as servers, storage and network connectivity.

Obviously the cloud needs a reliable and fast internet connection to exchange data between servers and devices. It also requires adequate security at both the client and server level. It is concerns over the latter that some organisations even today refuse to use the cloud for certain parts of their business, deeming the data to be too sensitive to travel on the public cloud, as encrypted as it might be throughout its journey.

Cloud computing is being applied in a variety of different ways; some of these are shown in Figure 12. As the IOT continues to grow, more and more devices will be connected to the internet and they in turn will join the cloud. The big tech players know just how big the cloud is going to get and are all key providers of cloud services, the top five of them (for 2013) being: Salesforce.com, Amazon, Microsoft, Oracle and Google, with Google launching a new cloud platform in November 2014.

Cloud computing requires huge data centres to store servers and network equipment. These centres are now so large that they account for at least 10 per cent of all energy consumption worldwide, and as the IOT gathers pace, that percentage is going to rise further. The unintended consequence of the explosion of the internet is that it is less green than, say aviation, which utilises half as much energy globally.

Pulling It All Together...

According to PwC, the IOT, wearables and virtual reality will all drive internet traffic and boost consumer spending more than any other product or service over the next five years. PwC believes that internet connectivity (broadband and related services) will generate sales of $636 billion worldwide by 2018.

Also by 2018, consumer internet revenue from apps, games, music, etc. is expected to reach $780 billion and ad spending is expected to grow to $640 billion, and by then internet advertising will account for one third of all ad spending worldwide.

Emerging market consumers are predicted to contribute the fastest growth in internet related spending in the next few years. China, Brazil, Russia, India, Mexico, South Africa, Turkey, Argentina and Indonesia will together account for 21.7 per cent of global revenue in 2018, up from 12.4 per cent in 2009, according to PwC.

The main areas of interest to us as investors in this next phase of the internet's growth are becoming increasingly apparent, namely:

1. Further "infill" disruption in

what might now be called the conventional internet, i.e. new apps, new retail channels and specialised and disruptive sites;

2. The expansion of the well-established but still infantile "sharing economy" where everything from cars to rooms to pets can be shared;
3. The Internet of Things (IOT), where the connectivity of objects through the internet will improve efficiency and productivity; and
4. The development of interconnected virtual reality as a target of internet developers.

What Should Investors Consider?

With so much activity in this space, all taking place at a mind-boggling pace, it is difficult to know which companies will emerge as the outright winners and which ones will fall by the wayside. One of our suggestions would be to consider Google, which in itself has evolved into a sort of government of the net, and although already highly capitalised, could still deliver good returns to shareholders.

Then there is Rockwell Automation, Honeywell and Cisco, all US-listed firms, and very active in the "nuts and bolts" of the internet. Cisco's equipment connects manufacturing floors, energy grids, healthcare facilities and transportation systems to the Internet. Its mission statement is based on the fact that when an object can represent itself digitally, it can be controlled from anywhere.

Intel is another high quality company that has been a world leader in chip design and manufacturing for several decades. Chips will play a vital role in the internet of things and unimaginable quantities of them will be needed over the next decade or so. We like Intel as a long term investment.

Also worth considering are companies that provide internet services, particularly

those "last mile" services into people's homes. The increased usage of bandwidth will grow extraordinarily with the IOT and the continued growth in mobile video. Companies well positioned to capitalise on these trends include Comcast and Verizon in the US, Vodafone in the UK, Softbank in Japan, and Telefonica in Spain. All of these companies are likely to enjoy renewed growth.

pio3 / Shutterstock.com

Then of course there is Apple, which is likely to come up with desirable and popular IOT products, along with increasingly useful wearable devices. Apple is also a large company but will deliver reasonable returns over the next few years.

For readers looking for more international exposure, there is a company called Naspers, headquartered in South Africa. Naspers is a pay TV and print business with some really amazing internet investments on the side. It purchased Tencent shares in China (China's largest internet content company); and it has a stake in Mail.ru, the leading internet company in Russia. It sells at a significant discount to the sum of its parts and looks like an interesting way to get international exposure to the growth of the internet.

Watch out also for Airbnb and Relay Rides, as they will likely list in the near future.

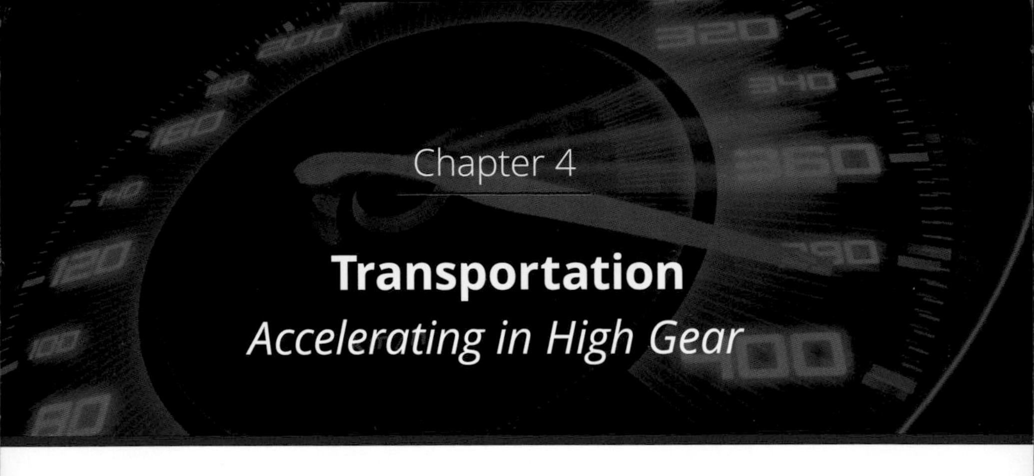

Chapter 4

Transportation

Accelerating in High Gear

In 1968, a movie named *2001: A Space Odyssey* was released that changed the way people thought about the future. Directed by Stanley Kubrick, it has become something of a cult film, playing as it does on a futuristic description of human protagonists pitted against rogue humanized computers on board a space mission to Jupiter.

The film was in many ways prescient, as it foretold of a world in which artificial intelligence (AI) is widely used, and in that way it heralds Ray Kurzweil's idea of the *Singularity.* Its ambition in terms of the level of technology that mankind would supposedly achieve by 2001 was towering, and in most ways has not been attained even today.

Mankind is still many years away from a manned mission to Jupiter, and the Singularity is still some way out, but the general direction of travel pursued, scientifically speaking, was bang on course.

It is instructive to think that a mere hundred years ago cars were a novelty, with their ownership confined to the rich, air travel was very rudimentary, the aeroplane then being less than twenty years old, and space travel was at best an imaginary figment. Fast forward to today, cars and trucks have become ubiquitous, air travel is universal, and space travel is routine, though not to the extent of going to the frontiers portrayed by Stanley Kubrick's film.

Yet somehow many people feel that we have been in a period of stasis when it comes to travel innovation.

"It is instructive to think that a mere hundred years ago cars were a novelty, with their ownership confined to the rich."

Planes, with the exception of war machines, don't fly much faster than they did in the 1970s, especially after the retirement of Concorde. They have become more fuel efficient and bigger though, and their avionics have become more sophisticated.

It is a similar story for cars, which despite being more reliable and electronically capable, are more or less the same as they were in terms of shape and configuration, and are still mostly powered by fossil fuels. Ships and trains, while faster and in the case of ships, larger, are still relatively similar to their forty year old cousins. While there is a lot of talk about a transport revolution, the evidence of it is relatively scant, at least in relation to other areas in which technology has powered ahead.

However, we believe that is about to change. The areas that we see as having the greatest potential are: space exploration, the automation of travel including driverless cars, new forms of train travel, new propulsion systems transforming air and sea travel, the use of electricity and hydrogen to power vehicles, and the coming pervasiveness of drones.

Transport systems are always slower to change than other areas of economic activity because of the entrenched nature of existing infrastructure and the very long lead times to develop new transport platforms. Yet despite that, there is much change afoot.

For where we are today in terms of new development in transport types, the year 1914 is a good exemplar. The First World War sped up the development of new forms of transport, including improvements in aeronautical technology and the development of mechanised vehicles including tanks. Subsequently, the manufacturing revolution initiated by Henry Ford led to the mass production of cars. During the Second World War, the invention of modern rocketry and the jet engine transformed transport technology from the 1940s to the 1970s immeasurably. However, we believe that the relative gradualism of improvements to transport systems since the 1970s is about to change as new technologies come to the fore.

Flights to Mars and More Prosaic Space Exploration

Since Neil Armstrong first set foot on the moon in 1969, with his famous pronouncements about a giant step for mankind, the early promise of space exploration has not really materialized. Sure, there were subsequent lunar landings, and the surface of Mars has been explored to some extent. Also, prior to its retirement, **NASA's** Space Shuttle made low Earth orbit travel more routine, and the **International Space Station (ISS)** has now been in service since 1998, although it is due to be decommissioned in 2020.

But the dream of space travel as envisioned in 2001: A Space Odyssey or **Star Trek**, or even **The Jetsons** is still many years out. The main reason is due to economics; it is hugely expensive to maintain an organisation such as NASA, and without tangible economic benefits, it became increasingly more difficult to justify a full-scale US space exploration effort. As well, the breakup of the Soviet Union made the space race a lesser priority in Russia as it tackled its huge economic problems. Emerging space nations such as China and India are as yet too far behind in technology to make a serious leap forward in space exploration.

This is changing. Thanks to technological developments, rockets are becoming cheaper and reusable; digital technology is now so advanced that a smartphone today has several thousand times more computing power than the original lunar landing mission. More computing power vastly improves the capability of monitoring systems and communications, and new materials enable engineers to design and construct superior space vehicles.

Reality TV has sensed an opportunity: The Dutch TV giant **Endemol** has teamed up with a non-profit organisation to create **Mars One,** a one way expedition to Mars by 2025, designed to take four colonists to the red planet. They will supposedly live in inflatable pods after a seven month uncomfortable journey to the red planet, and every two years thereafter, they will be joined by an additional four intrepid volunteers, with the intention of building a self-sustaining community there.

About 200,000 people applied for the job (bearing in mind there is no return journey to Earth), and 700 were initially selected. The selection process has reduced it further to 400, with the oldest candidate likely to be nearly 80 by the time lift off occurs. Final selection will take place by 2017.

All the technology for this mission is available today, especially with the **Space X Falcon** rocket now tested and working. This is the reusable rocket system developed by uber-entrepreneur Elon Musk, who also founded **PayPal** and **Tesla Motors,** the electric car company.

The initial training of the astronauts will begin in 2015, and it will be filmed to provide the funds for the expedition. (Interested readers can find out more at this website: http://www.mars-one.com).

Once they arrive on Mars, the astronauts will have about 50 square metres of accommodation each, and will live relatively normal lives from a workday point of view. This work will consist of preparing the ground for further colonists and maintaining communications with Earth, and of course their commercial sponsors. They will grow their own plants, make tunnels and domes from compressed Martian soil, and explore the planet.

Regardless of whether Mars One ever gets off the ground (and we rate it as 50/50) it does demonstrate a renewed interest and curiosity in space travel. Cheaper rockets, superior technology, and the demonstration by the ISS that it is possible to live in space for long periods are all contributory factors to the new space race.

There is also the prospect of asteroid mining, although this is still under development and some time off from being a reality. After all, asteroids are the original source of pretty much all of the metals on or near our planet's surface when they bombarded Earth some four billion years ago. Materials potentially mineable in space include iron, nickel, and titanium. There is also the prospect of mining water and oxygen to sustain the lives of prospectors *in situ*, as well as hydrogen and oxygen for use as rocket fuel.

And of course there is *space tourism,* which is going to be a reality relatively soon. Already, some rich people have paid to go to the ISS, but with **Virgin Galactic's** long anticipated commercial space flights, and Space X working on space tourism initiatives, it won't be too long before non-professional astronauts start flying up to space on a regular basis.

Elon Musk's company Space X is at the forefront of all of this activity. It has now successfully carried four payloads of research equipment and food to the ISS, under nearly $2 billion of US government contracts, following the retirement of the Space Shuttle programme in 2011. Space X is a private company based in California, but it is likely to go public in the near future – and is one to watch. It has over $5 billion of forward contracts with over 50 launches on its manifest. Its **Falcon Heavy** rocket is being readied for crewed missions to Mars and beyond, and it is one-third of the cost and twice as powerful as its nearest competitor.

Another American company, **Orbital Sciences Corporation (NYSE:ORB)** has a similar contract to Space X with its **Cygnus** rocket. Orbital has so far completed one mission under a $1.9 billion contract with NASA. Both companies have reusable first stage rockets for the ISS, which are self-guided to return to earth. Space X is also readying its **Dragon** rocket to be crew-ready, so it can take over from government programmes to take and retrieve crew and people to and from the ISS.

For the moment, Orbital Sciences is the purest play space company available to invest in.

There are other proxies, such as **Lockheed Martin** or **Boeing,** but these companies are so big that their space programmes are relatively insignificant relative to their business as a whole. Orbital's extensive experience (it has launched 150 spacecraft including satellites since 1990) makes it probably the best stock to tuck away for the long term in this field. It is capitalised at around $1.6 billion at the time of writing.

Meanwhile, NASA itself is developing its **SLS** rocket, by far the biggest rocket ever made, which is scheduled for a 2017 initial launch. This **Space Launch System** is being designed for Mars and deep outer space. For its first test flight, the rocket will be able to launch 70 metric tons (77 imperial tons) of payload into low Earth orbit, almost three times as much as the space shuttle was capable of transporting.

Figure 13: The design of the new heavy-lift rocket, the Space Launch System (SLS). **Source:** NASA

Airplanes, Jets and Solar Powered Planes

While mankind once again prepares to go to the farthest frontiers of space, back on Earth moves are afoot to improve the speed of air travel. This is the one feature of air travel that hasn't much changed over the past few decades. Concorde proved to be uneconomic, and despite its great speed and convenience, suffered from some design faults which made it unviable. Most notable of these was its small passenger carrying capacity and the sonic boom it generated in its wake that limited the routes on which it could be used.

Today, a new revolution in aircraft design is underway, partly as a result of the development of new engines to propel them. Some are fanciful, some are practical, and some are closer to fruition than others. But taken together, it is likely that in the next twenty years, there will be in late development a rapid air transport system that will dramatically cut journey times for long haul flights.

One concept that has been mooted is that of a *magnetic launcher.* This is a *magnetic levitation,* or *maglev system* that propels vehicles at high speeds and effectively shoots them out of the atmosphere. The idea is to get enough traction and speed to reach orbital velocity as the vehicle is released off its track. This is in effect a sort of catapult, or new runway system – and in theory looks very attractive. The problem is the heat that would be generated by the very rapid acceleration along a horizontal plane, which might lead to the aircraft melting. As yet, this is purely a drawing board idea but gives a clue as to the number of ways designers are thinking about aircraft of the future.

A further drawing board idea is that of *wing-in-ground craft.* This approach takes advantage of what is known as *the ground effect,* which is observed when fixed wing aircraft fly close to the ground.

Figure 14: A Maglev launcher could be used to propel aircraft into orbit. **Source:** NASA

When under the ground effect, the wing generates more lift (around 75 per cent more) and experiences less drag.

The ground effect works when an aircraft flies at a height roughly equal to its wingspan. **Boeing** has a large-capacity transport plane called the *Pelican* in development using this technique, and Russia has developed the *Burevestinik-24,* which so far appears to be a bit of a Heath Robinson contraption (interested readers can watch a video of it in action on YouTube: (http://youtu.be/wPlVod_SD0k). Such planes would never fly fast (around 150 miles per hour) but their payload capacities could be very large and they could skim over water and ground.

The moneyed classes definitely miss Concorde and recently there has been a lot of talk of new private planes which could fly supersonically. The problem with flying at supersonic speeds is the sonic boom, which is why most countries ban them from flying over their land. Boston-based company, **Spike Aerospace** plans to develop the Spike S-512, a 12-18 seater supersonic private jet designed for commercial use and capable of flying from New York to London in under four hours. Spike S-512 is predicted to reach speeds of Mach 1.6-1.8 (1,060 to 1,200 mph) over the sea. Its putative cost, around $80 million, will make such a plane a play-thing of only the richest, if it ever gets off the drawing board.

In addition, **Aerion Corporation** of Nevada also has plans underway for a supersonic, private jet that would also be capable of reaching speeds of Mach 1.6, potentially carrying its first passengers by the end of the decade. Even more ambitious is **Hyper Mach Aerospace,** which has unveiled the blueprints for its *Sonic Star,* an aircraft that will attain speeds of Mach 4. That translates to New York to London in an hour! Hyper Mach is to feature *"electromagnetic drag reduction technology"* which is supposed to soften the sonic boom.

Next up is the *Waverider,* a hypersonic aircraft which uses shock waves generated by its own flight to improve lift-drag ratios and thereby fly faster. In May 2013, an unmanned **Boeing X-51** Waverider was launched successfully from 50,000 feet (15,000 metres) by a B-52 bomber and accelerated using a rocket to Mach 4.8 (3,200 mph, or 5,100 kph) at which point it separated from the rocket and ignited its *scramjet* (more on that below). The Waverider was then accelerated further to Mach 5.1 (3,400 mph, or 5,400 kph) and climbed to 60,000 feet (18,000 metres) before it was intentionally crashed into the Pacific Ocean.

A scramjet (which stands for supersonic combusting *ramjet*) is a type of jet engine in which combustion starts in supersonic conditions, so the plane has to be accelerated to that speed before the engine can work. Airflow in a scramjet is supersonic throughout the entire engine which allows the scramjet to operate at extremely high speeds. Theoretical projections have suggested that the top speed of a scramjet could be somewhere between Mach 12 (8,400 mph, or 14,000 kph) and Mach 24 (16,000 mph, or 25,000 kph).

Scramjets have three basic components: a converging inlet, where incoming air is compressed; a combustor, where gaseous fuel is burned with oxygen to produce heat; and a diverging nozzle, where the heated air is accelerated to produce thrust. Unlike a typical jet engine, such as a turbofan or turbojet, a scramjet does not use rotating fan-like components to compress the air; rather, the supersonic speed of the aircraft causes the air to compress naturally without moving parts. But scramjets need to be accelerated to the supersonic speeds by other means (usually to around Mach 4). Variants of launch systems include rail guns, turbojets, or rockets. The technical challenges of scramjets are only now being addressed, even though the concept first originated in the 1950s.

A British privately held company called **Reaction Engines Limited** is working on an improved type of scramjet that will accelerate under its own power to the point where the scramjet variant it carries can be turned on.

The idea is that this *SABRE engine,* initially powering a plane called Skylon, will be able to get to the opposite end of the world in less than four hours, and takeoff and land on a normal runway, or to take cargo into space more cheaply and quickly.

Ultra-lightweight heat exchangers are the key enabling components in SABRE engines for Mach 5 cruising speeds and aircraft-like access to orbit.

Reaction Engines, based in Oxford in the UK, has run the engine over 100 times in tests, and while initially Skylon will be used to transport satellites into space, ultimately variants could also be used to take people from, say London to Sydney in one fifth of the current time.

Currently, Skylon is designed to be an unpiloted, reusable plane intended to provide reliable and effective access to space. The vehicle will be capable of transporting 15 tonnes of cargo into space. The vehicles using SABRE's combined air-breathing and rocket cycles allow it to take off from an airport runway, fly up to earth orbit, then descend and land like a conventional aircraft. The UK government is investing about $100 million in SABRE, and first test flights are mooted for 2017.

Could Airships Make a Come-back?

Slowing things down substantially, there is a revival of interest underway in the use of airships. The airship in its original form took a dive (literally) when the **Hindenburg** crashed in New

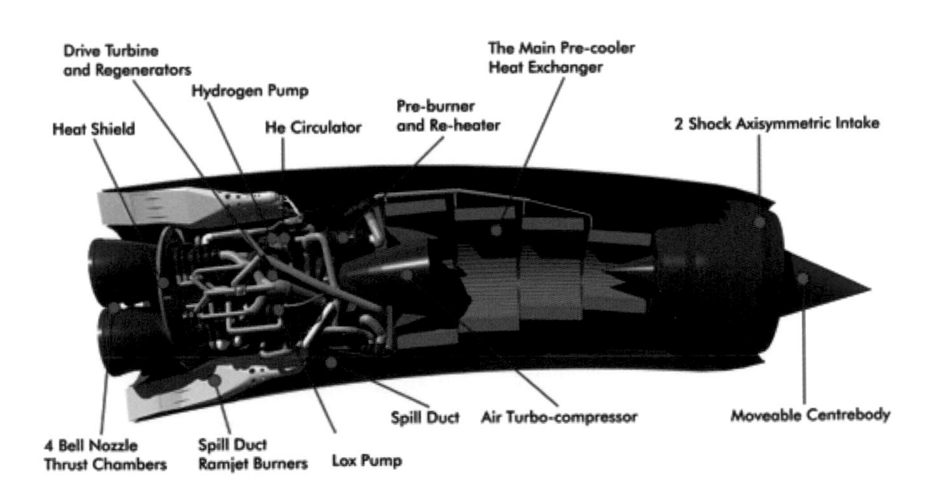

Figure 15: Reaction Engine's SABRE engine with built-in scramjet (annotated). **Source:** Reaction Engines (http://www.reactionengines.co.uk)

Figure 16: Rendition of Skylon aircraft in flight, to be powered by SABRE engines. **Source:** Reaction Engines (http://www.reactionengines.co.uk)

Jersey in 1937. It never really recovered as a mode of transport after that disaster, and its use since then has been largely confined to advertising.

However, with a different, inert type of gas, helium being used in modern airships, as well as new and much safer designs there is hope that airships could be used for transporting payloads into difficult areas. They are also able to carry much more cargo than conventional aircraft. An airship or *dirigible* is a type of aerostat or lighter-than-air aircraft that is propelled through the air by engine power. An aerostat stays aloft by having a large *envelope* filled with a lifting gas that is less dense than the surrounding air. In early dirigibles, the gas used was flammable hydrogen, due to its high lifting capacity. Nowadays helium is used, a non-flammable gas and almost as good as hydrogen. The trouble with helium is that it is relatively rare on earth and as a result from time to time there are shortages.

Since the 1960s airships have been used for advertising, surveillance, geological surveys and tourism, largely due to their ability to hover for long periods of time in one place. Today, due to improvements in design, they are about to be used as cargo transporters with almost minimal design risks.

They also have potential military applications, since the **UK Ministry of Defence** has recently tested airships and subjected them to high rates of small arms and military fire. Despite this ordnance, there was no critical loss of helium and all the of vehicles were able to return to base without crashing.

Aeros, a California company is developing the *Aeroscraft,* which combines fixed wing aircraft characteristics as well as lighter-than-air traditional airship technology. In addition, it possesses the vertical take-off and landing capabilities of a helicopter, meaning it has no need for a runway or airfield. The Aeroscraft is a rigid-hulled dirigible measuring 169 meters in length, with a payload capacity of 66 tonnes (with plans for a monster 250 tonne version), a cruising speed of up to 120 knots, and a range of 3,100 nautical miles.

In the UK, **Hybrid Air Vehicles** is developing a long endurance (five days) airship platform for such use as geological surveys, communications, and surveillance, as well as an airship designed to carry heavy payloads to difficult locations such as for disaster relief.

Other Contenders

In 2015, **Solar Impulse**, a Swiss aircraft powered entirely by the sun, will take off with two crew and attempt to circumnavigate the globe. The plane, which looks like a large glider, has been test flown with no problems.

Terrafugia, is an American company that has created the first street-legal aircraft in the world. This aircraft is called the *Transition.* The company has also announced the concept for a more automated hybrid version known as TF-X. (http://www.terrafugia.com). The company has described its first vehicle as the "first practical flying car." It is designed to fit in a single car garage, be safely driven on the highway, and be flown in and out of general aviation airports. It had its first flight in 2013, and while the Transition only has two seats, its successor, the TF-X will have four, and will use electric rather than fossil power.

Drones

All of us have become familiar with drones, mostly because of their military use, and also because of Amazon's attention-grabbing announcement that in the future it plans on delivering some of its orders by using drones.

The military use of drones as substitutes for manned aircraft is increasing, for several good reasons: avoidance of casualties, greater precision and the cheaper price tag attached to drones in comparison to fighter and other military aircraft. Interestingly, the US is finding it hard to get enough trained drone pilots, as flying them remotely – often thousands of miles from where the drone is in action – can be tedious and tiring.

Military applications aside, there are many other uses for drones, such as in agriculture to improve the efficiency of inputs such as water and fertilisers. Drones are much cheaper to own and operate than traditional aircraft and can provide farmers with all the information they need. Mini-drones can be bought (for instance from **3D Robotics)** for less than $1,000 and while military versions are much more expensive, the application of drones to civilian surveillance, monitoring of oil pipelines and environmental surveillance studies are just some of the many ways drones can be deployed. British giant **BAE Systems** is a leader in drone technology and is an investment we like for the long term.

The day when drones will be able to deliver pizzas, fight fires and search for missing people are not so far away, but before we can get there drones must be made safe – and by that we mean they don't crash into people or things, especially in urban environments. In that respect, the technology isn't quite there yet. **Integrated Robotics Imaging Systems** has a radar unit that weighs 12 ounces (about 340 grams) and these units are getting lighter with each new generation of releases. **Sagetech,** another US-based company has managed to get the weight of a transponder that shows up on air traffic control systems down to just 3 ounces (85 grams) versus 3 pounds (around 1.4 kilograms) for a regular aircraft.

The Federal Aircraft Administration (FAA) in the US is about to issue guidelines to allow drones below 55 pounds (25 kilograms) to fly below 400 feet (122 metres) without special permits, as long as they are within sight of a human operator. Amazon is developing *"Amazon Prime Air,"* a system it says will deliver packages in 30 minutes or less using drones that will be able to travel at speeds of more than 50 mph (80 kph) and carry payloads of up to 5 pounds (2.3 kilograms).

"One day, seeing Amazon Prime Air will be as normal as seeing mail trucks on the road today," the company has declared.

And of course, Google is in on the act and is testing its own drone delivery systems in Australia, though not, as yet, for e-commerce purposes.

Drones will become a big market. **Teal Group,** an aerospace research company, estimates that by 2023 the drone market will be worth at least $11.6 billion a year.

Trains – A Railway Revival

In many countries, trains are now recognised as environmentally friendly, rapid transportation systems that deserve far more investment than they received during the twentieth century. Until recently, trains had fallen out of favour as a mode of transport (for passengers and cargo) relative to automobiles, trucks, ships and planes.

That is now changing, and countries in Asia, including China, Europe and even North America are introducing variants of high speed rail networks. The first high speed trains began operations in Japan in 1964 and they are commonly known as *bullet trains.* High-speed trains usually work on modified standard gauge tracks, which have been continuously welded and have wide turning radiuses in their layout.

High speed rail typically refers to any train service that travels at over 200 kph (125 mph). Today, after commencing work only in 2007, China has already constructed the longest high-speed rail network in the world, with over 15,000 kilometres of track including the world's longest line from Beijing to Guangzhou (2,298 kilometres). China also has the world's first high speed maglev line in Shanghai. China's rail network is projected to grow to 18,000 kilometres of track by 2015, about a third of which will be able to handle trains travelling at speeds of over 300 kph (188 mph).

In Europe also, there has been an explosion in the construction of high speed rail networks. The first *Transport à Grande Vitesse (TGV)* lines were built in France in the 1980s and since then the network has been extended into many other countries in the European Union, incorporating trans-border services.

France has the second largest high-speed rail network in Europe, second only to Spain. *TGV Euroduplex* started service in 2011 on the new Rhine-Rhone high speed line, and is the world's

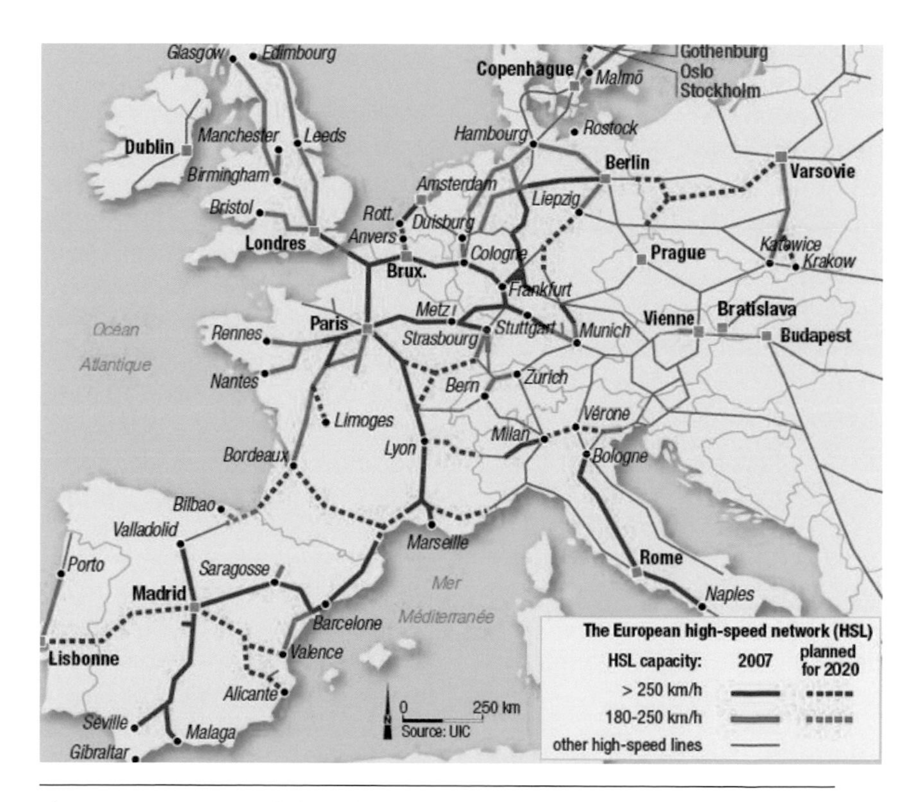

Figure 17: Europe's extensive high speed rail network. **Source:** UIC, International Union of Railways

first double-decker high-speed train, carrying up to 1,020 passengers in each train set.

Italy runs the fastest train network in Europe, with the *AGV Italo* operating at a regular speed of 360 kph but having reached a speed of 575 kph during its test run on the East European high-speed line in April 2007. AGV Italo is built by **Alstom,** a partly state owned company in France. Other key investable companies involved in the train business globally are **Siemens** of Germany, **Bombardier** of Canada, and **Hitachi** of Japan, all of which are listed on their respective country's stock exchanges.

The US has lagged significantly behind most of the developed world in terms of developing a modern train network. Where there is a rail service, it tends to be for slow freight trains rather than high-speed passenger trains. In fact, the passenger services in the US are generally awful. This is because the low speed passenger trains available are not competitive when compared to driving or flying.

However, there has recently been more blue-sky thinking about train travel from the US than anywhere else - but for now, these ideas remain confined to the drawing board. For instance, the modern concept of a *vactrain*, or vacuum tube train travelling through evacuated tunnels using maglev technology was first developed in 1910 by an American engineer Robert Goddard. His proposed train was posited to travel from Boston to New York in just 12 minutes, averaging 1,000 mph (1,600 kph).

Vactrains re-emerged as a topic in the 1970s when Robert Salter of the **RAND Corporation** came up with detailed plans for a tube train shuttle system, using little energy except gravitational force and running in evacuated tubes. Because of design limitations, these trains would only operate for relatively short distances, and didn't employ maglev technology, then in its relative infancy as a concept.

Maglev uses magnetic levitation to propel trains fitted with magnets rather than with wheels, axles and bearings. With maglev, a vehicle is levitated above a guide way (the equivalent of tracks) using magnets to create both lift and thrust.

The technology is only now, after decades of research, being refined and high costs and complexity mean that there are only a few maglev train systems in operation globally. One is in Shanghai, as we mentioned earlier, and the others are in Japan (a small operation), Beijing and South Korea.

Maglev trains are smoother than conventional trains, accelerate and decelerate faster, and are unaffected by the weather. However, they are subject to the same drag forces as regular trains, so energy usage is comparable. They are also very expensive to build.

Vactrains that would use maglev technology in sealed tubes with minimal air friction are being looked at closely, even if it's only conceptually for now. The vactrain theoretically would eliminate the drag forces and enable speeds of thousands of miles per hour to be achieved. The high cost of maglev trains, however, as well as the difficulty of maintaining a vacuum over large distances, has prevented this type of system from ever being built to date.

Our favourite over-achieving entrepreneur, Elon Musk has developed the *Hyperloop* train concept, which is a solar-powered, city-to-city elevated transit system that would be able to take passengers and cars from Los Angeles to San Francisco in just 30 minutes. Musk claims that this would be cheaper and faster than air travel in what is one of the busiest air corridors in the world. The Hyperloop would cover the 354 mile (570 km) route at an average speed of around 600 mph (960 kph), with a top speed of 760 mph (1,220 kph).

The Hyperloop is a variant of the vactrain but has about one millibar[1] of pressure, allowing the quasi-vacuum to be maintained over a long distance.

Turntables would change the direction of ski-mounted aluminium capsules at either end, and Hyperloop would use an electric compressor fan on the nose of each pod to transfer air pressure from the front of the pod to the rear, thereby reducing air drag

---

[1] *Atmospheric pressure = 1 bar, 1 millibar = one-thousandth of a bar.*

at the front. The Hyperloop will travel on air to reduce high speed friction. Musk has described the system as a combination of a Concorde, a rail-gun, and air hockey - and magnets will give the capsules their initial thrust.

Although Musk claims that the system can be built for $6.5 billion, which is a relatively trivial amount considering the distance and challenges faced, *The Economist* magazine believes that, at the very least, the estimate is unlikely to *"be immune to the hypertrophication of cost that every other grand infrastructure project seems doomed to suffer."* In truth, the costs of such a system could range anywhere from $10 billion to as much as $100 billion.

Musk is a dare-to-dream kind of guy and it is not inconceivable that such a system could one day be built. He has made the design open-source as a result of which all sorts of tweaks have been proposed.

All of these developments reinforce our belief that a *Second Age* of the train is upon us. Our favourite companies to invest in this realm include Siemens and Bombardier (mentioned earlier), both large companies, but ones which should offer a stable and decent return to investors over time.

Driverless Cars and Road Trains

At the forefront of just about every technology that consumers use on a daily basis is the California-based giant Google.

This company perhaps is the best example of the power of disruption. Incorporated only in 1998, Google already commands a huge market capitalisation and has an extensive range of services, such as internet search (Google), maps (Google Maps), electronic wallet (Google Wallet), cloud storage (Google Drive) and mobile technology (Android OS and Google play), just to name a few.

But Google is just getting started; it has even more ambitious plans in the pipeline. Our conversations with the company reveal the scale of its vision and power. It has a fascinating approach to planning its next moves - Google uses forward thinking to develop models of the future, then reverse engineers them back to the present.

Perhaps the most exciting innovation that Google has been working on is its highly publicised *driverless car,* which is now close to becoming a reality.

These driverless vehicles have logged over 700,000 miles (1.1 million kilometres) on the road and so far, accident-free.

Driverless cars make tremendous sense in the age of the *sharing economy.* It is possible to imagine that Google software or the equivalent could be incorporated in a high proportion of vehicles, both cars and trucks within the next decade or so.

The advantages are clear, namely: a big reduction in road

Figure 18: Lexus RX450h retrofitted by Google for its driverless car fleet. **Source:** Steve Jurvetson derivative work: Mariordo for Wikimedia Commons

accidents, which currently cause about 1.2 million deaths a year around the world; an improvement in efficiency, as cars which are directed by computer will go at the ideal speeds and trajectory for road conditions; and a higher utilisation rate – most cars spend 95 per cent of their time sitting in garages or parking lots[2].

Also, if driverless cars form part of a road "train" they would benefit from reduced drag and improved energy efficiency (whether they are running off fossil fuels or electricity). Furthermore, people who are disabled, too young or too old to drive at the moment under current licensing laws can use such cars to go from place to place – think of the millions of hours currently being spent every day ferrying around the old and the young by family members and friends.

Driverless cars would challenge the rationale of even owning a car, especially if they can be called up whenever needed, enabling them to be shared widely. It is even a possibility that trips taken in driverless cars could be paid for by advertising (after all that is still the source of around 95 per cent of Google's revenue). We are not sure how passengers would react to being bombarded by advertisements throughout their journey, but if it's cheap or free even, people will undoubtedly tolerate such annoyances.

And of course, having driverless cars on the road means all the people that used to be drivers become passengers, liberating them to read, play games with fellow passengers, work, watch movies, enjoy the view, and even have a nap.

Google is building 100 prototypes of its driverless two seater vehicle, which have no controls except on /off buttons, and while some car manufacturers such as **Mercedes, Volvo** and **Audi** have been working on driverless or semi-automated cars, no company is anywhere near as far along as Google. Full production is expected by around 2020, and while Google is building its own cars to begin with, it is much more likely to licence its technology to car manufacturers rather than getting into full blown production itself. This is because standard pod-like driverless cars will likely end up being priced as commodities.

[2] *McKinsey Quarterly, March 2014.*

The mass adoption of Google's driverless technology is far from certain; roadblocks include the fact that the current cost of the electronics in a Google car is thought to be around $80,000, so the price has to come down dramatically for the technology to become economically viable. Such cost reductions are very likely as production is scaled up and component prices are driven down as a result of Moore's Law.

Google cars employ a roof-mounted laser which generates a detailed three-dimensional map of their surroundings; this map is then compared with high-resolution maps of the world to produce the ability to self-drive. There is a still a lot to do to refine the system, as well as local legislation. For example, only California, Florida and Nevada in the US allow robotic cars on their roads at the moment, and even then a human is required to sit in the driver's seat, ready to take control should it prove necessary.

In addition, the building of *intuition* into the driverless systems needs more work. For instance, if a ball flies onto a road, a human driver would normally expect a child to follow and would slow down or stop. It is not clear how a driverless car would handle such a situation.

There is also the issue of cybersecurity; how will auto manufacturers protect their driverless systems from being hacked? One company addressing this is London-listed **NCC Group (LSE:NCC),** which engages in *penetration testing* for major car manufacturers, to render cars "hack proof."

Another way of playing the driverless car phenomenon, is by buying shares in tyre giant **Continental AG (XETRA:CON).**

This German company is right at the forefront for developing systems, and has even partnered with IBM to develop an Electronic Horizon (eHorizon) platform, which will use digital maps to anticipate the road ahead, augmenting the horizon beyond what is immediately visible.

There are plenty of start-ups and big companies around involved in driverless or autonomous vehicles. Nissan claims it will have its first fully autonomous vehicle by 2020, and at the other end of the scale there is British start up **RDM Automotive,** which plans to have three pod cars on British roads by 2015.

But for driverless cars to work, they need to have two characteristics: ubiquity, in other words everyone needs to be using them; and a standard operating system (such as Google's.) So, there might be many different types of cars we will be getting into, but all will directed by a single system.

As with many disruptive technologies, the acceptance and adoption of driverless cars as standard will lead to wide-scale job losses in the transportation sector. These include truck drivers, taxi drivers, bus drivers and people who work in auto insurance. Google, indeed, is now pressing Californian officials to start trialling a driverless motorbike - the ultimate insult to Hells Angels everywhere!

Electric and Solar Vehicles

Electric vehicles have been around for a long time, predating fossil fuel powered automobiles. But high battery costs and low driving ranges, combined with a lack of convenient recharge stations, have been significant barriers to their wide adoption... until now.

At long last, *the electric vehicle (EV) revolution* is here and it won't be long before sales of electric or quasi-electric vehicles begin to take-off in a meaningful way. The key drivers will be: universal availability of fast charging stations; a remarkable improvement in battery technology and a concurrent fall in prices; government subsidies to encourage low/no emission vehicles; concerns about the availability of gasoline and its pricing; and last but not least, a longer range, which is overcoming the so-called "range anxiety" of earlier electric vehicle owners.

Even taking into account the manufacturing of the battery packs, which itself causes emissions, EVs are significantly more environmentally friendly than internal combustion vehicles. A study from the UK concluded that EVs could reduce carbon emissions over the vehicle lifecycle by 40 per cent, including emissions from the power needed to recharge EV batteries and the power used to mine the metals for the batteries (typically lithium, copper and nickel).

There are now some 25 models of electric vehicles, mostly cars, around the world not including hybrid gasoline/electric vehicles. Japan has the lead in this area, although the US (with Tesla at the forefront) is catching up fast. The Nissan Leaf is the world's bestselling electric vehicle with cumulative sales of 100,000 by the beginning of 2014. Currently in the US, only four per cent of the cars sold are electrically powered but that percentage will grow substantially as prices fall and new models are introduced. Seeing the huge market potential, even luxury brands such as **Bentley** and **BMW** are introducing electric or hybrid cars.

The traditional OEM car dealership business model works on the basis that oil filters need to be changed and other moving parts require servicing/replacing periodically. Electric vehicles require much less servicing, which is why dealers have been resistant to selling them as actively as traditional cars. The battery operator model, first started by Israeli company **Better Place,** may come back as it potentially offers garages a new profit incentive. This is the model where batteries are leased rather than owned, and are separated from the car at the time of sale of an EV. The EV is therefore much cheaper to the consumer, the battery provider (through garages most likely) will make a decent return on servicing, providing and leasing batteries, and owners will be assured that all they have to do is to occasionally bring the batteries in for replacement, or more frequently if they are going on very long drives.

Think of this as the rough equivalent of the Pony Express, where ponies were swapped out at various points as messengers rode across America in the pioneering days. For this to be scalable there needs to be standardisation in the industry of both charging systems and batteries.

The most well-known EV manufacturer is Tesla Motors, founded by entrepreneur Elon Musk. Tesla started work on its first electric vehicle in 2004, and by 2008 it was delivering the *Roadster* to customers. The company's second vehicle is the *Model S*, a fully electric luxury sedan. Tesla also sells electric powertrain components, including lithium power packs, to other automakers such as Toyota and Mercedes.

Tesla is publicly traded but we believe its shares are too expensive to contemplate investing in. Tesla is working on building one or two mega battery factories to bring economies of scale to the production of the most expensive part of its electric car – the battery packs, which make up roughly half the cost. Tesla's main achievement has been to produce a car that to all intents and purposes performs like a regular vehicle, and although it still takes longer to recharge than to refuel a regular car, that time is coming down rapidly.

Sanford C. Bernstein, a US financial firm, projects that when the cost of batteries drops to below $200 per kilowatt-hour, electric cars will become competitive with conventional ones without the subsidies currently granted by many governments. The *Gigafactory* that Tesla is building, which will produce batteries for 500,000 cars a year, could bring the company's battery costs close to that level, especially with improved power management electronics.

In addition, Tesla plans to introduce a $30,000 car in the next few years, making it much more competitive with conventional car prices. Also, EV operating expenses when compared to a gasoline powered car are much lower. Nissan estimates that its Leaf's 5-year operating costs to be $1,800 versus $6,000 for a gasoline car in the US. In the UK, Nissan says that the operating costs of the Leaf are £1.75 pence per mile, compared to 10 pence per mile for a conventional car.

An absolute key to the acceptance of EVs is the development of better batteries and the ability to charge them in a comparable time to refuelling conventional vehicles, or faster. EVs generally use *deep cycle* batteries that are designed with high amp hour capacity. The smaller and lighter the batteries are, the better the energy to weight ratio and the better the performance of the vehicle.

The current range of the Nissan Leaf is only 83 miles (133 kilometres). The range of the Tesla Model S is about 300 miles (480 kilometres). But improvements in battery technology are happening at a staggering pace and as a result the market is exploding. It has been predicted that by 2020 the market for automobile traction batteries will be worth over $37 billion.

Additionally, fast charging stations are now becoming more common, though nothing yet on the scale needed to be competitive with the refuelling convenience of gasoline vehicles. That however, could change quite quickly; Tesla cars can now travel East-West and North-South across the US and find recharging stations (free for their upmarket models) along the way. It takes 20 minutes at a recharging station for most cars to get about an 80 per cent charge, and that time is improving continuously. So far, the tiny nation of Estonia is the only country in the world to have a full network of charging stations, but that will certainly change in the near future.

Batteries currently used in EVs are lithium-ion based. These can suffer so-called *thermal runaway* and *cell rupture* if they overheat, or are overcharged, and this has led to a few isolated cases of fires in some EVs, most notably in three Tesla cars in the US. Lithium-ion batteries also have a limited life, although in its latest models, Tesla claims that its batteries have an endurance of seven years at 40 miles (64 kilometres) of driving per day (the average daily distance driven in the US).

Tesla uses a combination of many modified laptop batteries, in contrast to a single battery pack that other cars have, but they all employ the same basic chemistry, using a lithium cobalt oxide cathode and a graphite anode.

Consequently, we think there is considerable upside in lithium and graphite miners as a result of the upsurge in demand for both of these minerals as EVs become more popular. In this respect, we recommend Australia-listed **Triton Minerals** for graphite (also used in graphene) and **Critical Elements** in Canada for lithium. Both look like very good long term investments to us.

LG Chem, a South Korean company is working on a *lithium-manganese spinel*[3] battery expected to last up to 40 years. Silicon *nanowires,* silicon *nanoparticles,* and tin *nanoparticles* are expected in due course to deliver several times the energy density in the anode, while *super-lattice* cathodes also promise significant density improvements. Battery costs, measured in kilowatt hours, are coming down fast; in 2007 they were approximately $1,300 per kilowatt-hour, and by 2015 they are expected to be $300 per kilowatt-hour, with a forecast of $125 per kilowatt-hour by 2022. This will boost the chances of EVs becoming the dominant force in autos, trucks and buses in due course. To overcome the fire problem, an *intumescent*[4] chemical is used and so far this seems to be effective.

Battery makers will benefit, and our favourite investment in this area is **GS Yuasa Corporation**, a Japanese company listed on the Tokyo Stock Exchange and likely to grow at an above average rate over the next twenty years or so. The price of its stock is not expensive at the time of writing, in our view.

As far as car manufacturers are concerned, almost all of the major ones either have electric vehicles already in production or in the works. Driving ranges are improving all the time; a **Daihatsu** *Mira* for instance has achieved a range of 623 miles (997 kilometres) without recharging. **Zonda**, a company from China, has produced an electric bus with a range of 310 miles (496 kilometres). Both are highly competitive when compared against internal combustion vehicles.

A new *aluminium air* battery, developed by Israel-based Phinergy and Alcoa (from Canada), appears to more than treble the range of electric cars.

The battery mainly comprises aluminium panels that generate a chemical reaction in the presence of water, creating energy. These batteries work alongside regular lithium-ion batteries to extend the range of the vehicle to roughly 1,000 miles (1,600 km). The weight of the aluminium air battery packs is about one fifth of those used in the Tesla Model S batteries, making them a very attractive battery technology.

One of the "problems" with electric vehicles is their stealthy silence; unlike internal combustion engines, electric motors are smooth and quiet, which makes it much harder for humans to become aware of their presence in an urban environment, especially for the hearing impaired and cyclists. As such, companies are exploring ways to make electric vehicles as noticeable as their fossil-fuelled counterparts, such as installing external speakers that make some sort of sound, such as whooshing or humming. Who would have thought there would be issues with a vehicle that is too quiet?

One alternative to batteries as power sources for EVs are so-called *ultracapacitors* (also known as *supercapacitors.*) These store energy in electric fields, physically on the surface of electrodes, unlike batteries which store energy chemically, and charge and discharge quickly, allowing cars to accelerate faster and to capture more energy through braking.

Toyota is trialling ultracapacitors in hybrid cars, where it can add a burst of energy for acceleration, and is then recharged as the car decelerates or brakes. Ultracapacitors are not yet as efficient in producing energy as conventional batteries, but they are getting there, with recent capacitors producing about 30 to 40 per cent of the energy density of batteries. This will improve as graphene and carbon nanotube technology develops. Ultracapacitors last much longer than batteries: at least one million charging cycles versus a few thousand for batteries. They are currently in use in at least 20,000 hybrid buses around the world, and are about to be used in trams in Guangzhou in China, and in some trains.

Finally, we would like to briefly mention *fuel cells*, which convert hydrogen into electricity. Although it may one day emerge as the solution to our transportation energy needs, the technology remains in development, and cost factors are unlikely to allow its commercialisation within the timeframe of this book. Recently, a company called **Intelligent Energy** listed on the London stock market, raising over $100 million

[3] A mineral comprising aluminium and magnesium.

[4] A substance that swells as a result of heat exposure, thus increasing in volume and decreasing in density.

and working in partnership with **Suzuki Motors**. Its fuel cells are designed for use in transport as well as for mobile phone battery charging in remote places and other applications.

Like other fuel cell companies that have raised money in London, such as **AFC Energy**, Intelligent Energy has so far been a disappointment for investors.

Marine Vessels

In marine technology, the main advances of the past two decades have been the steady increase in size, and therefore efficiency, of cargo and passenger ships. This is about to be further facilitated by the expansion of the **Panama Canal,** which will be capable of handling super-sized ships (neo-Panamax vessels) before the end of the decade.

Almost certainly, the need to install crews on ships except for safety purposes will further diminish over the next two decades, as automation takes the place of human operators.

This combined with better fuel efficiency will help to push costs down in this highly competitive business.

The neo-Panamax ships will be 160 feet (almost 50 metres) tall and 180 feet (55 metres) wide, and will be able to carry over 13,000 standard containers. There are even larger ships in the **Maersk** fleet which will be unable to go through even the widened Panama Canal.

A nearby neighbour of Panama, Nicaragua is supposedly planning to construct a rival canal, and although a longer route, it will be wider and deeper than the Panama Canal. It will be a 172 mile route from the mouth of the Brito River on the Pacific Ocean side to the Punto Gorda River on the Caribbean. The cost for such a major undertaking is estimated to be $40 billion.

There is room for both canals, as trade between Asia and North America is expected to more than double over the next fifteen years.

Worth a quick mention from a technological innovation point of view, is so-called *supercavitation.* This involves surrounding the boat with a bubble of gas to reduce drag, which improves speed and stealth, but as yet is very expensive and confined to military use, and is unlikely to translate to commercial shipping for many years if at all.

Disruptive Apps for Getting Around

Most of our readers will be familiar with the company **Uber,** the disruptive app and limousine service that is inciting mass protests from taxi drivers around the world. There are a number of competing services to Uber, namely **Lyft** (from the US) and **Tencent** and **Alibaba's** offerings in China. The Uber business model is simple: an approved driver and car is given some basic training and the driver app is provided. Customers can contact Uber drivers by using the Uber customer app on their smartphones from which they can request a pick-up time and location and specify their destination.

Customers will be quoted a price for the journey, and payment is made through a pre-registered credit card. Because Uber and its ilk don't suffer the same burden of licencing as conventional taxis, there has been an outpouring of venom directed at them. But the Ubers of the world are the future, and whatever form these app-based driving services eventually take on, they are here to stay. This is evidenced the eye-watering valuations accorded to Uber and Lfyt in recent funding rounds. Uber, which started only in 2009, recently raised nearly $2 billion on an $18 billion valuation, which ranks as the highest ever for a start-up. It is now available in many countries around the world, and in over 100 US cities.

Uber's revenues are estimated at be over $30 million a week, and it typically takes 20 per cent of drivers' receipts, so in theory, it should enjoy good margins as it doesn't own the cars. However, we are not big fans of this industry because it was very simple for Uber to enter the market and disrupt it, albeit with a brilliant idea. Low barriers to entry means the door is open for challengers to emerge and compete on price. Almost anyone with a decent car and a clean driving record can become an Uber or equivalent driver, and so much venture capital money has gone into this industry that competition will be fierce. In fact, Uber and Lyft are already engaged in a price war.

The taxi drivers are unlikely to prevail as Uber and Lfyt use the power of their customers to overwhelm opposition, but nonetheless, this remains a commodity business in the making. Indeed, Uber is now getting into the business of financing the purchase of cars, which makes it more like a conventional taxi fleet operator than a true disruptor. It is talking of getting into delivery and logistics, and possible car-sharing, but eye-watering valuations on it and its competitors reflect optimism and hype rather than the reality of commerce. Taxis are using app-based systems to combat the threat to their businesses, (**Hailo** in the UK, and **Flywheel** in the US). In China, Alibaba and Tencent are bleeding money on their services, which network conventional taxis, and even with 100 million registered users each, they are unviable. There is even an airline equivalent to Uber, and guess what, it is in partnership with Uber. Operating out of California, SurfAir is a subscription-based business, offering unlimited flights for a joining fee of $1,000 and a monthly fee of $1,750.

The future for conventional taxis looks bleak. In many cities around the world, either time (in London the *Knowledge*) or money (in cities such as New York, Paris and Hong Kong the medallions) are required to get a taxi licence. This accumulation of economic value in restricted licenses will disappear. Gordon Tullock, an American economist has called it a *"translational gains trap"* and it is a little like the catastrophic losses suffered by buggy whip manufacturers when the automobile first came along.

Putting the taxi wars aside for a moment, we wanted to also mention a company called **Waze** (owned by Google of course), which specialises in providing up-to-the-minute road traffic conditions to drivers so that routes can be selected to avoid congested sections. This type of service is finally reaching a critical mass of subscribers, helping drivers shave valuable time off journeys.

There is a great deal happening in this space, all thanks to GPS and mobile software. Marc Andreesen, entrepreneur and investor famous for co-founding the *Netscape browser*, has said that *"software will eat the world,"* and Uber is a good example of that. That doesn't mean that it will make its most recent investors any money though.

Energy

Renewing the Charge

Energy is fundamental to every aspect of our lives. Much of it we use for transportation and in the form of electricity for the home and office for lighting and to power all sorts of appliances and gadgets, and to heat and cool our indoor environment.

Since the Big Bang about 13.8 billion years ago, the amount of energy in the universe has remained exactly the same. All of us remember being taught the law of conservation of energy at school, which states that energy cannot be created or destroyed, only converted from one form to another. For us living on earth, virtually all of our energy, past, present and future, originates from sunlight, with the one exception being nuclear power. The uranium used in nuclear reactors originated from an exploding star billions of years ago, but (fortunately for us) it is not from the one in our solar system; our sun will continue to shine for billions more years to come.

Up until relatively recently human energy needs were rather basic: we relied on fire to generate light, to cook food, to keep us warm in cold weather, and to melt and shape metals for making tools and weapons. We also used a few animals for their brawn to help us plough fields and for transportation purposes (horse power). There was a little wind and water assisted power here and there, but that was about it.

Then came James Watt's invention of the steam engine, kick-starting the industrial revolution and, after an initial lag of a few decades, our energy consumption began to grow at an exponential rate. Thanks to the steam engine, humans for the first time were able to generate and apply abundant mechanical power, many times our own strength. The industrial revolution also spawned the transportation revolution – steam ships and steam trains could cover great distances at speed carrying cargo and passengers. It was an era of rapid technological progress, or so people thought at the time.

The advent of the silicon transistor in the 1950s marked the birth of the computer age - a second industrial revolution that is still very much in full flow. The rate of advances in technology began to accelerate faster still, thanks in large part to the doubling of computer processing power every 18 months or so (Moore's Law). And as computer chips become smaller and cheaper, they are introduced into more "things". Most devices today that run on electricity will contain at least one chip inside them, while more expensive and complex products, such as automobiles, are built with even more microprocessors inside them. For example, a modern high-end BMW or Mercedes has around 100 processors. Even a basic new car these days contains 20 to 30 processors. Today's laptops, smartphones and tablets are powered by dual or quad-core processors as standard.

Add to this picture a rising global population, rapid urbanisation across many developing countries and a growing middle class across the world, all of which go towards explaining why total global energy consumption today is at unprecedented levels. There are more households, with more home appliances, more cars, more tablets, more smartphones, more flights, more data centres, etc. – you get the picture. And as this chapter is all about energy, you will no doubt have guessed where we are going with this...where will all this energy come from to power all these additional planes, trains, cars, appliances, gadgets, data centres, etc.?

Current Primary Sources of Energy

It will come as no surprise to many readers that we are overly dependent on fossil fuels, and that they in turn are damaging our environment. The current sources of energy in the world come from:

- Petroleum
- Natural Gas
- Coal
- Renewables, such as wind, solar and hydro
- Nuclear

Although this mix varies by country depending on energy policy and accessibility to natural resources, let's take a look at the United States' sources of energy given that it is the world's largest economy and one of the largest consumers of energy.

As shown in Figure 19, more than 80 per cent of America's energy comes from fossil fuels (petroleum, natural gas and coal). This is not only an exhaustible source, but it is also responsible for most of the carbon dioxide emissions, a greenhouse gas attributed to climate change.

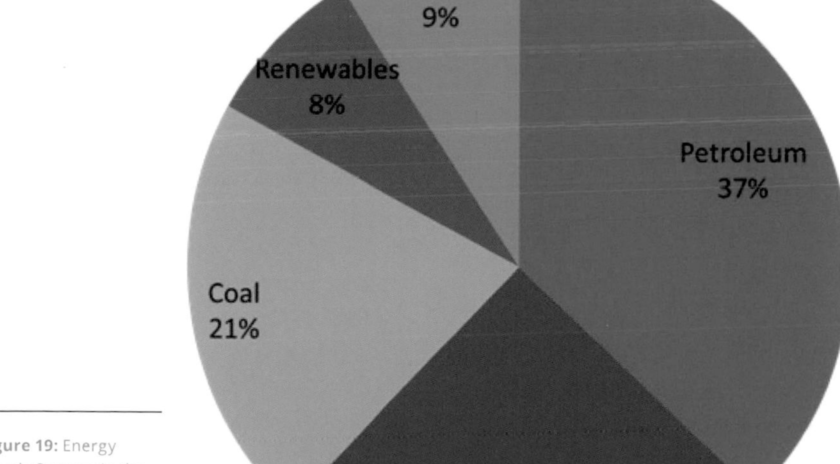

Figure 19: Energy Supply Sources in the United States **Source:** US Energy Information Administration.

Globally, 85 per cent of the energy currently produced comes from fossil fuels, and energy demand grows steadily at 2 per cent annually.

Given that most countries are heavily dependent on fossil fuels, it is unlikely that their use will cease overnight, as this would result in major economic disruptions which would be in no one's interest. But public pressure to move towards more sustainable energy sources, combined with efforts to curb carbon dioxide emissions have been driving innovation in renewable energy, and it is in this sector that we expect to find new and disruptive technologies. Equally exciting are new technologies for transmitting and storing energy. Although there may be some incremental improvements in energy from fossil fuels, we are more interested in clean and renewable sources of energy, as that is where we believe the best investment opportunities lie.

In the main, renewable energy is perceived by sceptics as being a token gesture at "saving the planet" and can only make economic sense when supported by government subsidies. However, what most people fail to realise is that fossil fuels themselves are heavily subsidised by governments to an equal, though generally disguised degree.

According to research conducted by the International Energy Agency (IEA), fossil fuel consumption subsidies worldwide totalled $544 billion in 2012, up from the preceding year. Despite pressure from the IEA on G-20 countries to phase out these subsidies, there remain challenging socio-economic and political hurdles to overcome. Readers can visit the IEA's online database to view the extent of the fossil fuel subsidies by country (http://www.iea.org/subsidy/index.html) which reveals that developing countries in the Middle East, Asia and South America are the main culprits in subsidising fossil fuels.

In a separate report published by the International Monetary Fund (IMF)[1], subsidies for petroleum products, natural gas and coal amounted to $480 billion in 2011, on a pre-tax basis, or 0.7 per cent of global GDP. Oil exporters were accountable for around two-thirds of these subsidies. The IMF states that this number increases to $1.9 trillion, or 2.5

per cent of global GDP, on a post-tax basis, which factors the negative externalities from energy consumption, namely carbon dioxide emissions. The IMF report also claims that removing these subsidies could lead to a 13 per cent reduction in carbon dioxide emissions and thereby lead to a reduction in overall global energy demand.

In contrast, the IEA's reported global subsidies for renewable energy was only $88 billion in 2011. So when compared on a global basis, fossil fuel subsidies are over 20 times greater than those for renewable energy. Governments and individuals alike are waking up to this fact and calling for a rebalancing of the skewed subsidies, one which will not only benefit the environment, but also the renewable energy sector as a whole. Indeed, renewable energy in some forms is now getting to the point where it may need no subsidy to compete with fossil fuels.

Shale's Impact on Energy Production

Most readers will have read something about shale gas and shale oil in recent years, which is usually associated with the word "fracking" – an abbreviated term for *hydraulic fracturing*. This is a process of injecting sand, water and chemicals into shale rocks deep underground to crack them open to release the trapped hydrocarbons within the rocks, generally using horizontal drilling methods. Fracking has been heavily criticized by many environmental groups as being a process that pollutes and drains underground aquifers, and claims have even been made that it increases seismic activity in the area. However, like it or hate it, the shale revolution is underway and there appears to be no stopping it. In the United States, shale will have a huge impact on the country's economy in terms of its trade balance and energy independence.

Since 2010, US natural gas production has increased by 25 per cent. This puts the US ahead of even Russia, making it the world's largest gas producer, and by 2020 the US is expected to become the world's largest gas exporter, once the facilities are in place to enable this.

[1] *International Monetary Fund. Energy Subsidy Reform: Lessons and Implications. 28 January 2013. Multiple staff authors, led by Benedict Clements.*

Oil production has also grown: since 2008 US oil production has increased by three million barrels per day, or 60 per cent. Before the end of the decade, the US will likely become the world's largest oil producer with 12 million barrels per day, surpassing even Saudi Arabia. And given the plentiful supply of shale oil and gas, these levels of production will be sustainable for decades. Removing its reliance on imported oil will mean that the US will be able to transform its huge trade deficit (which in 2011 was $354 billion) into a modest trade surplus.

This bodes well for America in the twenty-first century, as it will be able to support economic growth for many years to come using cheap, domestically produced energy, as well as being able to export its surplus oil, gas and petrochemicals. Not relying on imported oil, which typically comes from unstable hotspots such as the Middle East, will slowly re-shape America's foreign policy and alter the geopolitical landscape. Technology is also helping increase the efficiency of the fracking process; Conoco, an American oil giant, has worked out that by using more *ceramic proppant,* a sand-like material, it can better open the cracks where oil and gas is trapped, increasing the amount released in most wells by 30 per cent.

Other countries such as China and the UK are also looking at shale oil and gas with aspirations of attaining energy independence. As more shale oil and gas goes into production around the world, it will apply downward pressure on prices, in particular gas, and will hurt many of the oil and gas exporters, namely OPEC member countries.

The shale revolution is not great news for climate change and carbon dioxide emissions, but there is continued pressure by most large economies to increase the amount of energy generated from renewables, of which our favourites are wind and solar.

There is also a certain type of biofuel which is emerging as a viable alternative fuel to diesel, petrol (gasoline) and possibly even jet fuel, and we also look at its longer term prospects as a serious contender, but shale oil will continue to threaten such alternatives. This is despite the fact that at the moment, shale oil and gas companies are way outspending their cash flows; one reason being that their cost of production is above the currently depressed oil and gas prices, which in turn is a reflection of the success of the efforts in the US.

Wind Energy

Wind turbines have been popping up all over the place in recent years, sometimes as a solitary structure, other times as vast wind farms spanning the horizon. Globally, wind power capacity grew to around 318 gigawatts (318 billion watts) in 2013[2], representing an annual increase of 12.4 per cent. China alone accounted for 16 gigawatts or half of this new capacity. The Global Wind Energy Council, an international trade association for the wind power industry, expects the annual growth rate to remain in the 12 to 15 per cent range through to 2020, which by then it expects capacity to reach 1,000 gigawatts or 1 terawatt. If this energy were generated using fossil fuels, it would emit nine billion tonnes of carbon dioxide annually.

The largest wind turbine in the world today has a rotor diameter of 150.8 metres and is able to generate 6 megawatts of power – that is enough to power around 5,500 homes.

Wind power is becoming more cost-competitive against other energy generating methods: since 1980, the price of wind power has fallen by 90 per cent[3]. In fact, when comparing the cost of building a new wind farm versus a new gas or coal power station, wind power costs the same or less than gas or coal[4].

[2] *Global Wind Energy Council. Global Wind Report 2013.*
[3] *Wind Energy Foundation*
[4] *Bloomberg Report: Global Trends in Renewable Energy Investment 2014*

Figure 20: A small portion of Alta Wind Energy Center wind farm looking from Oak Creek Road.
Source: Wikimedia Commons. Author Z22.

Obviously, gas or coal power stations that are already in operation can generate energy at a lower cost than wind, but that is not entirely comparing apples to apples.

In its 2014 Annual Energy Outlook, the US Energy Information Administration (EIA) published a table comparing various methods of energy generation. When looking at the so-called *levelized* cost of new energy generation entering service in 2019, wind power came in at $80.3 per megawatt hour, or 8 US cents per kilowatt hour, including transmission costs – and this figure is without any subsidies. Conventional coal came in at $95.6 per megawatt hour.

Wind is clearly becoming a serious contender, but it will never be the single type of energy generation simply because wind is unpredictable.

As of 2013, the world's largest onshore wind farm was located in Tehachapi Pass, California, where around 500 wind turbines have been installed to generate an impressive 1,320 MW; that is enough electricity for over 600,000 homes.

Although wind farms have become a popular source of sustainable energy across the US, wind energy only accounts for about 4 per cent of the country's electricity production.

Wind farms receive a lot of criticism as being an eyesore on the countryside, and one method to address this issue has been to locate them offshore. Not only does it get the turbines out of sight, the winds offshore tend to be more steady and consistent. One of the largest offshore wind farms is located in the Thames Estuary in the UK, with a capacity to generate over 600 megawatts, which is enough to provide electricity to around 300,000 households.

Whilst we may see more wind farms in the coming years, the technology of wind turbines is already mature. Another drawback for wind power is maintenance – big moving parts means wear and tear so planned and unplanned maintenance adds to the cost of energy production. Having said that, we do believe there are going to be some interesting innovations in wind energy and we have found two companies as examples, one from the UK, the other from the US, that have come up with new ways to harness the wind.

The first company is UK-based **X-Wind Power.** We have spoken with Michael Blaize, its CEO and believe the company has enormous potential. Using talent from Formula One racing and the aerospace industry, X-Wind has designed a unique vertical axis wind turbine with two curved high efficiency double helix blades. The advantages of this design over conventional turbine blades are numerous: the blades are smaller, making them easier to assemble and transport; the blades rotate at a lower tip speed, so they are much quieter; they can harness the wind from any direction; they are aesthetically pleasing to the eye, and could pass for an art installation so they can fit in quite comfortably in an urban setting. Given the compact size of the turbines over traditional horizontal axis ones, they can be installed virtually anywhere without being a hazard or an eye-sore. On the maintenance front, the turbines are designed to operate for five years between servicing. One of its biggest challenges will be the competition from existing horizontal axis turbines, as the high volume of production will no doubt make them cheaper than X-Wind's turbines. The company is currently privately held, but readers should follow this company for any announcements to go public.

The second interesting company that is developing a new way to harness energy from the wind is US-based **Altaeros Energies.** Founded at the Massachusetts Institute of Technology in 2010, Altaeros is working on an airborne wind turbine to harness the stronger winds that blow at altitude. Using a helium-filled shell (resembling a tubular airship), the turbine is mounted inside the shell. Attached to the shell are stabilising fins that align the turbine to the wind direction and keep it steady at altitude. The entire contraption is tethered to the ground so it can be turned on at ground level if there is sufficient wind, or floated to a higher altitude. The turbine is designed to operate at an altitude of up to 600 metres (around 2,000 feet), harnessing the steadier, stronger winds.

What makes the Altaeros turbine so attractive is its ability to generate electricity for remote sites around the world. These can be rural communities, mining sites, disaster relief locations as well as military applications.

Figure 21: Altaeros Energies' Buoyant Airborne Turbine (BAT). **Source:** Altaeros

The turbine is relatively cheap, emits no pollutants or greenhouse gases, it is light and reasonably portable and can start generating electricity without any installation time.

Solar Energy

When we first wrote about solar energy, more specifically PhotoVoltaic (PV) cells in our 2008 book *The Top Ten Investments for the Next 10 Years,* we were excited then by their potential since they were first introduced in the 1970s. Global installations of solar have been increasing on average by 50 per cent a year since 2006, with no sign of slowing down any time soon. With each passing year, solar is playing a bigger role in energy markets.

Mono & Poly-Crystalline PV

The vast majority (over 90 per cent) of PV solar cells are either *monocrystalline or polycrystalline,* and we shall explain what the difference is between them. Both types are made from silicon, which just happens to be the second most abundant element on the earth's crust.

Monocrystalline cells, as the name implies, have a homogenous orderly crystal structure, but are more expensive to manufacture, while the polycrystalline cells have an irregular crystal structure and are cheaper to produce. The advantage of monocrystalline over polycrystalline is slightly greater efficiency in converting sunlight into electricity, but only by one or two percentage points. The efficiency of these PV cells ranges from about 12 to 15 per cent with the latest modules achieving an efficiency of just over 20 per cent. This may sound rather low except that these PV cells have become so cheap to manufacture, and have such a long lifespan, that efficiency does not really matter, especially when they are installed in remote, sunny locations where space is not an issue.

Furthermore, once installed, they need virtually no maintenance and can continue to generate electricity for many decades – their true life span is not known but could easily be 70 or even 100 years.

The trouble with solar energy is that pretty much all of the production costs are required upfront and because the cells are getting cheaper all the time, it is tempting to keep deferring buying solar as it will be much cheaper in the future. But if that cost were to be spread out over 20, 30, or even 70 years, it would not make much difference. Getting help with financing the upfront capital expenditure is a huge catalyst to the adoption of solar at a household level, and we mention one company doing just that later in this chapter.

In the US, the cost of installing solar panels on rooftops of homes was $7 per watt in 2008, but by 2013 that cost had fallen to below $4. McKinsey & Company, a management consultancy, believes that this cost will fall further to only $1.60 by 2020.

And it is not just households that are moving towards energy independence; giant retailer Wal-Mart announced that it intends to be 100 per cent renewable power by 2020, from its current 20 per cent.

Overall, PV solar has been the fastest growing renewable energy since the turn of the century. By 2012, PV solar capacity exceeded 100 gigawatts, according to the European Photovoltaic Industry Association, and this capacity is expected to surpass 200 gigawatts by 2015.

One of the big PV solar manufacturers is a company from China called **JinkoSolar (NYSE:JKS).** In March 2014, the company announced that it had successfully achieved a major milestone in terms of manufacturing cost: producing solar modules for less than 50 US cents per watt; a target set by the US Department of Energy's SunShot Initiative, which seeks to make solar energy more cost-competitive with other forms of electricity by 2020. JinkoSolar expects to ship out around 2.4 gigawatts of solar modules in 2014.

Some of China's other leading PV companies include **Renesola (ADR on NYSE: SOL)**, **Trina Solar (ADR on NYSE: TSL)** and **Yingli Green Energy (ADR on NYSE: YGE).**

According to a report[5] by GTM Research, a renewable energy research company, PV solar module costs will continue to fall to well below 50 cents per watt, down to 36 cents per watt by the end of 2017.

China has invested heavily in PV solar production. As of 2013, there were more than 400 PV manufacturers in China, which together are responsible for about 60 per cent of global PV production[6]. For PV solar, the bigger the scale of production, the cheaper the modules get. In fact, with each doubling of production volume, solar module prices have decreased by 20 per cent. Consequently, China currently makes the world's cheapest PV solar modules. Naturally, this has hurt American and European rivals, and the US has indicated that it plans to impose more tariffs on Chinese solar panels. The US Department of Commerce indicated that this will range between 18 and 35 per cent. America's justification for this seemingly uncompetitive step is that it will help offset the subsidies given by China's government to panel makers, which of course China denies.

Concentrated PV Cells

So far we have been discussing monocrystalline and polycrystalline PV cells, which are cheap and have an efficiency of up to 23 per cent or so. But there is another type of PV cell that is able to achieve much greater efficiency, and these are known as **Multi-junction Cells,** which by the end of 2013 had reached efficiencies of about 45 per cent.

This is made possible by cleverly using multiple layers of different semiconductor materials stacked vertically, each one responding to a different wavelength band of light. In addition, to boost the sun's energy falling on these cells, a concentrator can be added, such as a lens or a mirror, which can concentrate the sunlight by 500 times. This is known as Concentrated Photo-Voltaics (CPV) and can boost the electricity generated by over 30 per cent.

Figure 22 shows CPVs leading the charge in efficiency gains over the past few decades when compared to other types of PV.

In 2013, a French semiconductor manufacturer called **Soitec (Paris Stock Exchange: SOI)** set itself a target to reach 50 per cent efficiency, having already achieved 43.6 per cent in May 2013.

At 50 per cent efficiency Soitec claims that the cost of energy would fall to 8 US cents per kilowatt hour[7] in hot, sunny areas. That is a very ambitious claim which if achieved would put Soitec's CPV technology on a par with the cost of coal energy. We will have to wait and see if the company can get there.

Another company that manufactures CPV cells is **Amonix.** Based in California, the company's cells are in use primarily across California and Spain. The company was founded in 1989 and remains privately held. Amonix is attempting to lower the cost of electricity to 6 cents per kilowatt-hour by 2015. It has been funded by some high profile institutions such as Kleiner Perkins and Goldman Sachs, as well as by the US Department of Energy, but it has not been a smooth ride for Amonix. In 2012, it shut down a factory in Nevada that was only a year old and re-structured the entire business. The tough times were put down to intense competition and lower than expected demand for CPV.

When we spoke with friends and colleagues in the industry, the general feeling was that CPV technology only makes sense where space is limited and where the sun's rays are consistently intense, otherwise rolling out polycrystalline panels would be much cheaper, even if they take up two or three times the area. Additional concerns are related to the lifespan of CPV cells as the intense sunlight concentrated on the cells leads to extreme heat generation, causing the cells to expand, and at night in a desert, the temperature can fall dramatically, causing the cells to contract. This repeated expansion-contraction cycle is very punishing on the cells and would no doubt affect their longevity and efficiency.

Another concern pointed out to us was that the lenses require frequent cleaning to wipe the dirt off them otherwise the efficiency of the CPV cells would fall significantly, and this regular maintenance adds to the overall cost of energy production.

So all in all the jury is still out on the economic viability of CPV cells, especially in massive solar farm applications, and if the mono and polycrystalline cells continue to get cheaper, the

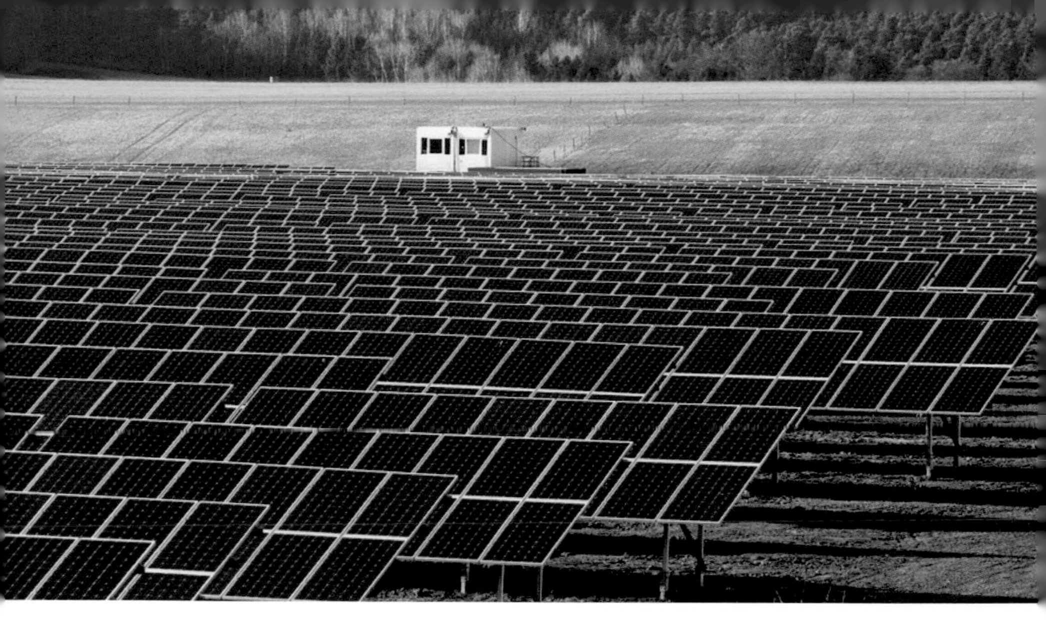

case for CPV cells will fade unless its manufacturers are able to achieve the same longevity as the mono and polycrystalline cells.

There are other solar technologies currently being tested in laboratories around the world, such as those that use nanoparticles called colloidal quantum dots, but as with all new technologies, it will take years before they become commercially viable and competitive with the incumbent technology. Moreover, if we are to keep installing more solar to decrease our dependence on fossil fuels, we need to buy what is available today at the most attractive price, which for at least the next decade will be silicon-based solar technology.

Nuclear Power - Fission

Nuclear energy is a rather polarising topic. Those for it emphasise its reliability, affordability and its zero carbon emissions.

---

[5] *GTM Research, Shyam Mehta, "PV Technology and Cost Outlook, 2013-2017," 18 June 2013.*

[6] *Jäger-Waldau, Arnulf (September 2013) PV Status Report 2013. European Commission, Joint Research Centre, Institute for Energy and Transport.*

[7] *Renewable Energy World. CPV Solar Manufacturer Soitec Sets Its Sights on 50% Efficiency, Jennifer Runyon, Managing Editor, July 16, 2013.*

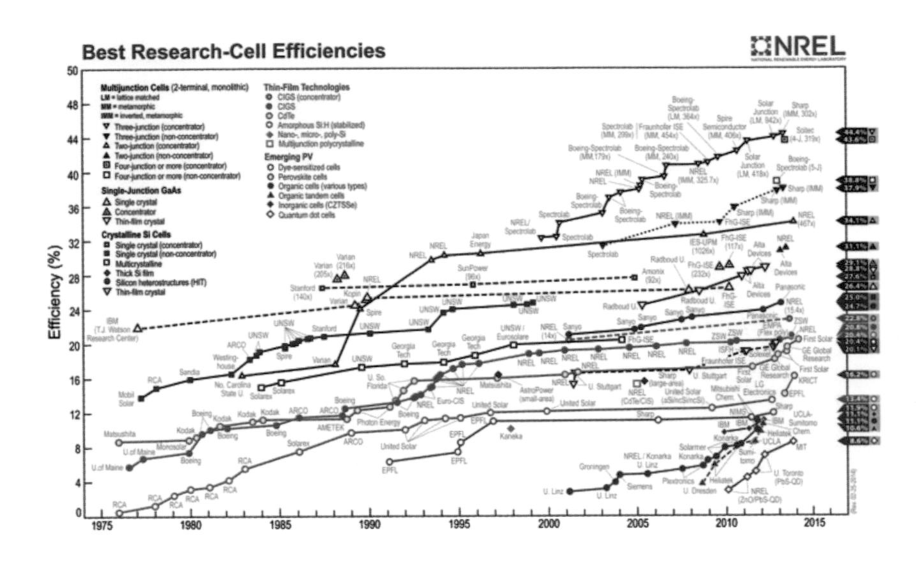

Figure 22: Timeline of solar cell energy conversion efficiencies (from National Renewable Energy Laboratory (USA). **Source:** National Renewable Energy Laboratory (NREL), US Department of Energy

Those against it believe the risks, however remote, make it an unattractive energy source, citing the disasters of Chernobyl and Fukushima. They also point out that the nuclear waste must be contained for many thousands of years before its radiation levels are safe for the environment.

Those in the pro nuclear energy camp believe that, in the short to medium term, there is no alternative clean energy that can realistically meet demand. The power stations of Chernobyl and Fukushima were old and badly run. The modern nuclear power reactors being commissioned around the world today (known as Generation III) are incredibly safe, robust and reliable, with Generation IV reactors expected to be operational by 2020.

Generation III reactors have improved efficiency, passive safety systems and standardised design. They also have a much longer operation life, which is 60 years instead of 40 years for the Generation II designs. The 60 years is extendable to a further

Company Spotlight: SolarCity Corp (NASDAQ:SCTY)

Company website: http://www.solarcity.com

A better known solar company is California-based **SolarCity.** It is yet another innovative venture backed by Elon Musk, the man who is also behind Tesla Motors, the electric car maker, and SpaceX, the space transport services company.

Unlike other solar companies, SolarCity installs and finances solar panels to homes, businesses, schools and governments. As of the end of 2013, SolarCity had installed around 4.3 gigawatts of solar panels.

Since it was established in 2006, it has expanded to 14 states across America.

With a market capitalisation of $5.5 billion at the time of writing, SolarCity isn't exactly a bargain – its share price has risen by around 400 per cent since its IPO in December 2012 and the company remains unprofitable. But the management team is innovative and its business model is a financing and distribution business, and a networked utility business that threatens to disrupt the traditional utility companies. It is worth including SolarCity in a portfolio, but probably best to wait for a correction in its stock price.

60 years with a major overhaul. Given how expensive nuclear reactors are to build (several billion dollars), and how time consuming they are to construct (about five years) this added operational life further reduces the cost per kilowatt of energy produced over their life time.

As of the beginning of 2014, there were 430 commercial nuclear power reactors in 31 countries with a total power capacity of 370 gigawatts, or 370,000 megawatts[8], representing over 11 per cent of the world's electricity supply.

There were also around 70 new nuclear power reactors under construction, many of them in China.

The raw material required to make the fuel pellets necessary to power a nuclear power reactor is uranium which is mined from a number of countries around the world. The table below lists the top ten countries where most of the uranium reserves lie.

Country	Reserves as of 2009	World Share	Ranked by 2012 Production
Australia	1,673,000	31.0%	3
Kazakhstan	651,800	12.1%	1
Canada	485,300	9.0%	2
Russia	480,300	8.9%	6
South Africa	295,600	5.5%	12
Namibia	284,200	5.3%	5
Brazil	278,700	5.2%	12
Niger	272,900	5.0%	4
United States	207,400	3.8%	8
China	171,400	3.2%	9

Table 1: List of countries by uranium reserves (in tonnes). **Source:** OECD. Uranium 2009: Resources, Production and Demand. OECD NEA Publication 6891. 2010.

[8] *Source of data: World Nuclear Association*

These 10 countries together account for 89 per cent of the world's uranium reserves. It is interesting to observe that the countries with the largest reserves are not necessarily the ones that produce the most uranium.

Australia, for example, has by the far the largest uranium reserves, yet it ranked only number 3 in terms of production, and South Africa which has the fifth largest reserves ranked 12th in terms of production.

The price of uranium has been on a wild roller coaster ride since 2005, but the price fluctuations have a minimal impact of the cost of energy produced as so little uranium is required compared to the power generated using fossil fuels, where the price directly impacts the cost of energy produced.

For example, 1kg of coal can generate 8 kWh of heat, whereas 1 kg of uranium-235 can generate around 24 million kWh – 3,000 times more heat.

The 2011 Fukushima nuclear accident has no doubt had a great

Figure 23: The price of uranium per pound in USD since 1995. **Source:** infomine.com

Company	Tonnes U	% of world production
KazAtomProm (Kazakstan)	8863	15
Areva (France)	8641	15
Cameco (Canada)	8437	14
ARMZ - Uranium One (Canada)	7629	13
Rio Tinto (Australia)	5435	9
BHP Billiton (Australia)	3386	6

Table 2: The top 6 uranium producing companies in 2012. **Source:** World Nuclear Association.

impact on the price of uranium (see Figure 23) and has forced many countries to reassess their energy policy. By May 2012, all of Japan's 50 reactors went offline, making Japan nuclear free for the first time since 1970, even though nuclear energy provided around 30 per cent of the country's electricity.

However, enough time has passed now and the practicalities of needing reliable, clean energy are re-emerging. Japan is expected to restart its nuclear reactors in the near future, which will be good news for the uranium price and uranium miners.

Table 2 lists the names of the companies that are responsible for mining most of the world's uranium. The clear stand-out there is Areva, a French company and the second largest producer of uranium, yet France ranks approximately 20th when it comes to uranium reserves. As many readers will know, 75 per cent of France's electricity comes from nuclear energy.

Not only is it enough for France, it has enough to sell to its neighbours; hence France is also the world's largest net exporter of electricity. Interestingly, France is able to generate 17 per cent of its electricity from recycled nuclear fuel.

Nuclear energy is by no means a one way bet. In addition to the health and safety concerns that many people against nuclear energy have, it is also very difficult to quantify its true cost of energy production because it enjoys many implicit and explicit subsidies. For example, in the UK, there has been a great deal of controversy in relation to the government awarding France's EDF Energy the contract to build and operate a 3.3 gigawatt two reactor power plant at Hinkley Point, near Bristol. The plant, which will eventually provide around 7 per cent of the country's electricity, is expected to be completed in the 2020s. To persuade EDF to accept the project, the government had to commit to a long-term contract to buy the electricity at a wholesale price of £92.50 per megawatt hour, which is not far off the retail price of electricity. This makes no economic sense at all. The wholesale price of electricity in the UK for the 2010s has averaged around £50 per megawatt hour. The government has defended its position by pointing out that this will avoid nine million tonnes of carbon dioxide emissions a year, and that it is vital for the UK to achieve energy independence.

In a memorandum to the UK's Environmental Audit Committee's enquiry into energy subsidies in the UK, Dr Gerry Wolff from Energy Fair[9], a think tank focusing on nuclear power subsidies, claims that nuclear power in the UK has been benefitting from seven types of subsidies. In his memo, Dr Wolff lists these subsidies as being the following:

1. *Limitations on liabilities:* The operators of nuclear plants pay much less than the full cost of insuring against a Chernobyl-style accident or worse.

2. *Underwriting of commercial risks:* The Government necessarily underwrites the commercial risks of nuclear power because, for political reasons, the operators of nuclear plants cannot be allowed to fail.

3. *Subsidies in protection against terrorist attacks:* Because protection against terrorist attacks can only ever be partial, the Government and the public are exposed to risk and corresponding costs.

[9] *Memorandum for the Environmental Audit Committee's enquiry into "Energy Subsidies in the UK," Dr Gerry Wolff, Energy Fair, May 2013.*

4. *Subsidies for the short-to-medium-term cost of disposing of nuclear waste:* In UK government proposals, the Government is likely to bear much of the risk of cost overruns in the disposal of nuclear waste.

5. *Subsidies in the long-term cost of disposing of nuclear waste:* With categories of nuclear waste that will remain dangerous for thousands of years, there will be costs arising from the dangers of the waste and the need to manage it. These costs will be borne by future generations, but they will receive no compensating benefit.

6. *Underwriting the cost of decommissioning nuclear plants:* In UK government proposals, the Government is likely to bear much the risk of cost overruns in decommissioning nuclear plants.

7. *Institutional support for nuclear power:* the UK government is providing various forms of institutional support for the nuclear industry.

Dr Wolff believes that should just one of these seven subsidies be withdrawn, the price of nuclear power would rise to at least £200 per megawatt hour. Compare that to offshore wind power which is currently around £125 per megawatt hour and suddenly nuclear power no longer seems so attractive. Further strengthening the case for offshore wind power is the expectation of further price declines in the coming decade by over 30 per cent through technological innovation and economies of scale in production.

Energy Fair lodged several formal complaints with the European Commission which opened a formal investigation into the matter in December 2013 to find out *"whether the construction of a nuclear power station could not be achieved by market forces alone, without state intervention."*[10] In other words, is the £17 billion that EDF going to receive in subsidies from public funds necessary?

In response to the investigation EDF released a statement insisting that the investment will not take place without a subsidy deal from the British government. It is not clear how long this investigation is going to last but the out-

[10] *Subsidies for UK nuclear plant could reach £17bn and 'may be unnecessary', Emily Gosden, The Telegraph, 18 December 2013*

come could greatly impact nuclear power in Europe as a whole.

The nuclear energy we have discussed so far all derived from a chemical process called nuclear *fission.* In simple terms, this is when a neutron is fired at the nucleus of a uranium atom, which causes the nucleus to become unstable and split into two. The act of the nucleus splitting releases vast amounts of energy in the form of heat. This heat is captured using water, which boils to create steam; the steam is used to turn a turbine, which drives a generator.

An alternative fuel for fission is *thorium,* which is at least three times as abundant as uranium and unlike uranium, is extremely difficult to convert into nuclear bombs. India and China are investing heavily into this alternative source of nuclear power, but it is too early to determine whether it will gain traction over the currently more popular uranium.

The other way to generate nuclear energy is by nuclear *fusion,* and we discuss briefly this in the next section.

Fusion

Nuclear fusion is currently confined to laboratories and not available commercially. The reason why it is often referred to as the solution to the world's energy needs is that it has many advantages over nuclear fission, namely:

- It generates far more energy per weight of fuel;
- Its fuel, called *deuterium* (an isotope of hydrogen), is abundant in seawater, which means that we would have enough supply for all the world's energy for millions of years;

- The nuclear waste created would be far less than generated by fission and would be confined to the reactor core;

- Dangerous levels of radioactivity from nuclear waste would last for around 50 years, instead of many thousands of years with fission waste; and

- The size of a fusion power plant could be a fraction of fission reactors for the same power generation.

Professor Steven Cowley is a professor at Imperial College London and Chief Executive Officer of The UK Atomic Energy Authority. As a leading authority on nuclear fusion, he is very optimistic about its commerciality, but he believes that the earliest we can expect this to happen is 2030. So whilst nuclear fusion stands to be one of the most disruptive technologies ever, it is still in its infancy and well beyond the time horizon of this book.

Investing in uranium, uranium mining companies and companies that commission fission-based nuclear reactors would be the best way to play the nuclear energy sector.

Biofuels

Several years ago biofuels came under heavy criticism and were accused of driving up prices of many of the world's soft commodities, such as sugar, corn and wheat, from which some biofuels are derived. *Ethanol*, one of the most common biofuels and is still in wide use, especially in Brazil. The problem with it is that on a net basis, it barely generates more energy than is required to produce it in the first place.

Another type of biofuel is *biodiesel,* which is derived from the oils of plants such as soy, palm, sunflower and jatropha, and it is this last one that shows promise of being a widely adopted fuel.

Originating from Central America, *jatropha* is a tough, drought-resistant plant that produces an inedible seed high in oil that can be refined to make low-carbon diesel or even jet fuel.

After a promising start last decade, jatropha became a victim of the global financial crisis and failed to gain enough momentum to become a recognised and viable biofuel. Dubbed as the next big thing in biofuels by Goldman Sachs as far back as 2007, jatropha experienced a spectacular boom-bust cycle.

But recent developments indicate that jatropha is making a comeback, albeit in a different strain to the last time. Thanks largely to advances in genomics, jatropha DNA can now be sequenced for just a few hundred dollars, instead of several hundred thousand dollars several years prior. An agricultural biotechnology company based in San Diego called **SGB** (which stands for Seeds, Genomics and Biomaterials) has emerged with a domesticated version of Jatropha, dubbed Jatropha 2.0. This version has greatly improved yields, more uniformity and reduced input costs.

Figure 24: Top of a Jatropha plant as part of a hedge. Photo by R. K. Henning

SGB claims it can produce a competitive biofuel from its Jatropha 2.0 strain. It is currently being tested as a viable jet fuel and biodiesel – several airlines such as Air New Zealand and Lufthansa have conducted test flights using Jatropha in one engine, and the results so far are encouraging.

Energy Distribution

Most of us use electricity from the electrical "grid," a network of cables and wires that transmit and distribute power from suppliers to consumers.

The suppliers tend to be few, namely power stations (coal, nuclear, hydro-electric, etc.), and the consumers are many (homes, factories, offices, streets, etc.) This set up is a legacy of the industrial revolution and most developed countries are suffering from an ageing grid infrastructure.

With energy demand increasing for the foreseeable future, the utility industry is trying to upgrade its network using modern, more efficient technologies. One key difference to today's energy production is the trend of decentralisation. There are an increasing number of smaller power producers selling electricity to the grid, not just businesses but also homes wanting to sell their excess electricity generation to offset their energy bills, or even to get paid by the utility company if they are a net seller. This is known as *Distribution Generation.*

Implementing a grid that uses automated technology to anticipate consumption behaviour is often referred to as a "smart grid" from which there is a more reliable, efficient and sustainable source of electricity. Both the United States and Europe have in place smart grid policies and its roll-out is underway.

Energy Storage

So far in this chapter we have discussed the various ways we generate energy, most of the time in the form of electricity, to meet our planet's growing demand, but we have yet to mention how we go about storing it. For a fossil fuel, such as coal, this is very straight-forward – a lump of coal is a store of energy which can be released when it is burned. For periods of high energy demand, simply burn more coal, and vice versa. Similarly for nuclear energy, the fuel rods store the energy and splitting atoms releases energy.

As we replace fossil fuels with more renewable energy sources over the coming years, we must figure out a way to stabilise the grid's energy supply because renewable energy sources such as solar and wind are very weather dependent.

For example, solar cells are not able to generate sufficient electricity energy at night time and on cloudy days and we must resort to an alternative source of energy to compensate for the energy shortfall. Wind energy is even more unpredictable; it could be windy at night, when demand is low and calm during the day, when demand is high.

That is why energy storage is so important for the future of solar and wind energy. There needs to be cost effective ways of storing the excess energy and releasing it during times of higher demand, or on cloudy and still days when energy production is low. And there is a buzz of activity in this space.

Batteries

Batteries are amazing things. They perform two valuable functions that make so many aspects of our lives possible: the first is that they provide us with electricity when we are on the move or when grid power is not available to us; the second is that they store electricity in the form of chemical energy, which is very useful when we are producing more electricity than we need at that time. In the first application, size, speed of charge, durability and weight are all important factors, as well as cost. In the second application, size and weight do not matter.

The battery was invented in the eighteenth century by Alessandro Volta, an Italian professor of physics. Batteries today use the same basic principle of having two electrodes of two different metals and an electrolyte.

Batteries for Transportation and Devices

Existing battery technology has become dated and is, in many cases, holding back our technological progress in areas such as electric vehicles and mobile devices. The next generation of batteries will have to be smaller, cheaper and lighter.

Most batteries today use metal ions to store their charge, such as lithium, which have a long cycle life relative to other batteries. However, lithium batteries remain rather expensive, despite coming down in price by 90 per cent over the past 20 years. The other downside of lithium batteries is their risk of combustion, as Boeing discovered after a string of lithium battery fires on its new *787 Dreamliner* aircraft.

So while lithium batteries are going to be around for a few more years, other types of batteries are being developed.

One such promising emerging technology is an organic battery.

EV QUICK
CHARGING POINT

The science journal *Nature* published an article featuring such a battery currently being developed at Harvard University[11].

This new battery technology uses small organic (carbon-based) molecules called *quinones.* The type of quinone being used is found naturally in rhubarb, yes rhubarb of all things! The finished product may end up using a different organic molecule but this research clearly indicates that innovation in battery technology is well underway and we will start to see their impact on our lives by 2020. Price, capacity and speed of charge will be the key innovation drivers.

That brings us to another limitation of current battery technology: the time it takes for a full charge. So we were very interested to read about a new type of battery that was demonstrated at **Microsoft's** *Think Next Conference* in Tel Aviv in April 2014. In the demonstration, a Samsung S4 smartphone with a completely flat battery was charged fully in 26 seconds[12]. The Israeli company behind this battery is a start-up called **StoreDot,** and is definitely one to watch. They are aiming to have a commercial product available within three years. This could be a game changer, but again cost and cycle life will be critical in this battery's success. It would definitely accelerate the adoption of electric cars if batteries could receive a full charge in, say a minute. This would be even quicker than filling up a conventional vehicle with petrol or diesel.

Another company with enormous potential is called **Ilika (LON: IKA),** which started out at Southampton University in England. What is special about Ilika is that in January 2014, it became the first company to make a stacked solid-state cell battery, which could halve the size of current lithium smartphone batteries.

Whilst its recharge time is not as impressive as StoreDot's 26 seconds, 10 minutes is still much quicker than the existing charge time.

[11] *A metal-free organic–inorganic aqueous flow battery, Nature 505, 195–198 (09 January 2014), Brian Huskinson, Michael P. Marshak, Changwon Suh, Süleyman Er, Michael R. Gerhardt, Cooper J. Galvin, Xudong Chen, Alán Aspuru-Guzik, Roy G. Gordon & Michael J. Aziz*

[12] *ABBC News, Technology. Battery offers 30-second phone charging, 8 April 2014.*

The company also believes it could last four times longer than the current lithium ion batteries.

There is another way of making sure our electronic devices do not run out of power that negates the necessity of a speedy charge. What if the battery in each device was smart enough to know when it was running low on power and was able to initiate a charge request from a nearby charging station, which would then proceed to charge the battery without the user ever getting involved? Sounds like science fiction doesn't it? And until recently it was. How could such a convenience be achieved? By charging the battery wirelessly. In August 2014, Hatem Zeine, the CEO of a company called **Ossia** demonstrated a prototype of his wireless charging technology called Cota, using a smartphone.

Wireless power may raise health and safety concerns with people but Ossia's technology operates in the same frequency range as Wi-Fi and Bluetooth which have both been widely adopted as safe wireless technologies.

The current prototype requires the device to remain stationary while the system locks in on the location before commencing the wireless charge. However, Mr Zeine is confident that future versions would allow devices to be in constant contact with the charging station, allowing an uninterrupted charge as the device moves around the room. As with Bluetooth, the range of wireless charging is around 10 metres, or 30 feet. Ossia is awaiting FCC clearance for its technology, which it requires to take Cota one step closer to becoming a commercial reality. With FCC clearance, consumer versions are expected to be available sometime in 2015. Mr Zeine's ultimate vision is to eliminate the concept of charging as a conscious act altogether.

Another approach to wireless charging has been taken by a couple of start-up companies, one called **Powermat Technologies** in the US, the other called **Chargifi** from the UK.

Their technology involves installing the charging hardware on the underside of tables, al-

---

[13] *http://news.starbucks.com/news/national-roll-out-of-wireless-charging-by-duracell-powermat-begins-in-starbu*

lowing devices placed on the tables to charge through magnetic resonance, not too dissimilar to how some electric toothbrushes are charged wirelessly today. The idea is to offer phone or tablet charging services at coffee shops and other chains, either for a fee or paid for through advertising. It sounds promising but it all depends on whether the big chains sign up to the idea. In this regard, Powermat has the upper hand as in June 2014, Starbucks announced that it was rolling out Powermat across its stores in the US[13]. Another positive for Powermat is that Proctor & Gamble (the parent company of Duracell) is a strategic investor, which was no doubt very valuable during the Starbucks discussions. Chargifi has made some headway on the other side of the Atlantic, launching its service at selected outlets in the UK, Ireland and Dubai at the end of 2013, and there is probably enough room in the global market for both companies.

Storing Excess Renewable Energy for the Grid

We mentioned earlier that for wind and solar to become more appealing sources of energy, we must find a way to store their excess energy production very cheaply, and be able to feed it into the grid whenever required.

One battery company that has caught our attention and shows great potential (pardon the pun) in addressing this need is **Ambri** (www.ambri.com). Founded in 2010 by MIT Professor Donald Sadoway, Ambri's objective is to produce cheap batteries that are flexible enough to meet the demands of the grid. To achieve this, the company developed a liquid metal battery, which as the name implies uses two different metals in liquid form at high temperature, one low density and the other high density, with molten salt as the electrolyte.

The batteries are available in modular form, stackable in a standard 40 foot container, which when filled with the Ambri batteries are able to store 2 MWh of energy.

This can be scaled further by stacking the containers themselves to provide multiples of 2MWh of energy.

In April 2014, Ambri raised $35 million in equity financing, which it believes is sufficient to build its first commercial-scale production facility and to continue with the battery technology development. Ambri has already received orders for its prototype across the US, from Massachusetts to Alaska.

We are very excited about Ambri's prospects because cheap energy storage is probably one of the most needed technologies in the coming decade. It is definitely worth following the company's progress and we will be watching out for any announcements to go public.

Another company that has established itself as an energy storage specialist is California-based **Primus Power.** Founded in 2009, the company has raised a total of $35 million in equity, from the likes of Kleiner Perkins (a successful venture capital firm that has been around for over 40 years) and Chrysalix (a venture capital firm specialising in new energy).

Primus's modular, stackable storage cells each have a capacity to store 280 kilowatts (kW). They are being marketed to utilities producing solar and wind energy, as well as to companies who may want to better manage their energy consumption by using their own stored energy supply during peak, expensive hours and grid power during off-peak hours.

There may be enough room in the storage market for both Ambri and Primus, but it will likely come down to cost, lifespan of the battery and the ability to deliver on large orders.

Pumped Storage

Today, the most common method of storing excess energy generated is known as pumped storage. As the name implies, the excess energy is used to pump water to a reservoir situated on a hill. In times of peak demand, the reservoir water is used to drive a turbine located on lower ground. Pumped storage is able to achieve an energy efficiency of 75 to 85 per cent.

Germany, for example, has around 7 gigawatts of pumped storage power plants.

There are a number of disadvantages with this approach, the most obvious one being that it is only feasible in hilly areas, which is not necessarily where the energy production is located. That brings us to an interesting alternative.

Compressed Air

A relatively old method of storing excess energy is being given a new lease of life. Compressed air energy storage has been around since the 1970s yet there are only two such plants in the world: one is in Germany and has been in operation since 1978; and the other is in the US and has been in operation since 1991.

The principle of compressed air storage is relatively straight-forward: instead of using the excess energy to pump water up to a reservoir, it is used to pump air into an underground cavern (obviously one that is air-tight). Air pressure builds up to around 70 bar, where bar is a unit of pressure and 1 bar is approximately equal to atmospheric pressure. In times of high energy demand, the compressed air is released and used to drive an air turbine, which in turn drives a generator.

The reason why this technology has had limited adoption is to do with efficiency. Unlike the 75 to 85 per cent efficiency achievable using pumped storage, the efficiency achievable using compressed air storage is in the 40 to 55 per cent range, and this is not because of any pressure leaking, it is to do with energy lost through heat. As we all know when we pump up our bicycle tyres, the pump gets hot because air releases heat when it is compressed. So this hot air must be cooled before it is stored in a cavern, hence heat energy is lost.

Conversely when the compressed air is released, it cools and this cold air must be re-heated before it can be used to drive a turbine. Usually, natural gas is used to heat this air, which consequently releases carbon dioxide into the atmosphere.

So in order to make compressed air energy storage a more attractive method of storing energy, it must be more efficient and carbon neutral.

One of Europe's utility companies, **RWE Power** believes it has developed a new method to address both of these shortfalls.

RWE's approach, which it hopes to have in operation in 2016, captures the heat generated when the air is compressed in large, highly insulated cylinders located above ground. This time when the compressed air is released from the underground cavern it is heated using this stored heat before reaching the turbine. Not only does this approach not require natural gas, hence zero carbon emissions, it is also able to achieve an efficiency of around 70 per cent. RWE expects to be able to install this technology alongside some of its renewable power plants to store around 1 gigawatt hours to be released during periods of high energy demand.

RWE is not the only player in this space; we also found two American companies with a similar method. In California, there is a company called **LightSail Energy** (http://www.lightsail.com) which has developed a similar approach, claiming to be able to obtain a roundtrip thermal efficiency of 90 per cent; and on the east coast in New Hampshire, there is a company called **SustainX** (http://www.sustainx.com) which also boasts of being able to achieve a high thermal efficiency.

The role of energy storage will become increasingly important in smart grids as the cost of storage continues to fall.

As far as energy production, distribution and storage is concerned, we believe the most disruptive technology in energy by 2020 will be in batteries/energy storage.

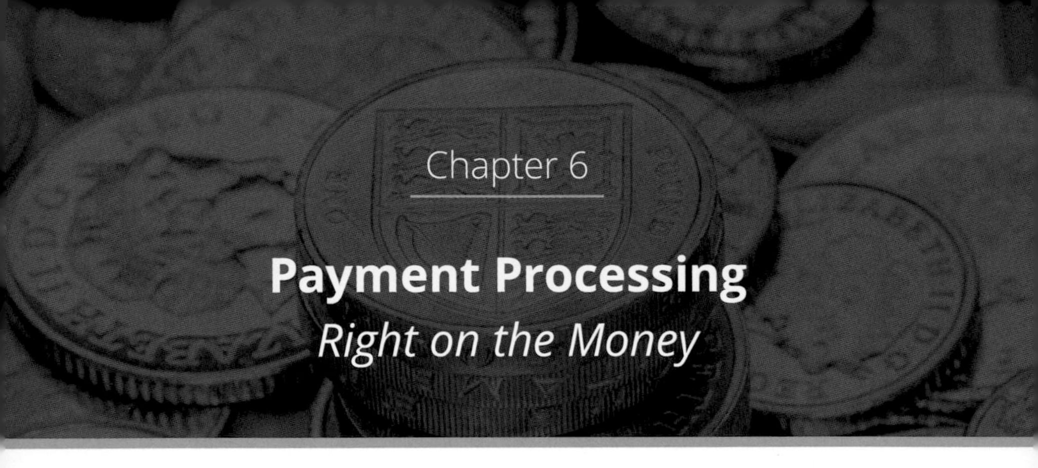

Chapter 6

Payment Processing

Right on the Money

Money is the medium through which humans exchange goods and services, and it is used universally. Money is also a store of value, acting as a way for surplus capital (i.e. savings) to be recycled back into the economy. Financial contracts of all kinds are one of the key foundations on which all modern societies are based. Monetary value is occasionally destroyed as a result of intermittent financial crises. These crises have led to an evolved model of finance that is based on state intervention in times of turmoil.

Early forms of money included beads, feathers and stones, yet today's money is so complex that understanding its machinations and layers can be beyond even the savviest economists. Derivatives, multi-layered bonds and high frequency trading are just a few examples that illustrate these complexities. Billions of payments around the world every day are still settled using notes and coins, which given where we are technologically as a society, seems antiquated. Their replacement is the most obvious feature of the future landscape of payments. Indeed, there is a great deal of activity in electronic payment systems to indicate that notes and coins are finally on their way out. Some examples include the use of e-wallets, near field communication (NFC) and crypto-currencies such as Bitcoin to make payments.

Mobile money (M-Money) is expected to grow exceptionally. In a report by Citibank, M-Money volumes are forecast to grow by over 80 per cent annually, reaching around $450 billion in 2016.

The way that money is transmitted, lent and borrowed throughout the world is also changing

Series 2
Series 3
Category 4
Category 3

quickly. Banks will soon become unrecognisable, fundamentally altered by technologies centred on the internet. The fat margins enjoyed by the incumbents will be disintermediated by such things as peer-to-peer lending, crowd-funding and the slow but sure erosion of the ascendancy of the main currencies. The latter will take much longer than the proponents of Bitcoin and other crypto-currencies would suggest, but nonetheless almost every aspect of money and its transmission, along with the entire financial industry as we know it, will evolve into something quite new.

That said, the basic function of money will remain unchanged; it is still the most convenient way known to mankind of swapping one form of labour for another. The evolution of money up to this point has taken many centuries: from barter, to coinage (which became too heavy to carry around), to banknotes (originally used in China). These first notes were backed by traders' promises, then by precious metals held by banks and governments, then by government promises (known as fiat money). It has been a long journey with fundamentally little technological innovation.

The banking industry has evolved increasingly sophisticated models of lending, of taking customer money and of obfuscation to increase and to justify margins. Some of these margins come with systemic risk, the consequences of which we foresaw in our book *WakeUp! Survive & Prosper in the Coming Economic Turmoil,* published in 2005.

In the golden age of technology, almost everything in finance will change, even though these changes are only slightly apparent today. For instance, contactless payments, either via mobile phones or cards are becoming increasingly prevalent, as are e-wallets. According to research by Adyen, a payment platform company, mobile payments accounted for 19.5 per cent of all transactions worldwide in December 2013, representing a growth of 55 per cent year-on-year. Using notes and coins is not only more cumbersome, it is more expensive to manage. Tufts University estimates that the cost of transit, security and theft of physical money to US businesses runs at over $55 billion a year. The consultancy McKinsey estimates that the digitisation of money in the form of notes and coins will add at least $340 billion to US GDP over time.

In the near future, borrowing money will become largely internet-based, and money transmission and savings will also be centred on the internet. Office-based banking is going to fade away, and companies will be financed through forms of crowd-funding, with multiple new exchanges for shares in such enterprises emerging. Even today, many of our readers will probably not have been near a physical bank branch for some time.

Almost all of our financial transactions will move online, and traditional banking will be severely disrupted. This will pose enormous challenges to established financial institutions, as their business of lending, taking deposits, selling financial services and insurance will face intense competition online. The transformation will pose enormous regulatory challenges, as new forms of virtual financial institutions, such as peer-to-peer lenders, will require supervision and adequate capitalisation. In addition, crypto-currencies such as Bitcoin are going to pose big challenges to the established issuers of money, i.e. governments.

In order for traditional banks to remain relevant, they have to adapt to the changing landscape, which means big cuts in overheads, such as those associated with running a physical branch network. Banks will need to become more specialised, and will have to use their might and capital base to counter the web-based lenders and deposit taking institutions.

With an ever increasing number of transactions taking place electronically, cash will become largely redundant within ten to fifteen years in the developed world. Even traditional credit cards and debit cards will quickly be replaced by embedded systems in mobile phones or wearable devices. Contactless payments, currently confined to low value transactions, will become the norm, and sending money via the internet will be available with much lower transaction fees than today.

Credit card merchants are already anxious to bypass the high fees imposed on them by the credit card issuers, and new technologies will allow these fees to be compressed. According to the Nilson Report, a payment card trade publication, merchants in the US alone spent $71.7 billion on these fees in 2013.

Conventional lending will become a thing of the past. Almost all lending, with the possible exception of mortgages, will be done online employing sophisticated algorithms and credit checking databases to assess risk.

In this chapter, we focus on three areas that are likely to have the greatest impact on traditional banking, these being:

- Contactless, near field communication and mobile payment systems;
- Crypto-currencies, especially Bitcoin; and
- Peer-to-peer lending and crowd-funding.

Contactless, Near Field Communication and Mobile Payment Systems

Apart from cash, most of us also use a number of other ways to pay for things, depending on where we are in the world. Common alternatives to cash include bank cheques, debit cards and credit cards. The popularity and adoption of a payment method largely depends on the (1) convenience and speed of transacting; (2) acceptance of the payment method by the merchant (seller); and (3) willingness of the buyer (consumer) to use the payment method. All three are, in a way correlated, but ultimately if a payment method is popular and widely adopted by the consumer, merchants end up having to accept it too. For instance, credit cards are popular with shoppers, and most merchants accept them even though they resent paying high commissions to the credit card companies, particularly merchants operating in low margin businesses. Merchants have been known to impose a surcharge for purchases made using a credit card; this can be in the form of a flat fee or a percentage of the transaction amount, typically 3 per cent. However, in some countries and states in America, merchants are legally prohibited from imposing a credit card surcharge.

The convenience and popularity of credit cards with consumers over the years has made the credit card companies vast profits. Naturally, for a new payment method to supplant an existing popular one, it must be superior in some way. Credit cards are popular because they allow the consumer to shop without having to withdraw the correct amount of cash beforehand. They also allow consumers to spend money they have not yet earned, which gives the credit card companies the opportunity to charge high interest on unpaid balances by the due date every month.

A Tale of Two Contrasting Smartcards

In 1990, NatWest Bank in the UK decided to develop a form of electronic cash it named *Mondex*. NatWest partnered with Midland Bank and proceeded to pilot the new payment system in a town called Swindon in 1995. Mondex smart cards were issued to participating consumers. ATMs began to allow card holders to pre-load e-cash on their Mondex card and participating merchants installed terminals to process Mondex payments. The pilot was deemed a moderate success. A couple of years later, Mondex was rolled out across a number of major cities around the world, where a healthy uptake among early adopters was expected. To cut a long story short, Mondex never took off and can be classified as a failure, even after *MasterCard* acquired a controlling stake in it in 1997. Mondex died a quiet death and most people today have never even heard of it.

Mondex failed because it didn't provide an incentive for consumers to change the way they paid for things and it didn't simplify the process of transacting. Quite the opposite in fact: consumers had to squeeze in a Mondex card into their already stuffed wallets, and make sure that it was regularly topped up with money from their bank account.

The Mondex story illustrates how for a new payment system to be successful, it must offer an incentive for the consumer to use it, regardless of whether the technology is superior or not.

Contrast that with the case of Hong Kong's Octopus card, introduced in 1997 by a consortium of public transport companies, the majority shareholder being the Mass Transit Railway (MTR). Anyone who has been to Hong Kong will concur that Hong Kong is a congested place. With an official population of seven million people, and on average an extra one million visitors in any given week (most of whom are from Mainland China), public transport is crucial to keeping the city moving, and the use of public transport is estimated at over 90 per cent, the highest in the world. There are a number of modes of public transport available in Hong Kong, all used extensively – bus, public light bus, tram, train, light rail and ferry. However, high passenger flow rates were resulting in unnecessary delays and bottlenecks associated with people fumbling around with change to buy tickets for their journey. Waving a contactless smartcard at a card reader would speed things up considerably by collecting the exact fare instantly. Initially the Octopus card was introduced only for MTR journeys (in 1997) and within three months, three million cards had been issued.

Octopus cards are issued for free with a refundable deposit of 50 Hong Kong dollars (around $6.40). Cardholders then have to pre-load cash onto the contactless card through designated machines, with an option to having it automatically re-load cash through a pre-registered credit card. As an incentive to its use, fares on MTR journeys are cheaper for passengers paying with their Octopus card.

Its rapid adoption led to the system being extended to other modes of public transport, and before long a number of merchants started to accept Octopus Cards as a form of payment too. For example, today it is accepted at Starbucks, McDonald's, 7-Eleven, Circle-K, as well as local supermarkets and restaurants.

According to data published by Octopus[1], there now are more than 25 million Octopus cards in circulation, with 99 per cent of the population having one. It is accepted by 14,000 retail outlets and 12 million transactions are made using the Octopus card every day, totalling over HK$140 million ($16.6 million.) Octopus is now working on launching its online payment system using near field communication enabled smartphones.

Contactless Smartcards on the Rise

Payment systems using stored value cards and chips embed-

[1] *http://www.octopus.com.hk/octopus-for-businesses/benefits-for-your-business/en/index.html*

Figure 25: Octopus card reader on a bus in Hong Kong. Photo by Ka890 for Wikimedia Commons

ded into smartphones and other devices are on the rise and are starting to replace cash as well as traditional debit card and credit card transactions.

We used the Octopus card earlier to illustrate how this form of e-cash has been deployed with a 95 per cent adoption rate in Hong Kong. Greater London has the *Oyster* card based on the same technology, but it is currently only used to pay for public transport. Other cities around the world use contactless smartcard systems, from San Francisco to Helsinki, mainly for public transport. The technology is based around so-called RFID (radio-frequency identification), which uses radio-frequency electromagnetic fields to transfer data between the card reader and the microchip inside the card.

Contactless payment systems currently take the form of modified credit and debit cards, smartcards, key fobs, mobile phones or anything else that uses RFID to facilitate secure payments. These payments are about twice as fast to make as conventional card payments. They are also secure without requiring PIN codes or signatures, and they tend to encourage consumers to spend more (about 30 per cent more according to MasterCard[2].)

Contactless smart card readers use radio waves to read and write data onto the chip in the card, smartphone or other device. When used for electronic payment, the terminals are typically located near cash registers. When the cards are used for public transport, the terminals are located on turnstiles and station platforms as standalone units.

With security being a major concern for contactless cards, there are a variety of techniques in use to guard against potential fraud. These include looking for attempts to corrupt or disrupt data transmission. In addition, payment processors combat eavesdropping designed to steal private information and employ methods to disable stolen devices automatically. Based on the evidence thus far, fraud levels are lower with contactless payment systems, which is reassuring.

In the UK, early adopters such as McDonald's, Boots, Pret a Manger, Stagecoach and Lidl have introduced contactless payment systems, but it will not be long before it becomes the norm for making payments. Understandably, MasterCard and Visa are embracing this trend, partly to shore up their own positions as the dominant credit card issuers globally. They have recently agreed to a set of standards for general "open loop" payments on their networks, with over 150 million cards deployed thus far in the US, UK and France.

In the UK, as an example, there were around 35 million contactless cards at the end of 2013, and over 300,000 terminals. More payments systems are on the way. In 2015, Barclays intends to roll out a wristband called bPay, available to all bank customers of whatever bank, to enable fast, contactless payment. There are also plans to use *bPay* to enter sports stadiums, concerts and other events.

---

[2] *http://newsroom.mastercard.com/press-releases/new-mastercard-advisors-study-on-contactless-payments-shows-almost-30-lift-in-total-spend-within-first-year-of-adoption/*

Many smartphones by Asian brands such as Samsung, Sony, HTC and LG are already NFC-enabled, as are some models by Motorola and Nokia. In total, around one billion NFC enabled smartphones shipped in 2013. Unusually, Apple has been slow to incorporate NFC into its iPhone, although the new iPhone 6 is NFC-enabled. With 800 million iTunes accounts, comprising mostly loyal and typically high-income earners, an Apple branded payments system, which has been dubbed *Pay*, could therefore be exceptionally valuable.

As the hardware becomes universal in all phones, there will be an explosion of activity in NFC payment systems. NFC technology requires a "secure element" within the phone that securely stores sensitive data, such as bank account details and other credentials.

Banks are terrified and excited at the same time by the adoption rate of contactless payment solutions, and most have decided to launch their own version. Citibank, American Express, JP Morgan Chase, RBS, Barclaycard and Lloyds are among the many banks who now offer it as standard. This is despite the efforts of many retailers and non-bank financial institutions to bypass the traditional banking networks and their high "interchange" fees by setting up their own cooperatives.

In the US, for example, the likes of Walmart, Banana Republic, Target, Gap, Wendy's and Kmart have joined forces to form a group called the *Merchant Customer Exchange (MCX)* in an effort to develop a mobile payment system across all participating merchants that bypasses the credit card companies. The idea is to allow the participating retailers direct access to customer bank account details and customer data. As yet, however, the project has gained little traction, despite the use of loyalty schemes to encourage customer adoption.

For their part, Visa and MasterCard are naturally throwing their weight behind their own technology, dubbed EMV (Europay, MasterCard and Visa.) This technology has evolved from being a common standard for "chip and pin" cards to a common standard for contactless payments. It is expected that this new technology will push more fraud liability to retailers if they do not upgrade to terminals that are able to process the new cards. In return, retailers are hoping that the move to EMV will reduce the high fees imposed on them on the basis that there will be less fraud, which has always been the main reason card issuers use to justify their high interchange fees. It remains to be seen whether banks actually pass on these savings to retailers.

The high credit card interchange fees are the bane of all merchants, so much so that the biggest retailer of all, Walmart, has filed a lawsuit against Visa in the US, alleging that the latter has "engaged in a conspiracy with some of the nation's largest banks to illegally fix and inflate various fees."

Cloud-Based Payment Systems

Contactless cards and NFC enabled phones are generally linked to electronic wallets or "e-wallets," such as Google *Wallet*, or to a credit card, such as MasterCard's *PayPass* and Visa's *payWave.*

Most e-payment systems, including Google Wallet, PayPal, GlobalPay and GoPago, adopt a cloud-based approach, placing the mobile payment provider in the middle of the transaction. This involves two separate steps: first, a cloud-linked payment method is selected and payment is authorised via NFC or an alternative method. During this step, the payment provider automatically covers the cost of the purchase with its own funds. Second, in a separate transaction immediately following, the payment provider charges the purchaser's selected, cloud-linked account for the funds. If the account is a credit card, then the provider will usually charge a fee; in the case of Google Wallet, that fee is 2.99 per cent of the transaction value, with a minimum charge of 30 US cents per transaction.

Google Wallet, initially available only in the US, is being rolled out elsewhere in the world from late 2014. Also based around NFC, Google Wallet is a payment system that allows its users to store all of their loyalty cards, debit cards, credit cards, and gift cards on its system. Users can also transfer money to other people using Google Wallet for free. Google Wallet can be used either with an Android-enabled phone or with a physical card, and is linked to Visa and MasterCard.

It is also integrated with Gmail, allowing users to send money through Gmail attachments.

Given the size of the opportunity associated with mobile payments, it is no surprise that big disputes between various players have arisen. PayPal, already a leading e-commerce payment platform, is suing Google for misappropriating trade secrets from PayPal's mobile payment business.

In another dispute, Verizon, the US's largest mobile network operator, is actively blocking its subscribers from installing Google Wallet, claiming that not all of its subscribers' handsets are NFC enabled to allow sensitive data to be stored. However, in November 2013, Verizon launched its own NFC enabled e-wallet with AT&T Mobility and T-Mobile USA, calling it *Isis*[3]. Isis comes pre-installed on all new handsets issued by the three partner network operators, and transactions are settled through a linked credit card. At the time of writing, Wells Fargo, American Express and Chase had signed up as participating card issuers, so there is plenty of corporate muscle behind the Isis e-wallet.

This is clearly squeezing out Google Wallet, and if the company intends to support its e-wallet offering, it will have to persuade Isis to unblock it from its network partners. This will not be easy given that such an action would have no benefit to Isis, so Google will have to think creatively, or failing that, it could file a law suit.

PayPal

PayPal was one of the first e-commerce payment platforms, dating back to the dot-com era of the late 1990s. It was acquired by eBay in 2002 shortly after it listed on NASDAQ, and it still thrives today. With 150 million active users, PayPal's 2013 revenues were $6.6 billion with a 25 per cent EBITDA[4] margin. Total payment volumes were close to $150 billion and the company is tentatively valued at $40 billion. Although there have been rumours that PayPal would like to offer its platform on a white label basis to Apple, we don't believe there would be much in it for Apple. That said, we expect PayPal to announce some sort of e-wallet strategy in the near future, either on its own, or in partnership with another player.

[3] *In July 2014, Isis announced plans to re-brand following the militant group's adoption of the same name.*
[4] *EBITDA stands for earnings before interest, taxes, depreciation, and amortization.*

There is also the case against Google for the alleged theft of its intellectual property; the outcome of which would no doubt influence how it proceeds with its e-wallet offering.

New Players to Watch

So far we have mainly written about what the big boys are up to in the e-wallet space. However, there are a few new companies that show potential in this space that we believe are worth a mention.

First up is a really good app called **Venmo** that is quickly gaining mind share in the US. Venmo is an e-wallet app that is a kind of fusion of social media and PayPal. Using their smartphones, users can exchange payments with people in their social circle. The app is free to download and is available on both Apple and Android devices. As with most other e-wallet offerings, Venmo links to the user's banking account, debit card or and credit card (using a credit card carries a 3 percent transaction fee). The app also links Facebook friends and email contacts to the user's bank account. Rather scarily, friends who are "trusted" can automatically withdraw money from their friend's account. Expenses among friends can optionally be displayed in a Facebook-style feed, and Venmo payments can either be "cashed out" to a designated card, bank account, or kept for later use.

Venmo is owned by US credit card processor **Braintree.** The system works really well; better, in our opinion, than PayPal or Google Wallet and is ideal for cash-strapped twenty-somethings who are used to making micro payments between friends, for instance, after settling a restaurant or bar bill.

Next is a UK-based company called **Weve,** a company launched in September 2013. Weve is a joint venture between the three largest mobile network operators: **EE, Telefonica UK (O2)** and **Vodafone UK.** The purpose of Weve is to promote the development of contactless mobile payment systems with a view to creating a pan-European platform. Weve is set-up in a similar way to America's Isis platform that we discussed earlier, although Weve is slightly behind in its development.

Other Mobile Payment Solutions

In the developing world, the use of mobile payments has attracted public and private funding by organizations such as **US Aid** and the **Bill & Melinda Gates Foundation.**

Originating in Africa, *M-Pesa* (*M* for mobile, *pesa* is Swahili for money) is another type of mobile phone-based money transfer and micro financing service. M-Pesa was started by **Safaricom** and **Vodacom,** the largest mobile network operators in Kenya and Tanzania. One of the most developed mobile payment systems in the world, M-Pesa allows users with a national ID card or passport to deposit, withdraw, and transfer money easily using their mobile phone. The system allows its users to send balances using SMS technology to other users (including sellers of goods and services), and to redeem deposits for regular money. Users are charged a small fee for sending and withdrawing money using the service. M-Pesa has spread quickly to become the most successful mobile phone-based financial service in the developing world. By 2014, there were about 18 million M-Pesa users in Kenya.

In Tanzania M-Pesa has five million subscribers and the service is now also available in Afghanistan, South Africa, and India. Indeed, throughout the emerging world mobile financial services are being used to address the "unbanked" market, estimated to be half of all adults on the planet.

A survey conducted by the GSM Association, an industry group that encompasses some 800 mobile operators in 250 countries, found that operators were offering 219 money transfer services in 84 countries at the end of 2013, up from 179 such services in 75 countries a year earlier. Mobile money services were rolled out in 2013 in nine new markets – Bolivia, Brazil, Egypt, Ethiopia, Guyana, Jamaica, Tajikistan and Togo.

A similar system is currently being rolled out in the UK is an app called *Paym,* which is being offered by many of the big banks and building societies. To use the money transfer service, recipients are required register and link their bank account number to their mobile phone number.

Senders also need to register, after which they can use the mobile phone number of the recipient when making transfers. More than 90 per cent of UK current accounts support Paym.

Although Barclays in the UK already support Paym, it has developed another app called *Pingit.* Unlike Paym, Pingit facilitates money transfers without the need for a smartphone, making it more like the M-Pesa platform.

Not wanting to miss out on an opportunity, British entrepreneur and billionaire, Sir Richard Branson has teamed up with one of PayPal's founders Peter Thiel to develop a payment platform dedicated to transfers of small amounts of money called **TransferWise,** a space is currently dominated by banks and Western Union. TransferWise uses the web to charge much lower fees than the incumbents. Based in the UK and currently privately held, the company has received $25 million in funding and is worth following.

Another new company entering the increasingly competitive arena is **Square,** a payment system company from the US that some readers may already be familiar with. Founded by Twitter entrepreneur Jack Dorsey, Square has received significant funding from venture capitalists and there is talk of an IPO in 2014. Square is a credit card accepting mechanism linked to mobile phones, with a flat fee of 2.75 per cent per swipe to merchants, not much lower than what credit card companies already charge merchants today. However, the difference with Square is that it comes with a suite of analytical tools that allows merchants to keep track of all their payments and inventory. Square also makes small business loans through Square Capital, and is involved in money transmission through Square Cash. For the time being, Square operates in the US, Canada and Japan, and has gained considerable traction.

In our opinion Square is more of a merchant software than a revolutionary payment system. It takes advantage of the fact that chip and pin technology is not yet widely used in the US, but it is likely that Square will be leap-frogged by NFC technology, which will become ubiquitous.

Similarly, in the UK, there is a company called **Powa**, a mobile payments technology company that has raised nearly $100 million from Wellington Partners. Dan Wagner, the irrepressible UK entrepreneur has developed a system where a mobile phone can take a photograph of an item or service and the object can be purchased on the spot.

"If I see an ad in The Telegraph, I will be able to buy it just by lifting my phone and pointing it at the ad," Mr Wagner has said. *"I can do that with a mail-order catalogue or a TV commercial or even walking past a shop window."* Powa works seamlessly with smartphones and uses a pin device that comes with the app. The system has not yet been rolled out, but so far shows promise.

UK-based company **Monitise,** listed in London (LON:MONI) is an interesting play on the "backbone" technology for mobile payments. As well as having a strong alliance with IBM, it has partnerships with several leading financial institutions, such as Visa, Bank of China and HSBC.

Moving on to Latin America, mobile payments have taken off in a surprising application: e-invoicing. In the same way that the use of M-Pesa has become widespread in Africa for transfer money, e-invoicing for businesses has become the norm in Latin America. E-invoicing requires buyers and sellers to register a transaction as it occurs with the relevant tax authorities. Starting with Chile, the technology is now used in almost every Latin American country, and in general the technology is as quick as a credit-card transaction. As a result, the region has gone from being at the forefront of tax evasion, to being amongst the most effective in collecting commercial taxes. So much so that PwC thinks that if e-invoicing became universal it could add $100 billion to governments' tax-takes.

Crypto Currencies – Will They Attain Global Acceptance?

By now, everyone has heard of **Bitcoin.** Most people, including those who use it, find the whole concept of a *crypto-currency* confusing. We are all used to thinking that currencies are centrally issued by national governments or supranationally by organisations such as the European Central Bank. Crypto-currencies are decentralised, internet-based, highly volatile and put into circulation by arcane means, typically described as "mining".

They have also been associated with criminal and shady activities, exemplified by the now-defunct Silk Road website, which allowed Bitcoins to be traded for drugs and other illegal products. Silk Road was shut down by the FBI in 2013, where they seized 144,000 Bitcoins, worth $28.5 million at the time. The collapse of *Mount Gox,* a Japanese exchange and repository of Bitcoins cast further doubt over ownership and provenance of Bitcoins.

That said we believe crypto-currencies are here to stay, even though their adoption may be slower than many proponents believe. Indeed, over the next couple of decades crypto-currencies will evolve into a useful and widely circulated international currency/ies, and it might one day even supplant the US dollar as the principal global trading currency. For this to happen, however, several significant hurdles have to be overcome: first, security of ownership and transmission will have to be vastly improved; second, the crypto-currency of choice will have to settle into a pattern of much lower price volatility, with reference to its exchange rate compared major currencies such as the US dollar; and third, crypto-currencies must become well understood and be demonstrably superior to existing currencies, for at least some purposes.

These are high hurdles but the notion of an electronic universal currency is not so far-fetched. Crypto-currencies do have some advantages over regular currencies: they are generally anonymous (though ultimately traceable); and they are produced in limited numbers offering their holders protection against high inflation that may be triggered by government-backed quantitative easing. For example, Bitcoins are used by some Argentinians as an alternative to the peso to store value and avoid capital controls.

Crypto-currencies also have low "friction" or transaction costs, as transmission is directly between internet users (peer-to-peer) and as a result bank charges and other related transaction fees are avoided. Generally speaking, the cost of acquiring, holding and transacting in crypto-currencies is very low.

Bitcoin 101

In this section, we attempt to explain Bitcoin in as simple terms as we can. In essence, Bitcoin is a decentralised, internet-based, currency introduced as open source software by a mysterious person named Satoshi Nakamoto in 2009. No one has ever discovered the true identity of Satoshi Nakamoto, despite a wide search and several false sightings.

Bitcoins are best described as entries in a giant electronic ledger, known as a *"block chain"*, which contains the transaction history of every Bitcoin in circulation. This ledger is kept up to date by a global network of tens of thousands of computers, with the block chain kept public as a way to keep the system secure.

Several levels of cryptography are employed to add further layers of security. Users make payments by digitally broadcasting "signed" messages to the network. Transactions do not identify the payer or payee by name. Instead, transactions transfer ownership from one Bitcoin address to another are broadcast using readily available software applications, the most common of which is version 9 (Bitcoin Core) of the original client that Nakamoto developed.

Bitcoin servers validate these transactions, then add them to their copy of the ledger (block chain) and then broadcast these ledger additions to other Bitcoin servers. It is important for Bitcoin owners (of whom there an estimated 150,000 worldwide) to protect their "private keys" linked to their Bitcoin addresses.

Roughly every ten minutes a group of Bitcoin transactions, called a "block", is confirmed to the block chain ledger. This confirmation process is described as "mining," and it carries a reward to the people who keep the Bitcoin servers running, which equates to 25 Bitcoins per "block" added to the block chain. To claim this reward, the miner includes in the block a message called the "coin base" which allocates the reward Bitcoins to the miner's address. All Bitcoins in circulation can be traced back to such coin base transactions.

The block reward of 25 Bitcoin will be halved to 12.5 Bitcoins in 2017, and again approximately every four years thereafter. By 2140, (yes, they are thinking far

Figure 26: A sign that indicates the presence of a Bitcoin ATM. **Source:** Mrnett1974 for Wikimedia Commons

into the future), there will be a total of approximately 21 million Bitcoins (the purported maximum) and transaction processors will be solely incentivized by transaction fees. There are currently around 12 million Bitcoins in circulation.

The most efficient mining servers are designed specifically for Bitcoin creation to allow for faster mining and lower power consumption. This is vital because the cost of running computer servers for many miners is higher than the reward of new Bitcoins they receive.

Reward Bitcoins are the means by which new Bitcoins enter circulation. The easiest way to acquire Bitcoins is to buy them online for cash in many different currencies, using credit cards or cash transmission. There are many online exchanges for Bitcoin, but their reputation has been severely tarnished following the collapse of *Mount Gox* in Japan, the largest exchange of all.

Today the biggest exchanges are in China and Europe. There is also an increasing number of Bitcoin ATMs that credit Bitcoins onto an individual's smartphone in exchange for depositing bank notes into the ATM.

Using an online exchange to obtain Bitcoins poses significant risks, as many of the smaller exchanges have failed. In addition, because Bitcoin purchases are irreversible, sellers of Bitcoins must take care to ensure receipt of traditional funds from buyers.

There is one further problem with the Bitcoin system: a particular "mining pool" called GHash.IO, has almost a 50 per cent share of the Bitcoin network. Although this has not so far disrupted the network, it could theoretically allocate all of the mining rewards to itself, destroying trust in Bitcoin and causing a crash in prices. This would not be in GHash.IO's interest, it being a major Bitcoin player, but nonetheless it is a risk that could undermine the crypto-currency.

Until recently, Bitcoin was mostly the domain of speculators, with relatively few legitimate businesses prepared to accept it as a form of payment. This is changing and merchants are increasingly prepared to take Bitcoins over credit cards because of the substantially lower transaction fees. Another reason is that, over time, Bitcoin has appreciated and there is a growing view that accumulating Bitcoins has some upside in the exchange rate when compared to traditional currencies. As of November 2013, there were about 1,000 brick-and-mortar merchants and over 35,000 online stores globally that accepted Bitcoin as a form of payment. As the illicit use of Bitcoin is whittled away by law enforcement agencies, the adoption rate of Bitcoin will continue to increase.

But the volatility of Bitcoin's price since inception has also been a major reason behind its slow adoption rate. Bitcoins were trading for as little as 1 US cent each in 2010, before reaching

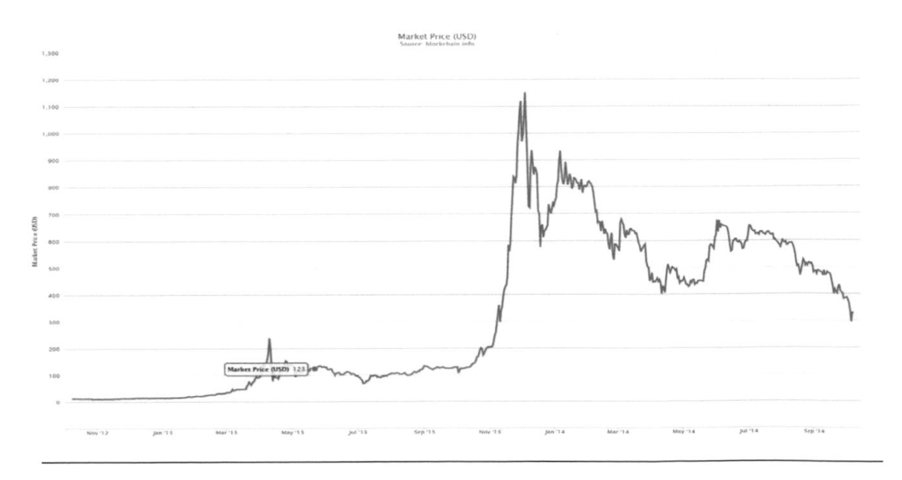

Figure 27: The volatile price of Bitcoins in USD from Oct 2012 - Oct 2014. **Source:** blockchain.info

parity with the US dollar in 2011, then rising to as high as $1,200 in late 2013, before crashing to just below $450 at the time of the Mount Gox failure, thereafter remaining in a generally downward trend (see Figure 27).

Thankfully, money doesn't usually swing in price as wildly as Bitcoin on a daily or annual basis (except in areas of extremely high inflation or political risk). A car selling for $20,000 is likely to be more or less the same price from one month to the next. Referenced in Bitcoin, it would be difficult to judge what the likely future cost of that car would be. Hence it is vital for the future acceptance of Bitcoin that its price volatility is reduced. Equally the general price of Bitcoin needs to rise over time against regular currencies to create the view that it is a store of value.

Other factors that would help Bitcoin gain popularity are:

- Its use and acceptance in more countries around the world (for instance, China does not allow Bitcoins as a means of exchange);
- Improved security; and
- Its acceptance by tax authorities as a currency to avoid taxation being applied to unspent Bitcoins. Otherwise, governments could kill off Bitcoin by taxing it to death.

The regulation of crypto-currencies is also a subject of considerable debate, with the US Senate itself having opined that virtual currencies were a legitimate financial service in November 2013. So far though, there has been no formal framework to regulate crypto-currencies, other than outright banning them in some countries.

In 2013 Bitcoin suffered a technical glitch that caused a "fork" in the block chain, with one half of the network adding blocks to one version of the chain, and the other half adding to another. For a period of nearly six hours there were effectively two Bitcoin networks operating at the same time, each with its own version of the transaction history. Fortunately, its core developers quickly rectified this and the new software code appears to be much more stable.

One of the strong points of Bitcoin is that it is open to all participants; the system is described as "permissionless," encouraging innovation to develop multiple applications for it, most of which have not even been thought of yet. For example, Bitcoin might be used to represent ownership or partial ownership of things where an item, say a car, would only operate with a key that included a Bitcoin token.

There is a string of start-ups that are working to develop Bitcoin for new applications, such as the ownership of a car example above. It is being dubbed "internet of money" and "Bitcoin 2.0" protocols. Some of these companies are **litecoin, namecoin, novacoin, worldcoin, quarkcoin, feathercoin** and **alphacoin.** Some crypto-currencies are being designed for specific applications, such as **Colored Coins** and **Mastercoin,** which are being developed to enable the trading of financial assets, such as stocks and bonds. There is also a company called **Ethereum** that is working on a new block chain with a complete scripting language on top of it, allowing anyone to develop applications for it – a very ambitious undertaking. A competing approach to Ethereum has been adopted by **NXT** (pronounced Next), which is being built with pre-installed features to allow it to be used for, say secure asset exchange, or encrypted emails.

Ethereum is the open platform approach, but the risk is that it will have to rely on third parties to develop the applications for it. **Ether,** Ethereum's internal currency, powers its applications and acts as a "token of exchange" on its decentralized network.

For the time being, it is difficult to see how investors can profit from Bitcoin, apart from buying some as a hedge against depreciation of other currencies. Ethereum is possibly a contender to go public in the US, and should be watched.

Naturally, there is huge debate underway as to whether crypto-currencies will work at all. On one side of the fence, we have the sceptics, such as Professor John Quiggin, an Australian Economist, who has forecast that *"Bitcoins will attain their true value of zero sooner or later, but it is impossible to say when."* On the other side we have the optimists: Bank of America recently published the analysis of its strategist David Woo forecasting a maximum fair value of Bitcoin of $1,300 and a maximum market capitalization of $15 billion. We fall somewhere in between, believing an investment in Bitcoin will likely be a reasonable, albeit an unspectacular, success. Merchants and consumers alike will slowly feel more comfortable with the concept of a crypto-currency and, barring any security scares, Bitcoin and/or others will slowly gain traction.

Peer To Peer Lending / Crowdfunding

Having covered mobile payment systems and crypto-currencies, the third exciting growth area in technology-enabled finance is P2P, or peer-to-peer lending, also sometimes referred to as person-to-person lending, peer-to-peer investing, crowdfunding and social lending. P2P lending is the practice of lending money to unrelated individuals or "peers." This lending bypasses traditional financial institutions, such as banks, and takes place online on dedicated lending platforms.

Most peer-to-peer loans are unsecured personal loans, although that is changing. Typically, loans are made to an individual rather than a company, and the borrower does not provide collateral as protection to the lender against default.

Some P2P platforms have started to offer business loans, including secured loans, known as crowdfunding, although the same term is also used for non-loan funding platforms that are designed to raise money for new ideas.

A good example of a business loan platform is **Funding Tree** in the UK, which allows investors to be matched with equity opportunities in start-ups and small businesses (www.fundingtree.co.uk)

In less than a decade, a handful of crowdfunding websites around the world have organised billions of dollars' worth of small loans to individuals and businesses by matching individual or corporate lenders with borrowers and by offering superior interest rates to banks. P2P lending is effectively an alternative financial service, conducted for-profit (for the web platforms) and always online.

P2P loans are generally spread among a variety of lenders to diversify the risk of default, and unlike traditional, regulated banks, they are not backed by government insurance. Increasingly however, some websites are offering default insurance "pools" as a backstop to default by individual borrowers.

Seeing a potential threat to their business, traditional banks and lenders are starting to show an interest in P2P lending, as are investors. For instance, two former Lehman Brothers bond traders based in New York have launched a fund to invest in P2P lending, describing it as a rapidly growing asset class. In 2014, P2P lending in the US totalled around $4 billion. In five years' time, this figure is expected to grow to over $25 billion, with a large institutional component.

Given how rapidly P2P lending has grown, it has attracted the attention of financial regulators who have started to explore the risks it poses as an unregulated sector. While these lending platforms share the common characteristic of not having a physical branch presence, they also tend to lack a capital buffer to ride out financial storms. The default risk is passed directly onto the lenders; all it would take is for one nasty default to occur for regulators decide to bring in P2P lending under their umbrella, which would include imposing stricter reserve capital requirements. Despite such a possibility, there has been a surge of interest in the sector as a whole, partly due to a backlash against traditional banks post Great Recession.

Just as with traditional banks, P2P lenders check the credit history of the borrower, typically charging more interest to those who have a poor credit history. Unlike banks, however, they use new technology to keep overheads low, and interest rates are largely determined by lenders.

With the permission of the borrower, the lending platforms can sweep social media profiles and look at online bank accounts to approve or reject loans within seconds, using algorithms that are increasingly smart at avoiding defaults. Of course, the automated due-diligence process that allows platforms to keep their costs low can also be manipulated by criminals, and there have been cases where this has happened, highlighting the platform's vulnerability.

For example, in its first few years of operation, **Prosper,** the second largest P2P lender in the US, had a default rate exceeding 20 per cent. After enhancing its systems, Prosper's default rate fell to around 3 per cent. Compare that to Zopa, the UK's largest and the world's first P2P lender, which has been able to bring down its loan default rate to less than one per cent.

Securitised Debt, Anyone?

Lured by the higher interest rates compared to government bonds and banks, hedge funds and large wealth managers have been making loans through P2P platforms. They are fast becoming major P2P lenders; US platforms such as Lending Club and Prosper are trying to reallocate some of the lending opportunities to retail investors for fear of being swamped by institutional money. Such is the influence of institutional lenders over the P2P market that the infamous practices of debt securitisation have emerged in the industry. In October 2013 a New York-based hedge fund securitised about $53 million worth of P2P loans from Lending Club, repackaging them into bonds that could be sold on to a wider array of investors. In November 2013, alumni-based student lender Social Finance, together with Barclays and Morgan Stanley created a bond backed by P2P student loans worth $60 million.

Debt securitisation allows the larger lending platforms to expand their loan books more rapidly - the top five US P2P lenders account for over 85 per cent of loans, and over 60 per cent of loans made through Prosper and Lending Club are now believed to be backed by institutional investors.

UK P2P Market

In the UK, where the crowdfunding landscape remains dominated by retail investors, the British branch of Bank Santander has done a deal with **Funding Circle** in which Santander sources capital and loans for Funding Circle. This move is indicative of the P2P lending industry's willingness to partner with traditional banks, which is ironic given that the industry once claimed to avoid large financial institutions.

For traditional lenders, P2P provides a new business channel and possibly a way to circumvent regulatory and capital

reserve requirements. In June 2014, **Money & Co.**, a P2P lender, arranged a loan of £1 million for Mecmesin, a small manufacturing company in what is believed to be the largest manufacturing loan conducted through P2P thus far. Another P2P loan example is Odyssey Airlines, a start-up hoping to introduce a London to New York service, which raised £1.9 million through UK-based P2P **Thin Cats.** Thin Cats has so far lent about $100 million, all to businesses, funded by its 2,600 members with an average lending rate of 9 per cent.

Zopa is the largest site in the UK, followed by Funding Circle and RateSetter. Zopa has placed about $800 million of loans since it was launched in 2005. With around 54,000 registered lenders, Zopa's average loan size is £7,500, with lenders typically receiving a net interest rate of 5 per cent. As is common practice in the industry, lenders are charged a 1 per cent fee. Defaults in the UK are lower than in the US, reflecting somewhat tighter lending criteria.

The UK industry became (some-

what) regulated in April 2014, but lenders' money is still not protected by an official safety net, such as the Financial Services Compensation Scheme's (FSCS) £85,000 guarantee per person.

The Financial Conduct Authority (FCA) has identified 25 companies involved in the P2P lending market, five of which account for more than 95 per cent of outstanding loans. The FCA now requires P2P platforms to ensure that their lenders have the information they need, particularly the risks they face, so they can make informed investment decisions. This is far less onerous than the requirements imposed on traditional banks.

The main P2P sites have started to establish pools into which borrowers pay a small amount, to serve as a backstop should a borrower default on a loan. RateSetter was the first lender to do this in 2010, and several other sites across the world have followed suit.

The popularity of P2P lending in the UK has resulted in numerous new entrants to the market. At least 10 companies have been formed recently. These firms vary from the more sophisticated outfits such as **Assetz Capital,** which makes secured loans to businesses and property developers, to smaller start-ups such as **eMoneyUnion,** which is basically an online payday loan company.

Due to unscrupulous practices and usurious interest rates, the payday loan market is moving towards greater regulation. To date, this market has been dominated by self-funded companies such as Wonga, so it is encouraging to see the P2P model being applied to payday loans, as it is likely to push down interest rates, which will lighten the burden on the borrowers who are typically low income earners.

As P2P lending grows further, there will no doubt be a split between those platforms that remain selective about their borrowers in order to keep default rates low, and those that pursue looser lending criteria, accepting a higher default rate.

Regulators are keeping a close eye on how things develop.

The total alternative finance market in the UK doubled in size in 2014 to £939 million of new loans, of which approximately 30 per cent were to businesses.

Readers interested in investing in the UK P2P lending sector should consider AIM-listed investment company, **GLI Finance (LON:GLIF),** which has invested in several P2P lending platforms, including Funding Knight, a business lender and Platform Black, an invoice financing company. There are limited options to directly invest in P2P platforms for the time being.

US P2P Market

In the US, the market operates in a slightly different way to the UK. Investments in P2P loans can be as low as $25, and once enough investors commit to funding a particular loan, the actual loan is originated by a federally insured bank partner and then sold to a P2P platform, such as **Lending Club.** The platform then issues notes based on the underlying loan to the lender and services the loan, i.e. it collects the monies and interest back from the borrower. This complex process is designed to prevent Lending Club (which has 75 per cent of the US market) and its competitors from being regulated as traditional banks and having to maintain capital reserves. 70 per cent of borrowers on P2P platforms are using the loan to refinance existing debts, which is reflective of the market worldwide.

With such market dominance, Lending Club has made over $4 billion worth of loans since it was founded in 2006 to the end of 2013, and it is likely to add $3 billion more to its tally for 2014. It is by far the largest player in the US and is moving into facilitating unsecured business loans of up to $100,000.

Lending Club has announced that it plans to go public in 2014/15 and is one to watch closely. It is estimated to be valued in the region of $4 billion, and is expected to raise at least $500m in its IPO. Lending Club is the biggest in the world, and appears to be very well managed. Google Ventures invested in an earlier round, as did Kleiner Perkins, a leading venture capital firm.

Another difference in the business model of typical P2P platforms when compared to the UK is US investors (lenders) are typically charged one per cent of all cash returned, and in addition to the fixed interest rate on the three or five year loan, borrowers are also charged a fee of one to five per cent which the P2P platform shares with the originating bank. The loans are usually registered as securities with the SEC to allow retail investors to participate. This system is now working well for Lending Club and others, but its complexity provides a considerable barrier to entry for new players.

P2P in Other Countries

Although over the long term, P2P lending has the potential to be a global offering without country boundaries, the different levels of regulation and currency risk has made P2P lending fragmented, with different players in different countries. Although the UK and the US have the most developed P2P markets so far, there is plenty of activity in other countries around the world.

In China, nearly 1,000 P2P companies currently operate,

and over 100 have collapsed over the past year or so as borrowers have struggled to repay their loans, especially as China's property market and economy have cooled. The most prominent among those that remain are **Creditease** and **Sino Lending,** the former runs a huge branch network in major cities across China, and so is not a true P2P platform. Sino Lending has links to Lending Club in the US and concentrates on the online market. In 2013, loans issued through P2P platforms in China reached ¥68 billion (around $11 billion), about three times the 2012 figure, according iResearch. However it needs to be borne in mind that much of this lending took place off-line.

In Australia, **SocietyOne,** founded in 2012, has emerged as the first fully compliant P2P lender, but as yet remains very small.

In some countries, such as Japan and Israel, P2P lending is currently banned outright. Across the rest of the world in countries such as Argentina, South Korea, Italy, Estonia and India, P2P lending remains insignificant, hampered by stringent local lending laws and a lack of public awareness.

Not For-Profit P2P

In 2009, the US-based non-profit **Zidisha** became the first P2P platform to link lenders and borrowers directly across international borders without local intermediaries. Zidisha is a micro-credit lender to low income, small business owners in developing countries. Individuals in the US and Europe can lend as little as one US dollar and Zidisha's crowdfunding platform allows lenders and borrowers to engage in direct dialogue.

Non-Loan P2P

Some P2P platforms raise money that is not in the form of a loan. For instance, many readers will be familiar with sites such as **Kickstarter, Indiegogo, GoFundMe, Seedrs** and **CrowdCube.** Each one has a slightly different business model as described below.

Kickstarter, a US-based platform raises money for projects. These projects can be anything, from a start-up company to producing a film. In return for pledges, people are offered tangible rewards that are usually a product of the project. The most money raised on Kickstarter to date was a project to design a cooler with extras built into it, such as USB ports, a bottle opener and Bluetooth speaker. In August 2014, the "Coolest Cooler" raised over $13 million from 62,642 backers, who were promised delivery of the cooler once built at a big discount to the intended retail price.

Indiegogo, another US-based site is similar to Kickstarter. Indiegogo charges a fee of 9 per cent of donations unless the goal of the project's fundraising is reached, in which case the rate falls to 4 per cent. Based on the amount pledged, gifts are promised at some point in the future. In June 2014, a company called Solar Roadways raised $2.2 million through Indiegogo to manufacture solar panels that can be walked on, driven over, and can provide lighting for roads, as well as a host of other features.

GoFundMe is a platform that specialises in soliciting donations to raise money for personal matters, such as healthcare or social causes, with no strings.

Equity-based crowdfunding is also growing in popularity. UK-based platforms Seedrs and Crowdcube allow businesses to raise money by selling equity or debt securities, and as a result it is regulated by the FCA. Seedrs specialises in raising equity for early-stage start-ups across Europe. The minimum investment is as little as £10. Seedrs' business model takes a one-off fee of 7.5 per cent from any successfully funded start-ups, which covers all legal and administrative costs associated with the fundraising. Seedrs also takes a success fee from investors of 7.5 per cent of the profits investors make as a result of their investment, covering day-to-day management of the share register and on-going investor protections. It is an "all-or-nothing" platform where companies do not receive any funding unless they reach their declared investment target, but start-ups are allowed to accept more than the original target, so-called "overfunding." Of the various P2P business models out there, we find the ones involved in micro equity finance to be the most interesting.

Crowdfunding is an industry that is likely to grow rapidly. According to a report released in May 2014 by The Crowdfunding Centre[5] more than $60,000 were

[5] *Report titled "The State of the Crowdfunding Nation"*

raised on an hourly basis in the month of March 2014 through global non-lending crowdfunding initiatives. Of course, not all P2P platforms will survive, and some have already fallen by the wayside. For example, in 2011, UK P2P platform Quakle closed down within a year of launching due to poor quality borrowers, resulting in a default rate of almost 100 per cent. Bigcarrots and Squirrl.com are two more examples of P2P platforms that have closed down.

The Evolution of Finance

We expect the disruptions in finance to continue and gather momentum. The digitisation of currencies and the use of the internet to move money around the world more efficiently and cheaply; the use of the internet to disintermediate traditional banks, and contactless payments are just the beginning. AT Kearny, a consulting firm believes that worldwide, non-cash payments will reach $177 billion transactions a year by 2020, more than double the amount in 2010.

Which players are likely to emerge as the winners? We expect the traditional card companies will continue to do well, and although both MasterCard and Visa are listed, neither one is cheap. NFC chips will become increasingly embedded in wearable smart technology. Smart watches, rings and the likes of Google Glass might supplant mobile phones eventually as NFC devices of choice due to the fact that they don't need to be taken out every time a payment needs to be made. NFC is not necessarily perfect, but it is likely to be the dominant technology in payment systems for the next decade or so.

Some payment companies that are very active "behind the scenes" are worth looking at, such as semiconductor companies, software providers and POS makers. One such company that listed in June 2014 is called **Worldline (PARIS:WLN),** is a French business spun out of Atos, and it looks like a good long term investment. Worldline has revenues of more than $1.5 billion and employs over than 7,000 people.

It specialises in mobile payments for retailers, hoteliers and transport companies and is right at the heart of cashless payments.

Another company to look at is **Identiv (NASDAQ:INVE),** which is a leader in providing NFC systems to institutions, and although its financial performance has been erratic, we like the stock for the long term. **Clear Channel Outdoor (NYSE:CCO),** the largest outdoor advertising company in the world, is likely to be a winner in the QR code/NFC market, where consumers download information or buy from an advertisement. This is already a large company although it carries a lot of debt on its balance sheet, so growth is likely to be slow but steady.

Another large company with faster growth prospects is **VeriFone (NYSE:PAY),** which operates around the world and is the largest provider of secure electronic payment solutions globally. In 2011, the company acquired Global Bay, a leading supplier of mobile retail solutions. VeriFone is already the largest supplier of POS terminals in the world, and in our view is a good banker for the long term.

Coupon.com (NYSE:COUP) is an interesting company, though expensively rated. Coupon.com has over 2,000 brands from more than 700 clients, including Proctor & Gamble and General Mills, as well as drug and mass merchandise chains across the US. As its name implies, the company specialises in producing digital coupons; customers "clip" these coupons and add them to their store account (made easy by a "check all" function). Usage rates for digital coupons are about 30 times higher than with paper coupons.

Also worth a mention is Apple, which has been slow to adopt NFC (as mentioned earlier, the iPhone 6 will be the first of its phones to be NFC-enabled).

Its alternative offering called iBeacon has had a lukewarm response from the market and will not likely win out against NFC.

In the P2P space, Lending Circle and Zopa have the best prospects in our opinion, and Powa is worth keeping an eye on, along with the leaders in non-lending crowdfunding, such as Kickstarter and Indiegogo.

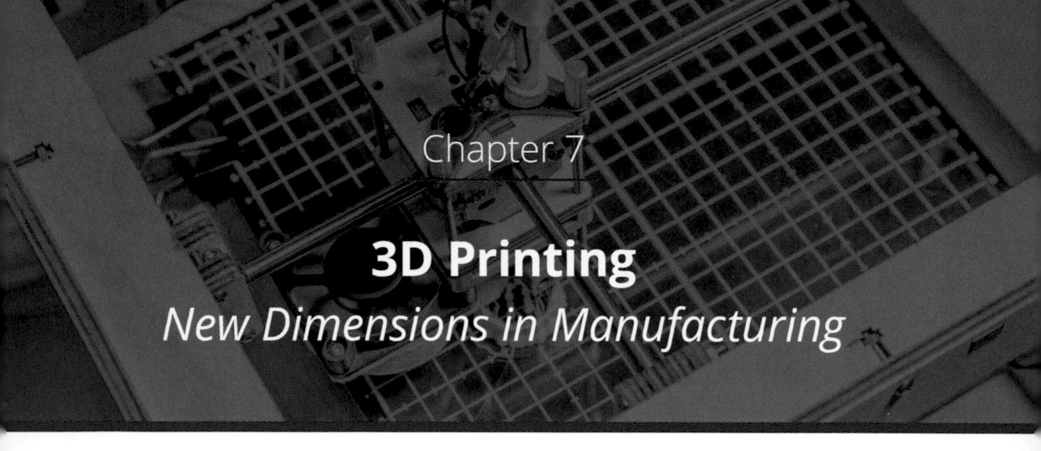

Chapter 7

3D Printing

New Dimensions in Manufacturing

This chapter is all about the exciting and rapidly emerging field of three dimensional or "3D" printing, which has been receiving a great deal of media attention, sometimes even being heralded as a second industrial revolution. We explore whether such bold claims have merit by digging below the sensational banners and give you our take on 3D printing, identifying the industrial sectors that have been its early adopters, as well as those that are starting to wake up to its potential.

In *Cracking the Code*, we only briefly mentioned 3D printing, mainly in the context of printing organs made of a bio-rubber that can subsequently be seeded with stem cells to bring the organ to life. As with all emerging technology, things have progressed rather quickly. So in this book, we definitely think 3D printing deserves an entire chapter, given how much has happened. Whereas a few years ago 3D printing was only familiar to certain engineers and industrial designers, today pretty much anyone living in the developed world has at least heard of 3D printing and at a minimum has a conceptual notion of what it is.

No longer confined to niche applications, 3D printing is starting to become useful in large scale manufacturing across many industries, admittedly with varying degrees of success so far. Like its 2D cousin, many of us will likely have a 3D printer in our homes within five years, but will it be just a novelty or will it serve as an indispensable household appliance? How influential could it be in the future of society?

Often referred to as *additive manufacturing* when used in an

industrial context, 3D printing is actually not a new technology and dates back to the early 1980s. The reason it has so many people excited today is because the cost of the printers and their "ink" is rapidly falling. The quality of the "prints" is also improving and the speed of the "printing" is increasing. Printers today are also more accurate, have the ability to print objects in different colours, and with an ever increasing choice of materials, such as rubber, porcelain, metal, plaster and glass.

We are of the view that 2014 will be remembered as the year 3D printing became a household term. According to a leading 3D printing consultancy, **Wohlers & Associates**, the industry grew by 35 per cent to just over $3 billion in 2013. This pace of growth is expected to continue, with the industry doubling to $6 billion in sales by 2017. Another industry research company, **Canalys**, is even more aggressive with its growth forecast, announcing that it expects the market size to reach $16 billion by 2018, which represents a compounded annual growth rate of 46 per cent between 2013 and 2018. That is a growth rate surely any investor would find very attractive.

3D printing has already proven its value in rapid prototyping, demonstration units and small volume production. But increasingly, we are seeing it being used for specialised industrial production applications as well.

Indeed, in July 2014, Amazon announced its own 3D printing store, where customers can order 3D printed items from a wide range of template designs. Goods printed on-demand include jewellery, toys and accessories. Amazon uses a "personalisation widget" that allows customers to modify products easily, without requiring any skills in 3D modelling software. **Mixee Labs'** *3D bobble head*, designed to look like the person ordering it, is one example of such a widget.

The three main factors limiting its further utilisation across more industries is the ability to print products that are at least as high quality as the traditional manufactured versions. Secondly, the processing speed can be frustratingly slow, which is okay if it is a single prototype, but unacceptable if it is a small batch of say, 20 units. Thirdly, the price; printers used to cost tens of thousands of dollars and were used mainly for in-house purposes by corporations for prototyping of products. By the 2010s, the price of a basic 3D printer had fallen to a few thousand dollars, with some basic models selling for under a thousand dollars. When we checked with the large US retailer **Staples**, we found a number of household 3D printer models for sale at its stores, the cheapest one being $1,000.

As the name implies, 3D printing is the process of making a solid, three dimensional object from the bottom up, by applying successive layers of the material(s), usually in a liquid or powdered form, which then dries before the next layer is applied. Imagine an inkjet printer but with layering abilities.

So why is there such a buzz about 3D printing? The advantages over traditional manufacturing methods can be enormous, namely:

- Each object that is printed can be a different shape, size or colour without the need to re-tool and with negligible variations in production costs. This mass customisation means each customer can buy a tailor-made product at a mass production price;
- Virtually anything can be 3D printed – the limitations from the traditional use of moulds do not apply;
- Very low wastage. Traditional manufacturing techniques such as cutting, drilling, extruding and injection moulding waste a great deal of material. 3D printing only uses the materials it requires to make the object;
- Reduced tooling costs. The same 3D printer can be used to make a variety of objects without retooling. If we use the inkjet printer analogy again, it makes no difference if we print out a spread sheet, a presentation or a document – there is no need to reconfigure the printer between print jobs;
- Time to market. As soon as the design of the object has been completed, the item is ready to ship out. Compare that to how slow the traditional manufacturing supply chain is today, especially with long transport times; and

- Low/No inventory risk. Vendors no longer need to guess how many units they expect to sell and pre-manufacture them; with 3D printing they can manufacture-on-demand.

As 3D printing becomes more prevalent, the actual making part of the manufacturing supply chain will become commoditized. Manufacturers will be forced to re-think where and how they add value to the process to differentiate themselves from 3D printing. We expect many manufacturers will shift their emphasis to innovation and design. In the same way e-books offer an alternative to physical hard copy versions that are shipped to the home, companies will be able to sell "blueprints" or designs of their products for printing at home. This has already started to happen for some items.

The Principles of Printing in 3D

We have already mentioned that the term additive manufacturing is preferred by those using the technology in industrial applications. Technically, it is a more accurate term and it also distinguishes 3D printing from the more traditional subtractive manufacturing, which for example, is using a lathe to shape a metal cylinder to the desired dimensions. But for consistency we shall continue to use the term 3D printing as the general broad term for making three dimensional solid objects from a digital model.

There are a number of technologies that are used in 3D printing but every object starts off as a 3D computer image. Using specialised software, designers can define the shape, dimensions, colour, even the material to use for the object. The file is usually in *STL* format (STL stands for Standard Tessellation Language). Once the object design is completed, the instruction to make it can be given.

The following are currently the three most common forms of 3D printing.

Material Extrusion

This type of printing is probably the one most people are familiar with and is also known as *Fused Deposition Modelling* (FDM). The process involves a nozzle containing the material from which the object is to be made, often a polymer that is squeezed out in a liquid form that quickly hardens shortly after leaving the extrusion nozzle, ready for the next layer to be applied.

Stereolithography

This method of printing works by concentrating a beam of ultraviolet (UV) light onto the surface of container filled with liquid resin. This resin is designed to harden when the UV light beam hits it, allowing the light beam to shape the solid object out of the resin. Once the first layer has hardened, the base of the tank moves up a fraction, preparing for next layer of resin to be hardened with the UV beam. This process continues until the completed solid object has been made, effectively from the bottom up.

Selective Laser Sintering

This process is similar to stereolithography described above, but instead of a liquid resin, a powder is used. This powder can be ceramic, glass, plastic or metal. Instead of a UV light beam, a high power laser beam is used. As the laser beam strikes the top layer of the powder, it solidifies. Then the base holding the powder is moved down a fraction and a new top layer of powder is applied using a roller. The laser then shapes the next top layer of powder, and so forth until the object has been completed.

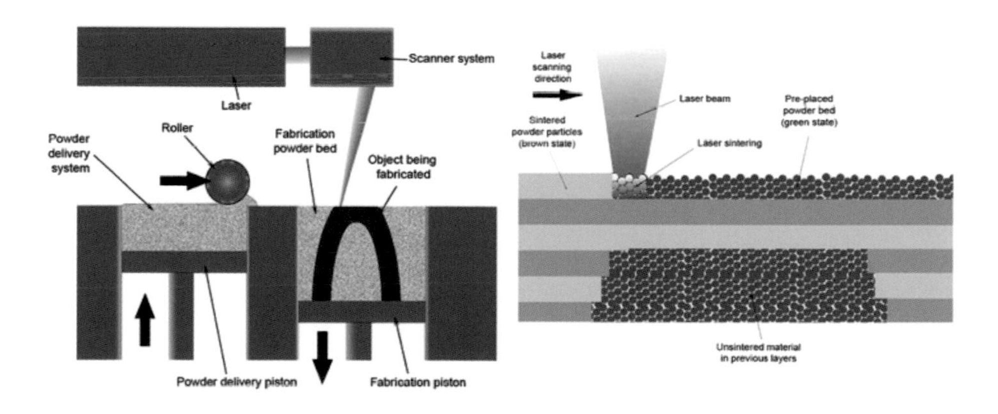

Figure 28: Selective laser sintering schematic.**Source:** Materialgeeza for Wikimedia

Applications of 3D Printing

There are literally limitless applications for 3D printing, which is on the cusp of being a truly disruptive technology.

Let's take a closer look at how 3D printing is being used today, as well as explore some of the fast emerging applications.

Medicine

One of the most exciting areas in which 3D printing has already started to demonstrate some real successes is the field of medicine. The amazing developments taking place today have already saved countless lives and it will save many more as the technology becomes more sophisticated.

Here are some of the ground-breaking developments.

Scientists in Melbourne, Australia are testing a "bio-pen" that can literally draw new tissue, such as bone, skin and muscle onto patients who have suffered a serious traumatic injury, such as a traffic accident. Surgeons are using the 3D bio-pen containing bio ink to build a bio-polymer scaffold, layer by layer onto the affected area. The bio ink contains stem cells that can repair damaged areas and ultraviolet light is used between the application of layers to harden the polymer gel and to protect the stem cells at the wound site. It is still early days for this technique but scientists believe they will be ready to start using the bio pen in human trials by 2020.

On a more macro level, there has been a great deal of scientific research in the 3D printing of human tissues and organs as a way to repair or replace damaged / malfunctioning parts of the body. This is currently done by printing a scaffold in the shape of the desired tissue or organ and then "seeding" it with stem cells from the patient and allowing them to proliferate. Using the patient's own stem cells reduces the risk of rejection from the body's immune system.

The scaffold itself is quite complex and is typically made from a biomaterial, known as a polymer, which can either be from a natural source such as collagen, or it can be synthetic. A scaffold can also contain fibres and other particles to achieve more desirable physical and chemical properties as well as better bioactivity and biocompatibility. Already such biomaterials have been used widely across a number of applications, such as skin, bone, tendons, nerves, bladder and liver.

In 2011, University College London (UCL) successfully printed a scaffold of a section of a cancer patient's windpipe or trachea then seeded it with the patient's stem cells. Prior to that, the patient had the malignant part of her trachea removed.

Similar procedures in the past have relied on windpipes from human donors, which involved waiting and were not necessarily an ideal fit. But with this procedure, the first of its kind, the windpipe was a perfect fit because the printed version was an identical copy of the patient's actual windpipe, after scanning it using Computed Tomography (commonly known as a CT scan).

Prosthetics is another emerging area for 3D printing. Current practices involve the use of pre-manufactured hands, arms and legs with some options on the size, but using 3D printing to make prosthetics means they can be designed to be an exact fit. Not only that, the waiting time for receiving a prosthesis is reduced and the cost of printing can be as low as $10. For children using prosthetic limbs, it means that they can receive replacements more frequently as they grow without worrying about the expense of the replacements.

Aviation

One obvious advantage of having an industrial 3D printer is the ability to save a small fortune on spare parts inventory. An aircraft maintenance facility, for example, is required to keep an extensive list of spare parts. Imagine instead, a solitary printer sitting in the corner of the hangar that can produce any one of the thousands of parts that are occasionally required for servicing an aircraft.

Today, when a part is not in stock, maintenance engineers have to wait for days, sometimes even weeks to receive the part from its manufacturer. Being able to print the required part in a matter of hours would be an enormous convenience – it could almost be viewed as teleporting the part directly to the engineer. Think of all the working capital that could be freed up by not having to stock such an extensive inventory of spare parts. Consider also any modifications that may be required for some parts – this would simply become a matter of updating the blueprints, no physical parts need re-working or re-ordering. Savings in shipping costs would also be made as all parts would be printed on site. The case for such a 3D printer is compelling.

Clearly, the 3D printer must be capable of fabricating the part to the same standard as the original manufacturer, and who better to sell such a 3D printer to aircraft maintenance companies than the original equipment manufacturer? The technology is not quite there yet in terms of being able to print almost any part on demand, though some parts are already printed using 3D technology at the manufacturer's factory, so it will take a few more years for the printers to be able to produce the required breadth of parts at an acceptable speed and a competitive price to the current methods.

In 2014 the giant German conglomerate **Siemens** started printing spare parts for its gas turbines[1] using 3D printing, making it the first global manufacturer to routinely print metal parts. The company believes that by doing so, it will be able to cut the repair time of damaged turbine burners to just four weeks from its preview 44 - a vast improvement! Siemens uses machines made by a fellow German company called **SLM Solutions,** which listed on the Frankfurt Stock Exchange in May 2014 (under the symbol AM3D). SLM could be an interesting play in the industrial space given than it has Siemens as an anchor client, plus it is a possible take-over target, either by Siemens itself or by another 3D printing company looking to gain access to or increase its market-share of the European market.

Across the Atlantic in the US, the industrial giant **GE** has also embraced 3D printing, using it to make fuel nozzles for its *Leap* aircraft engines. GE claims that the 3D printed version is 25 per cent lighter and five times more durable than the traditionally manufactured part. This is a big weight saving as each engine contains five such fuel nozzles. Unlike Siemens, GE has made the strategic decision to bring its 3D printing technology in-house by buying a company called Morris Technologies, which has laser melting as well as electron beam melting capabilities.

House Construction

As bizarre as it may sound, houses can be "printed" using a 3D printer. Obviously it needs to be larger than your regular desktop model and the ink is more of a quick-drying

[1] *Tanya Powley, Financial Times, 3D printing becomes a solid reality, December 26, 2013*

cement than a plastic or metal. And we are not making this statement as a prediction; it has actually started to happen.

WinSun Decoration Design Engineering, a private company from China announced that it had successfully printed 10 full-sized houses in just one day. Granted these printed houses are not the most elegant looking constructions by any means, but they are houses nevertheless, measuring 10 meters wide by 6.6 meters high with an area of 200 square metres, or around 2,000 square feet, so a comfortable size by most people's standards. To achieve this remarkable feat, a giant printer had to be built, measuring 32 metres in length, 10 metres in width and 7 metres in height. The printer's "ink" comprised a combination of cement and construction waste. The company claims that each house costs around $5,000 to make.

The printer's inventor is WinSun's CEO, Ma Yi He, who has been designing 3D printers for over a decade. He believes that his method of house building is not only cost-effective but also environmentally friendly.[2]

To build a house that is larger and more aesthetically pleasing would take more time, but not that much more. The University of Southern California (USC) is testing a giant 3D printer it has developed to see if it could build an entire house in just one day. The technology is very similar to that of WinSun, using a gantry that allows the full three dimensional movement of a nozzle squirting a variation of quick drying cement.

Not only could this bring affordable housing to millions of people around the world, it could also be used to build quick, temporary shelters in disaster stricken areas, while the more permanent homes are being rebuilt.

The designer behind USC's giant 3D house printer is Professor Behrokh Khoshnevis, who points out that house construction remains one of the last things in the 21st century that is still an entirely manual process, and is long overdue an upgrade. Obviously the challenge in making this a new industry standard is going to lie in the speed and cost of the giant printer, as well as its disassembly once a building has been completed. When it comes to building rows of houses of the same or similar dimensions and specifications,

---

[2] *Xinhua News. 3D printers print 10 houses in 24 hours, 25 April 2014. http://news.xinhuanet.com/english/sci/2014-04/25/c_133290171.htm*

the "assembly line" advantage is evident over the manual labour alternative.

We'll just have to wait and see how quickly this technology is adopted by the industry, bearing in mind that construction is one of the biggest employers in the US and elsewhere, and it is therefore likely to meet political resistance by those who are more interested in seeing the unemployment rate fall over having a new industry emerge that threatens construction jobs in the short-term but creates new ones in 3D printing in the long-term.

The Consumer Market

Earlier in the book we discussed how robotics will disrupt manufacturing and redefine the priorities of where companies choose to locate their production facilities. Up until now, the site selection decision has been overwhelmingly influenced by the cost of labour. That is why China has been able to become a manufacturing powerhouse for the world. But that is no longer the case; China does not have very cheap labour and most companies would openly say that if they were deciding on where to set-up their manufacturing facility today, they would not pick China. For those already invested in China, it is cheaper to stay there than to relocate elsewhere, but not for much longer.

Looking out to the end of this decade and beyond, 3D printing will play an increasing role in where companies locate their production facilities. With increased factory automation, labour costs will matter less, whilst proximity to important customers will matter more. As robots drive the cost of production down, the cost of transportation becomes more significant, so it would make sense to set up production near customers as this would reduce shipping costs as well as reduce order lead times.

If we develop this scenario further with influence from 3D printing, we come up with a rather intriguing picture: as 3D printers become more sophisticated and cheaper, we believe that they will become common household appliances alongside the TV, fridge and indeed regular 2D printers (which are likely to be combined with 3D printers). Once firmly entrenched in the home, 3D printers will take on the role of a manufacturing facility and a retail outlet. Many people today choose to download

Company Spotlight: Stratasys Limited (NASDAQ:SSYS)

Stratasys has dual-headquarters in the US and Israel. In 2013, it acquired MakerBot, a maker of a range of 3D printers targeted at the consumer and small business. Its entry price *Replicator Mini* started shipping in the spring of 2014 and retailed for around $1,400. Another subsidiary of Stratasys is a company called **Solidscape**, which serves small and medium-sized businesses. Solidscape specialises in high-precision 3D printers for making small parts, such as jewellery, consumer electronics and dental prosthetics. This is achieved by printing a 3D wax model from the CAD design and then using the model to cast the finished product.

Stratasys also produces larger, industrial scale models for making low volume finished goods.

The company is well-diversified in the 3D printing space, and is positioned to capitalise across all applications of 3D printing. Founded in 1998, Stratasys has a market capitalisation of around $6 billion at the time of writing and it employs around 1,400 people.

or stream music, film and TV shows over buying them on physical DVDs or CDs, allowing them to enjoy the entertainment within minutes or even seconds of the purchase.

A similar thing will develop for many physical products: online stores will emerge selling designs of items, or blueprints that allow people to print at home using their 3D printer. And just like the old days when downloading software or films would take many hours, printing times will be slow(ish) for the first few years, but nevertheless the adoption of 3D printers in the home will accelerate. By the mid-2020s, buying blueprints of items online for home printing will become commonplace, rather like it is today when buying items for home delivery. Crockery, is a good example of something that would be easy to print at home – simply buy a dinner plate design and print as many copies as you need. If one accidentally breaks or if someone

BE COOL

decides to host a Greek wedding, no problem, just print more!

Toys are another area that will see explosive growth in home printing. Companies such as **Lego** will be able to upsell, cross-sell and sell more of its products. And if you've misplaced that critical piece from your favourite *Star Wars* Lego set, simply print out another one.

There will definitely be patent and copyright issues to contend with. The industry today is just not set up to deal with printing "stuff" at home, and it will have to adapt or risk losing out to "illegal prints". No doubt efforts will be made to restrict the printing of items, but this will only lead to open source copy cats that will circumvent such restrictions.

If most every-day non-perishable or non-liquid items stand to become commoditised and easily copied, what must today's consumer brand companies do to stay relevant in the future? These companies still have a few years to come up with a new business model to maintain market share and preserve their profitability, but if they leave it too late, they will find themselves getting trampled over by newer, more agile companies emerging to take advantage of 3D printing.

One brand of 3D printers that focuses on the consumer market is called **MakerBot** (now a subsidiary of **Stratasys** - more on this company later), which has started to open retail stores in the US. The stores are designed to raise the profile of 3D printing and also to allow consumers to watch a 3D printer in action, as well as to see and touch some of the printed products.

Other 3D Printing Applications

In this section, we cover some of the less well-known applications of 3D printing. Some of them might seem a bit of a novelty and all of them are still in their infancy. Still, it illustrates that 3D printing is only limited by the imagination and that it could be an option for making literally anything. Whether this method ends up being superior to the existing methods of making things remains to be seen, but new applications will continuously be explored - no manufacturing process is safe from being replaced by a 3D printer in the long-term.

Fashion

3D printing's ability to make intricate shapes and patterns makes it ideal for creating jewellery, clothing, shoes, even make-up.

In May 2014 at the TechCrunch forum in New York, a company called **Mink** presented its unique business of allowing someone to capture any colour they like from a screen, magazine or real-life using their phone and then being able to print make-up, such as lipstick, that is an exact colour match.

Art

In Boston, Massachusetts, a company called **Wobble Works Toy Company** has started selling a 3D drawing pen. Known as the *3Doodler*, it originally sourced financing from **Kickstarter**, one of the crowd-funding sites, seeking to

Figure 29: The 3Doodler and a 3D drawing of the Eiffel Tower made using the pen. **Source:** WobbleWorks, Inc. (http://the3doodler.com)

raise $30,000, but ended up raising $2.3 million. The 3Doodler sells for $99 and is designed for children and adults alike. Similar to a glue gun, the plastic cools and solidifies shortly after being squeezed out of the pen, allowing the pen holder to create all sorts of 3D shapes and designs, from jewellery to sculptures.

The 3Doodler will not be alone in the market for long: we discovered another company called **Lix Pen** (www.lixpen.com) that, at the time of writing this chapter, was seeking to raise £30,000 on Kickstarter to develop its 3D pen. Lix Pen is a London-based company and like its American rival, it too far exceeded its target amount and ended up raising £731,690.

There will no doubt be other entrants into this new realm of 3D style of drawing, which could launch an entirely new art form.

Food

Readers who found the idea of printing a house peculiar will be astonished by the prospect of "printing" food. Now we are not implying that the same printer that can print a house will then be able to print lunch (wouldn't that be something?) This would be a food-specific printer containing edible ink, and it is already a reality. One of the leading 3D printer companies, **3D Systems Corporation** (covered in more detail later), makes a printer called the *ChefJet*, which uses sugar as its ink and is able to print the most intricate icing designs on cakes. The intricate patterns and art work made possible by 3D printing are unrivalled by any human efforts.

A company from Barcelona, Spain called **Natural Machines** has made a 3D food printer called **Foodini** that is capable of making a variety of savoury, sweet and fresh food. It is essentially a sophisticated food processor with a touch screen that is connected to the internet. Once a dish has been selected, Foodini will instruct the user which ingredients to put into the printer capsules, after which it can begin to print the meal. It is expected to go on general sale in 2015 with a unit cost of around €1,000.

Still in the lab stage of development, scientists are synthesising protein to create lab-grown meat. As this technology becomes more sophisticated, we may one day be able to print any type of meat without the need to farm animals.

Figure 30: A pizza printed using Foodini. **Source:** Natural Machines

Lenses

LUXeXcel (http://www.luxexcel.com), a privately held Dutch company that manufactures lenses for LED lighting, has developed a new type of 3D printing which it calls *Printoptical*. What makes it special is that the printer heads deposit droplets of liquid plastic in the shape of the desired lens, and these droplets remain in a liquid plastic state which allows them to merge into each other. Traditional 3D printing allows the liquid to set quickly after it is injected out of the printer heads, meaning that it is difficult to achieve a smooth finish required for lenses. Once the amalgamated droplets of liquid plastic reach the desired shape, ultraviolet light is used to harden the lens, so there is no need to polish the lens.

LUXeXcel is trying out this technique to make prescription lenses for glasses, and so far the results have been encouraging. These printers could be the only thing an optician needs to have to be able to print out lenses and frames for customers. There would be no need to tie up valuable cash in stocking hundreds of types of frames.

In time, 3D printers at home will have this capability, allowing people have their eyes scanned by their computer camera and print a new pair of custom-made glasses in a matter of minutes. Opticians will likely become obsolete within the next couple of decades as their role becomes fully automated and available in the home at virtually no cost.

Key Players in 3D Printing

Although not quite at the "gold rush" phase of growth, 3D printing does have quite a few established players, but given the sudden twists and turns in the development of the sector, it is still somewhat unclear which company or companies will emerge as the industry standard bearer, if indeed there does become one. A more likely outcome is that there will be a small handful of dominant players, any one of which could edge away from the pack with a new, innovative aspect to the way their devices print, or perhaps it could be low cost that triggers the purchase of millions of printers for the home. Getting reasonable specification 3D printers in every home will be the game changer in the consumer side of the industry.

Let us review some of the leading companies today in 3D printing.

US Companies

In the US, there are three major 3D printing companies that are listed. The first is **Stratasys Limited** (NASDAQ: SSYS, website: http://www.stratasys.com), which offers a broad range of printers and supporting software and devices. It sells its printers to industries such as aerospace, automotive, medical and dentistry. See earlier Company Spotlight on Stratasys.

The second big player in this space is **3D Systems** (NASDAQ: DDD, website: http://www.3dsystems.com), a company that is around the same market capitalisation as Stratasys. 3D Systems also sells a broad range of personal, professional and production printers. These two companies are currently the leaders in this field.

Also from the US is **ExOne** (NASDAQ: XONE; website: http://www.exone.com) which went public in September 2013. ExOne is at a much earlier stage of growth and since listing it has delivered disappointing results, although growth is likely to pick up as the company starts to invest some of that capital it raised when it went public. Its *ExCast* full service production centre is where much of its growth potential lies, offering an all-in-one solution, from design to printed metal parts (stainless steel, bronze or tungsten). The company claims that it is the fastest metal printer in its class.

Leading 3D modelling software company, **Autodesk** (NASDAQ: ADSK), announced in May 2014 that it was releasing its own 3D printer, the first time the company has entered the hardware market. In a similar approach as Google with its Android software, Autodesk plans to allow other 3D printer manufacturers to develop their own printers and use its software for free. By doing so, it hopes to further entrench its 3D modelling software into becoming the industry standard.

One potential player to watch is old timer **HP** (NASDAQ: HP), which so far has chosen to stay on the side-lines of the 3D printing revolution. HP plans to make an announcement sometime in 2014 to enter this market. Our bet is that it will do so with an acquisition rather than by trying to play catch-up with the leading players. With a market capitalisation of around $65 billion, it can certainly afford to buy even the biggest of the 3D printing companies, which are less than a tenth of its size.

European Companies

In the UK, **Renishaw Plc** (LON: RSW, website: http://www.renishaw.com) is a company that dates back to 1973. It originally started out in precision machining using Computer Aided Design/ Computer Aided Manufacturing (CAD/CAM) and entered the 3D printing market following its acquisition of UK-based MTT in 2011. Renishaw is a niche player in the 3D printing sector, only making printers for medical and industrial applications, using laser melting, or metal 3D printing. Today, almost 95 per cent of the Renishaw's sales come from outside the UK.

Arcam (STO: ARCM, website: http://www.arcam.com) is a company based in Sweden and listed on the Stockholm Stock Exchange that has developed its own patented Electron Beam Melting (EBM) technology for printing metal shapes. The higher energy beam is able to shape denser metals and with less voids than the laser beam equivalent printer. Arcam is targeting the aerospace and orthopaedic implant sectors, which is where it believes it can differentiate itself from the other players.

Lastly, we want to mention the German company, **Voxeljet** (NYSE: VJET, website: http://www.voxeljet.de/en), which listed on the New York Stock Exchange in October 2013. Voxeljet has a wide range of production printers, the largest one having a build space of 4m x 2m x 1m (approx. 160" x 80" x 40"). Voxeljet was founded in 1999 as a 3D printing company, selling its first particle material printers in 2002.

One Fund to Invest in them All

We often get asked if there is a single vehicle where investors could park their money that would give them the broad exposure to one of our themes, as many readers do not have the time or inclination to invest in individual companies in a particular sector. Most of the time there are Exchange Traded Funds (ETFs) that would allow investors to do just that, offering them a more diversified exposure to a particular theme or sector.

But in the case of 3D printing, it is a little trickier. Unlike sectors such as biotech, renewable energy and commodities, we could find no ETFs specialising in 3D printing at the time of writing. That is certain to change as the sector grows (as we mentioned earlier, 3D printing globally was only $3 billion in 2013) – double digit percentage annual growth is expected for the next decade or so.

We did, however, find one brave company in the US that launched an aptly named "3D Printing and Technology Fund" in April 2014. The minimum initial investment is $2,500.

When we last checked in May 2014, 10 companies (all publicly traded) accounted for 65 per cent of the fund's holdings, most of which we have discussed at some point in this chapter. These were: Stratasys, 3D Systems, Organovo Holdings, ExOne, Arcam, Dassault Systems, Voxeljet, Autodesk, GE and Proto Labs.

Readers can visit the fund's website to find out if it is something that suits their investment strategy by visiting: http://www.3dpfund.com.

2013 was a great year for investors in 3D printing, although 2014 has been a more volatile year, but the trend remains upwards to reflect the rapidly expanding sector.

4D Printing – A New Dimension Emerges

In the process of researching 3D printing, we came across something being referred to as *4D printing*. In science, the fourth dimension is usually time, but in this case the extra "D" refers to self-assembling 3D objects that change form over time. It sounds strange, we know, even to us, but apparently this is in development.

Our initial thoughts were that it was just a gimmick with no practical application, but then we started to read more about some what-ifs that were very intriguing. For example, imagine buying a piece of flat-pack furniture, and when it reaches your home, or wherever its intended destination may be, it starts to put itself together.

Some other interesting applications would be fabric or paint that can change colour based on the temperature or surroundings, which would lead to army camouflage uniforms that could automatically change patterns to ensure the best camouflage colours at all times. Similarly for army vehicles, such as jeeps or tanks, being able to change colour to be harder to spot would literally be a life-saver. For consumer clothes, a t-shirt could, for example, change colour to match other items of clothing, or it could retain more heat if it senses the wearer getting cold. Conversely, it could shed more body heat if it senses the wearer starting to sweat.

There are other potential applications too: imagine tyres that could change tread automatically based on the weather and road conditions, so for hot dry conditions on a smooth road, they could be smooth and without any tread, but if it started to rain, they could change into wet weather tyres. Similarly, this could work in snowy or off-road conditions.

Still think 4D printing has limited use? What about space? Consider the possibility of sending compact shapes into orbit or to the moon, and then have them self-assemble once they are in position. They may even be able to have repairing abilities if they are somehow damaged.

It came as no surprise to us to

discover that it was once again the clever researchers at MIT that are pioneering this technology, in collaboration with Stratasys, the 3D printing company we mentioned earlier that makes the MakerBot 3D printers. MIT has created a new Self-assembly Laboratory, led by Skylar Tibbits, who is an architect by training and is a Research Scientist at MIT's Department of Architecture. Readers who are interested may visit the Self-assembly Lab's website: http://www.selfassemblylab.net/.

It is still early days for 4D printing, but we wanted to inform our readers about how 3D printing will likely evolve, once it goes mainstream in the coming years. Obviously, 3D printers need to take off first, which they will as prices continue to fall and sophistication increases. At the moment, 3D printers are painfully slow and only make sense for one-off print jobs. Traditional manufacturing is still faster and cheaper for large batches but for low volume production, the threat to traditional manufacturing is very real.

New Materials

Before we close out this chapter, we wanted to include a section on materials, which are often-overlooked when it comes to technological innovation. Yet, without advances in material science, 3D printing would never have made it this far. Indeed, materials have played a vital role in most of mankind's technological progress throughout history.

Around 12,000 years ago, humans began making objects from natural materials, such as stone, wood, clay and skins. This era is known as the Neolithic Era, or "Stone Age."

Then came the "Bronze Age" around 3,000 BC, when humans became capable of making metal objects for the first time, namely alloys of copper. This was followed by the "Iron Age," which began around 1,200 BC, marking the start of the use of iron and much later, steel, thus propelling mankind's technological progress with more advanced and sophisticated objects, tools and structures, as well as improved transportation.

The next significant era of materials was probably the "Plastic Age." Plastics are made from long chains of carbon atoms, referred to as polymers. The first type of plastic came onto the scene in the mid-nineteenth century. Since then, hundreds of different types of plastics have been invented, many of which are still used extensively today – in fact it would be hard to find a man-made object today that does not contain some plastic parts. Derived from oil, plastics are cheap, easy to shape and quick to produce.

Then in the second half of the twentieth century, the "Silicon Age" arrived. The invention of the silicon transistor followed by the microchip sparked a new wave of innovation that is still in full flow today. Every new generation of microchips crams in more and more transistors onto the central processing unit (CPU), the Intel Core i7 chip shown in Figure 31 contains over one billion transistors; compare that to one of Intel's chips from the early 1970s which contained around two thousand transistors.

The i7 chip in Figure 31 is 32 nanometres[3] in scale, and already the latest chips are down to 14 nanometres, with the most optimistic prediction taking it down to 3 nanometres over the next few years. Beyond this point we enter the realm of quantum physics under which electrons no longer behave in a predictable manner. We therefore need to find an alternative to copper wires if we are to continue developing faster processing speeds.

The Graphene Age?

The most promising candidate thus far is a material called **graphene**, a two-dimensional

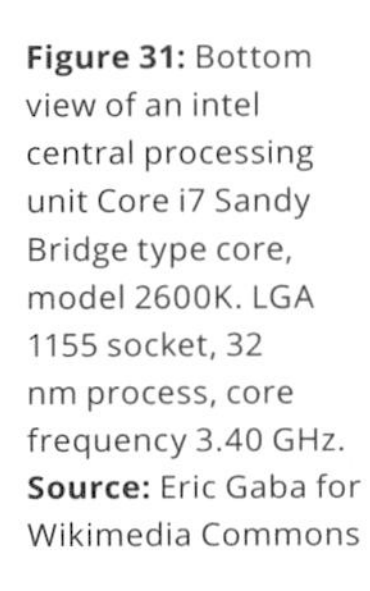

Figure 31: Bottom view of an intel central processing unit Core i7 Sandy Bridge type core, model 2600K. LGA 1155 socket, 32 nm process, core frequency 3.40 GHz. **Source:** Eric Gaba for Wikimedia Commons

[3] *A nanometre is a billionth of a metre.*

Figure 32: The ideal crystalline structure of graphene is a hexagonal grid one atom thick.
Source: AlexanderAIUS for Wikimedia Commons

allotrope of carbon – considered to be two dimensional because it is only one atom thick. It can be considered to be a one atom-thick layer of graphite, the material used in pencils that is misleadingly called "lead." Graphene has generated a great deal of excitement amongst the scientific community since its discovery around a decade ago due to its unrivalled strength, flexibility and superior conductive properties. Graphite is already mined around the world and used to make carbon composite materials.

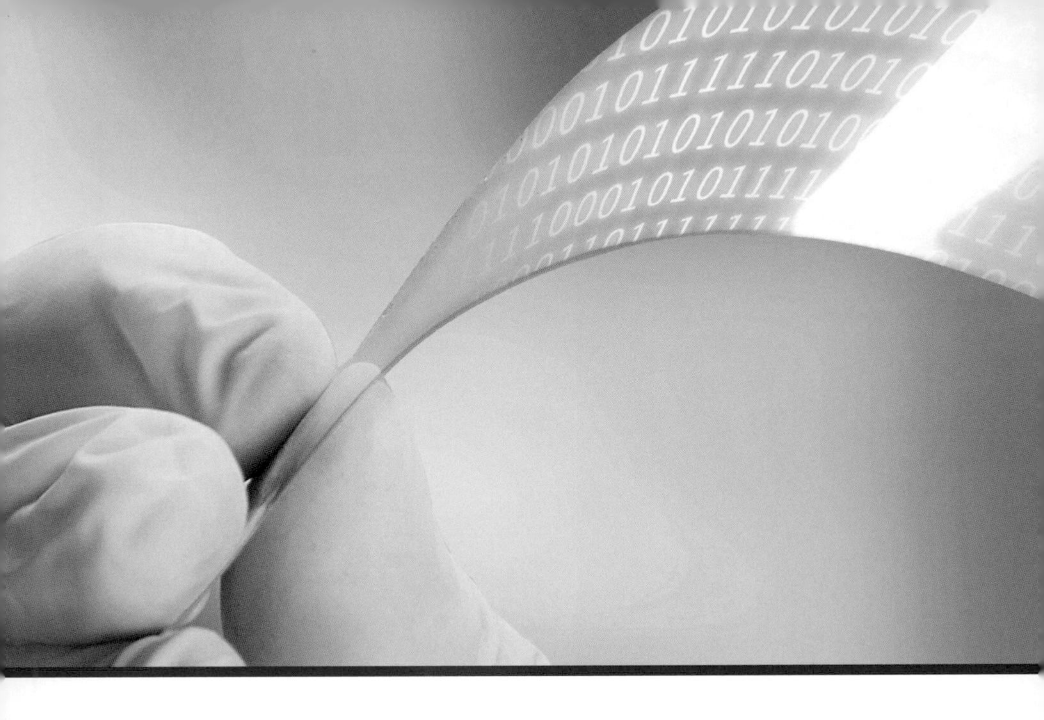

In chip manufacturing, graphene is being considered as a replacement for copper wires. Being just one atom thick, it generates less heat, costs less and requires less energy than copper. That said, graphene is still very much an experimental material, and it will be a number of years before we can expect to find it widely used to make our phones, tablets and laptops.

Another application of graphene that is currently in development is in *optoelectronics*, where its near transparency and ability to transmit 98 per cent of light makes it an ideal candidate for flexible and rollable LCD screens. Graphene is also being considered for use in filtration, photovoltaic cells, energy storage/batteries, insulation, composite materials, and even *nanomedicine*, where it can be used to deliver drugs to difficult sites in the body.

When graphene is rolled up into a cylindrical shape, it becomes a carbon *nanotube* with unrivalled strength and lightness. Again, we are not yet there in terms of being able to mass produce carbon nanotubes, but once we do, they can be used in making all sorts of things. Concrete structures could, for example, contain carbon na-

notubes instead of steel, making them stronger, cheaper and lighter.

We are only just starting to really discover the full potential of graphene, which is why we don't expect any commercial applications this decade but we do believe that it will eventually emerge as the most important material of the twenty-first century.

Ultimately, we are heading towards an era of molecular nanotechnology, where *nanorobotics* and *nanomedicine* will become dominant sectors that lead to accelerated technological breakthroughs.

Readers interested in investing in graphene at this stage can look for graphite mining companies, either at the exploration stage or in production. One such company we like is called **Triton Minerals**, listed in Australia (**ASX:TON**), which has a number of graphite mining projects in Mozambique.

Chapter 8

Media, Publishing, Education

Extinction of the Dinosaurs

In an earlier chapter, we discussed the rise of the internet and more specifically the emerging areas around what is termed as the "Internet of Things." In this chapter we take a closer look at how the internet has been changing the way people consume media content, and what the traditional media empires have had to do to remain relevant. Relatedly, we examine how the long-standing business models of publishing are being threatened as a result of the internet's ever-growing pervasiveness. Finally, we write about the education revolution that is quietly underway, and how it is transforming the centuries-old way that people have been taught.

Old Media vs New Media

As far back as the late 1990s, traditional media giants became acutely aware that the internet had started to encroach on their cosy print world of newspapers and magazines. In response, old media decided to try and join the internet age instead of fighting it. But an industry that has had a comfortable ride for so long was not set up to move quickly and adapt to the changing environment.

Old media's attempt to adopt new media channels was therefore not painless, and many new entrants leapfrogged the old guard with ease. Let us do a quick "before and after" exercise which involved a visit to the leading ranking website **Alexa** (www.alexa.com, now owned by **Amazon.com**), which we have used to browse through the list of the world's most popular websites, measured by how many visitors they get. What surprised

nix Studio / Shutterstock.com

us about the list was that the first old media company we found was ranked 59th; and that was CNN! Some of our older readers may remember that in the 1990s, CNN dominated the news, making its mark covering the developments of the first Gulf War. Today, CNN is just another channel among hundreds of competitors across the world. Incidentally, the BBC website was not far behind, ranked 64th.

So just what are the top ten most visited websites in the world, some of our more curious readers may be asking? It will come as no surprise that most of them are very established household names today that didn't even exist before the internet; they are all "pure plays", i.e. they didn't come from the offline world, but were born on the internet, so to speak.

Here is the full top 10 as ranked by Alexa:

1. Google.com
2. Facebook.com
3. YouTube.com
4. Yahoo.com
5. Baidu.com
6. Wikipedia.org
7. Qq.com
8. Taobao.com
9. Twitter.com
10. Amazon.com

When we ran the search again on Alexa but this time for the highest ranked news sites, this was the top 10:

1. Reddit.com
2. News.yahoo.com
3. Cnn.com
4. Huffingtonpost.com
5. Nytimes.com
6. Weather.com
7. News.google.com
8. Theguardian.com
9. Timesofindia.indiatimes.com
10. Forbes.com

The top 10 news sites crudely shows us that there is approximately a 60 per cent survival rate of companies from the pre-internet era that have successfully managed to build an online presence to complement their traditional business. These companies are **CNN, The New York Times, The Weather Channel, The Guardian, The Times of India,** and **Forbes.** Clearly the companies that have made the top ten are among the luckier ones. The less fortunate ones have gone bankrupt, are going bankrupt, or continue to struggle financially, often resorting to shedding staff and shutting-down their overseas bureaus to cut costs, which then cuts the quality of their reporting, leading to an irreversible downward spiral.

As an example of how much value destruction has taken place in the traditional news media since the advent of the internet, in 1993 The New York Times (a listed company) bought **The Boston Globe** for $1.1 billion, only to sell it in 2013 for a mere $70 million.

The single reason behind all the disruption in the media world comes down to advertising – the life blood of the media industry. Whereas traditionally there used to be a cosy 3-way relationship between the advertiser, the agency and the media company, the explosive growth of internet use has transferred many of those "eyeballs" online, allowing pure plays to charge for the privilege of advertising to their audience. Online advertising has allowed pure plays to circumvent many of the once all-powerful traditional media empires, crowning them the new kings of the industry.

Unlike a print ad in a magazine or newspaper, online ads can be more accurately targeted to the intended audience. Not only that, online advertisers are able to tell if the target audience saw the advertisement and if they reacted by clicking through to find out more about the product or service being advertised.

The online world allows advertisers to be very specific about whom they would like to reach; they can specify the location of the target audience, sometimes even within a city itself, gender, age, education level, etc. When advertisers can be this detailed in their focus, it is no wonder that the old style print ads are no longer as popular.

Online advertising is not necessarily cheap, and the cost of running these targeted ads can be difficult to determine, so the likes of Facebook and Google let the market decide by allowing real time bidding of ad space.

Over 95 per cent of Google's revenue is derived from online advertising, which translates to a staggering $50 billion or so per year, and it is still growing by double digits.

Total global ad spending for 2013 was $503 billion, $140 billion of which was in the US[1], which means that Google enjoys 10 per cent of the global advertising market and about one-third of the global digital advertising market[2].

As all the key players know, this is a fluid industry where no one dominant player can rest on its laurels. Already, the next turf war has begun, this time in the mobile sector, which in 2013 was where 81 per cent of the growth in ad spending came from in the US[3]. ZenithOptimedia, a digital advertising agency, forecasts that by 2015 the mobile advertising industry will be worth $33 billion, accounting for 25 per cent of internet expenditure and 6 per cent of all ad expenditure. Also by 2015, the agency expects that for the first time, online advertising spend will eclipse newspapers to become the second largest medium after television.

More and more online advertising is being automated, and there is a secular shift underway to so-called programmatic placement of ads and use of online exchanges to buy and sell ads. Indeed, the amount of advertising to go through programmatic channels in the US was over $3.5 billion in 2013 and this is expected to reach $7 billion in 2015. A US-based company called **Rocket Fuel (NASDAQ:FUEL)** is an interesting play in this area, and it is currently growing by about 80 per cent per annum. The stock is highly rated so we recommend only a small investment.

Multi-channel, global marketing campaigns are becoming increasingly more complex to manage. There is an opportunity for some of the players in the software industry to consolidate, coordinate, distil and interpret all of the many activities. This would prove to be a powerful tool for big business, providing them with real time feedback on marketing campaigns and on-the-fly optimisations to enhance reach and effectiveness. Achieving this would be no mean feat and only the software giants will likely have the technical know-how and the deep pockets to develop such a product; companies such as **IBM**, **Oracle** and **Salesforce.com.**

Media Disruption

There are essentially three ways that traditional media is being disrupted: firstly, in the way it is *consumed*; secondly, in the way that it is *delivered;* and thirdly in the way that it is *made.* We discuss each one of these in more detail.

Consumption

In terms of consumption, television, radio and print media used to be the main channels for reaching the consumer.

So when a popular television programme or sporting event was broadcast, the owner of the station could command a sizeable fee to run advertisements during the time slot of that programme or event. Similarly, for a popular radio show with millions of listeners, or a newspaper with a large circulation, companies paid hefty premiums for the privilege to advertise to their audience.

As costs came down and internet bandwidth went up, it opened the door for the transmission of high quality video, making the internet more of a direct competitor with television. Incidentally, about half of all internet traffic in the US[4] today is associated with two video sites, **Netflix** and **YouTube** (YouTube is a Google company in case some of our readers didn't know).

The television in many homes has become more of a big screen on which people watch some traditional television but increasingly, new media video. Add to this the introduction of tablets, smartphones and Google Glass, and now consumers have a number of ways to watch what they want, anytime, anywhere.

This dilutes the power of traditional media further, diverting those once captive eyeballs to other media channels, mostly

[1] *Source: Kantar Media, a marketing consultancy and subsidiary of WPP Group.*
[2] *Source: http://www.statista.com - The Statistics Portal.*
[3] *Source: ZenithOptimedia*
[4] *Source: The Guardian, 11 November 2013, Netflix and YouTube make up majority of US internet traffic, new report shows, Amanda Holpuch.*

new media companies.

Delivery

TV & Film

Up until the internet started shaking things up, media was delivered by a handful of powerful corporations, and state-owned media, such as television, radio and newspapers.

The internet started to fragment this cosy set-up as new channels for delivering media emerged.

Back in the 1950s, television enjoyed 100 per cent market share of viewers. Not only that, it had to be watched in real-time as it was being aired and there were no alternatives available. Fast forward to 2014, and people watching television broadcasts made up only 57 per cent of viewers. Next, with 23 per cent, were viewers who watched recorded video (such as TiVo), video on demand, and DVDs.

Next, social media started to come to the fore, and its influence became too significant to exclude from any marketing campaign. People suddenly had the option to watch their favourite television programmes on-demand on their way home from

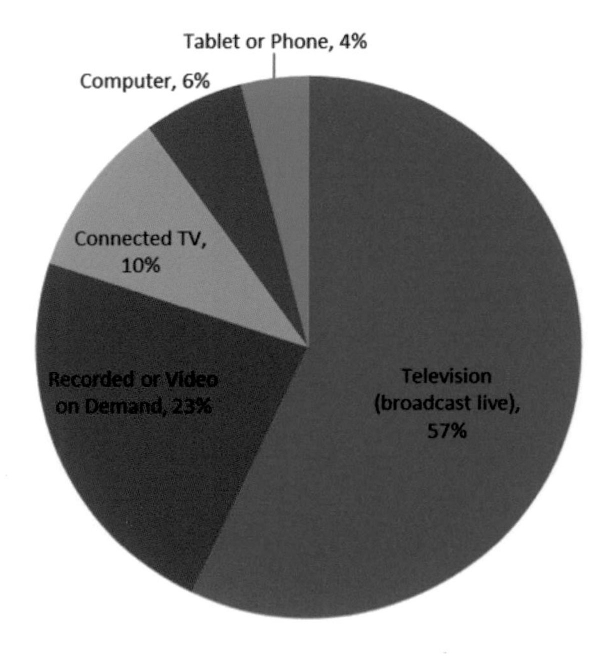

Figure 33: Figure 1: How US Viewers Watch TV Content in 2014. **Data source:** Horowitz Associates, State of Cable and Digital Media Report. April 2014. US internet traffic, new report shows, Amanda Holpuch.

[5] *John Hagel, Deloitte. May 2014.*

work on their smart phones, streamed directly over the internet. The likes of Netflix and iTunes started to hurt DVD sales as the ability to watch any film or TV show on-demand meant that people no longer needed to go to the store to buy them. It's tough to compete with instant delivery.

People watching a movie could also find out more about what they are watching, perhaps they like the actor in the film and would like to find out his name or other films he has appeared in. Within seconds, a website such as **IMDB.com** (owned by Amazon) could provide the entire filmography of the actor, as well as any upcoming films that he will be appearing in.

Traditional media are not going down without a fight though. In fact, some companies have been very successful online, with their on-demand channels for the TV, tablet and phone. For example, the **BBC** has a huge following of its **iPlayer** service, which was launched at the end of 2007 and is free to access for anyone in the UK, allowing viewers to watch anything aired by the BBC in the preceding 30 days.

In 2013, there were three billion iPlayer requests, up 33 per cent on 2012, making it another record year. The most popular show was *Top Gear,* where five of its episodes made the top 10 of the most watched shows.

Other traditional channels with popular on-demand viewing include **ESPN** and **HBO.**

On-demand viewing requires vast amounts of data storage and reliable, cheap broadband. Fortunately, data storage costs have been declining on average by 38 per cent annually since 1992, and broadband costs have been declining on average by 27 per cent annually since 1999[5].

Music

The way people consume music has also vastly changed because of the internet. Worldwide, almost half of recorded music is now sold digitally, both through streaming services (digital jukeboxes), such as Sweden's **Spotify,** and digital downloads through iTunes, Google Play and Amazon.

Streaming of music is forecast to grow by 13 per cent per annum over the next five years, according to PwC, and the subscription model suits an increasing number of music lovers who are granted unlimited access to vast libraries of music for a fixed monthly fee.

In 2013, 11.8 billion tracks were streamed by the various services globally, up 32 per cent over the previous year. Google is getting into the business and recently bought **Songza,** which tailors music choices to users' moods, and even to local weather conditions.

Spotify now has 10 million paying subscribers worldwide, and 50 million ad-supported members. Deezer has five million, and YouTube has signed up all the major labels for its own paid-for and ad-supported streaming services. One fifth of the $15 billion in revenue generated by the record companies in 2013 came from streaming of music and videos. Artists don't like it very much, as on average, they only receive 0.7 US cents per track played on a service such as Spotify – a lot less than selling a CD. Record companies like it even less than artists, reflected in their falling profits.

Streaming is starting to overtake digital downloads of individual tracks as the hottest part of the music industry. In 2013, music sales through digital downloads fell for the first time since 1999. Music videos now account for two thirds of the music consumed by teenagers, the prized demographic for record labels, and YouTube is absolutely dominant there.

In fact, YouTube is being accused of favouring large record labels over independents by signing deals that are more commercially attractive to the established labels, leaving independent labels out to dry. In an unappealing use of its hegemonic position, YouTube is in the process of removing videos from independent record labels that don't go along with its proposed royalty deals.

Production

Today, most smartphones are capable of recording high definition video, making everyone a potential producer of media content. Media channels such as YouTube can reach audiences of hundreds of millions of people. *Gangnam Style*, the 2012 catchy song by South Korean artist **Psy,** has had around two billion views – far more than any traditional-

media, such as MTV and VH1, could ever hope to achieve.

Anyone with a video camera/smartphone and internet access can upload a video on YouTube, or even set up a YouTube channel. Owners of popular videos can apply to become part of YouTube's partnership programme, allowing them to receive a share of the advertising revenue generated as a result of someone watching one of their videos.

The larger the audience, the more money can be earned through sharing the ad revenue. So appealing is this to some people that they have chosen to make it their main source of income. Popular channels can earn millions of dollars through YouTube.

At the time of writing, the channel with the most subscribers was called PewDiePie, a games channel with over 27 million subscribers and around 4.5 billion views.

YouTube's subscriber-base continues to grow at triple digit percentage rates. According to YouTube's own data, these are the number of subscribers and annual growth rates for its top five channels:

Channel	Number of Subscribers (millions)	Year on year growth May 2014 (in per cent)
Music	85	85
Gaming	79	79
Sports	78	78
News	35	35
Popular	28	28

These numbers are truly remarkable, especially when compared to top-rated television shows. For example, the hit TV series from the 1990s, Friends had an audience of between 20 and 25 million per episode in the US.

Obviously the production costs of a hit show like Friends are incredibly high when compared to a YouTube channel, yet the audience reach is in the same order of magnitude.

There is also an interesting new category of online media channels that has gained popularity in recent years, and these channels could be described as social content providers, the most popular of which is **BuzzFeed.** BuzzFeed specialises in publishing interesting facts, figures, quizzes, explanations, etc. In fact, at the time of writing, it was the single largest publisher on Facebook, with around 55 million "interactions", i.e. *Shares, Likes and Comments.* In August 2014 Buzzfeed raised $50 million dollars from *Andreessen Horowitz,* a US venture capital firm, at a valuation of $850 million[6].

The Huffington Post has the number two spot on Facebook with around 30 million interactions[7]. What makes Buzzfeed so much more impressive is that it was able to achieve the 55 million interactions with only 3,216 articles, whereas The Huffington Post had 16,664 articles for its 30 million interactions, making BuzzFeed's articles ten times more viral than The Huffington Post's.

By adopting a Facebook "piggy-back" strategy along with attention-grabbing headlines, BuzzFeed has been able to grow rapidly over a short period of time (it is growing by some 200 per cent per annum[8]).

Automated Writing

When it comes to print media, the role of human reporters and journalists is starting to be challenged by something known as

[06] *The Guardian, BuzzFeed valued at more than three times the Washington Post, Rupert Neate, 11 August 2014.*

[07] *Data source: NewsWhip (www.newswhip.com) as of February 2014.*

[08] *Source: comScore (www.comscore.com) – an audience analytics company. Figures as of March 2014.*

automated writing. For the time being, it is limited to reports that are relatively standardised in format, where the key facts and figures can be pasted into the right places.

Reporting basic facts about weather-related activities, sports results or company earnings is becoming commoditised, but we are still some years away from having an algorithm with the skills to write a full-length investigative feature on a deeply nuanced subject such as politics.

There is a Chicago-based company called Narrative Science that specializes in automated report writing of corporate earnings, for example. Automated Insights, based in North Carolina, is another interesting company in this space. Its Wordsmith platform is able to retrieve data, analyse it, then identify any interesting patterns, trends and insights, which it then formats in a meaningful way and publishes it. It is rather incredible at the volume of content that can be published in this way: in 2013, the company put out 300 million "articles" - content is probably a better description.

Automated Insights' approach to publishing is virtually the opposite of a traditional publication. Instead of writing a quality article that will be read by, say a million people, the company takes a scatter-gun approach, publishing millions of articles, trying to get at least one of them read by a million people.

Eye Tracking

An entirely new technology threatens to further rock the boat in the media industry - eye tracking systems. Making their debut in 2014, eye tracking systems use infrared cameras, which can be incorporated into headsets such as Google Glass, or by mounting a camera at the top of a tablet or computer screen. From such systems, websites will be able to further understand what readers are looking at, providing them with even more targeted marketing opportunities.

One of the leading companies in this space is a Swedish company called **Tobii Technology.**

Expect to see its eye tracking technology become more prevalent, especially in video games, where the games will be able to know where you are looking on the screen and react accordingly.

Another possible application of eye-tracking technology is to operate tablets, phones and computers themselves by looking and gesturing at specific parts of the screen. Once again, it is Google that is a first mover in this and in mid-2014 it released a new tablet with advanced vision capabilities[9]. South Korea's Samsung is also developing this technology and some of its existing smartphones already have eye-tracking features.

Net Neutrality

There is a very controversial debate underway, started in the US but with global ramifications, and it concerns the allocation of priority bandwidth to companies willing to pay for it, versus keeping the internet neutral, i.e. all data on the internet is treated equally, regardless of content, website, platform, application, user, etc.

Some of the heavy hitters in the industry would like to have priority for their company's traffic, a so-called "fast lane". In April 2014, the Federal Communications Commission (FCC) announced that it was considering a new rule that would allow Internet Service Providers (ISPs) to charge content providers to have their traffic be given priority over other internet data.

The ISPs are in favour of this as it would allow them to generate new revenue after years of lacklustre performance. Content providers with deep pockets would be in favour of this too, as providing superior internet speed would retain customers and attract new ones who may get fed up with slower internet access from the poorer content providers.

Those in favour of net neutrality argue that the internet should be there for everyone to use equally. Carving up the bandwidth would mean that the biggest companies will only get bigger and more dominant, as they would be able to afford to buy the lion's share of the bandwidth, thus crowding out any up-and-coming companies from getting a fair chance to compete, even if these smaller, younger companies are offering a better product or service. Giving ISPs the discretion to charge, block and discriminate between companies would no doubt kill internet innovation.

[09] *Source: The Wall Street Journal, Lorraine Luk and Rolfe Winkler, Google Developing Tablet With Advanced Vision, 22 May 2014*

Imagine if MySpace in its prime had done a deal with ISPs to block Facebook, or if Microsoft, sensing a threat, paid ISPs a premium to protect its Internet Explorer browser by blocking the likes of Firefox. There are countless other scenarios that demonstrate how stifling to innovation the internet would be in a world where ISPs and big business call the shots.

There has been a huge backlash against an internet fast lane. Tim Berners-Lee, the inventor of the World Wide Web and Vincent Cern, the inventor of the internet protocol, are among many who remain firmly in the net neutrality camp. They along with over 150 leading technology companies have signed a petition to the FCC calling it a "grave threat to the internet."

Although the debate continues on net neutrality, there are already instances of ISPs breaching it in the US, Europe and Canada. For instance, in the US Netflix is already rumoured to be paying Comcast, an ISP, tens of millions of dollars a year for preferential access to its networks. Chile is the only country thus far to enshrine net neutrality as a national principle.

On an episode of his satirical news show on HBO, British-American commentator/ comedian John Oliver has been particularly scathing on the subject. In his view, if the telecom companies succeed in imposing a tiered system of internet access, it would allow the big players to *"buy their way into the fast lane, leaving everyone else in the slow lane."* He claims that the assault on net neutrality has all the ingredients of a *"mob shakedown"* and points out that the head of the Federal Communications Commission, Tom Wheeler is a former cable industry lobbyist: *"The guy who used to run the cable industry's lobbying arm is now running the agency tasked with regulating it. That is the equivalent of needing a babysitter and hiring a dingo."* We highly recommend readers watch Oliver's segment on net neutrality, which can be found on YouTube; at the time of writing it had been watched over 6 million times.

We find it hard to believe that the US and indeed the rest of the world would accept a sort-of class system on the internet; it is a slippery slope and it goes against everything the internet has been designed to be. No doubt there would be countless appeals against the FCC should it decide to go ahead with an internet fast lane. Governments may have to step in, depending on the outcome and public reaction to it. We are at a critical juncture in the internet's evolution.

Fighting Over the Consumer

The centre of attention in the age of the internet is the consumer, around which all battles are being fought. There is the traditional way to reach the consumer, through the broadcast television networks and cable companies. Then there are the ISPs that sell consumers internet access to the home. Increasingly, consumers are using their broadband ISP service for news and entertainment that was previously accessed through their TV and cable network providers. Seeing the growing importance of the role of ISPs, Google decided to become one. It is rolling out its Google Fiber service, offering bandwidth speeds of 1,000 Mbps.

One of the main drivers of the change in consumer behaviour is **Netflix,** which allows viewers at home watch virtually limitless video content for a monthly subscription fee. Netflix has also started producing its own programmes, such as the hugely popular remake of the British political drama *House of Cards,* starring Kevin Spacey.

Not wanting to be left out, Amazon also has a streaming video service called *Amazon Prime Instant Video,* which has not been as popular as Netflix. In an effort to boost its presence in this space, Amazon paid $1.1 billion in August 2014 to buy Twitch, a video livestreaming company. Twitch has about 55 million monthly users, but whether Amazon will be successful in integrating and monetising Twitch with its Prime Instant Video service remains to be seen.

The mobile phone network operators, with the high bandwidth 4G and beyond are also interested in offering high speed internet access to the home which can be delivered through a phone SIM card, either directly into a device or into a router that can then provide a home Wi-Fi network.

It is clear from all of the current jostling going on that the future of the industry will not look like it does today. On the one hand, consumers will benefit from the increased number of choices to access media content; on the other regulators need to keep a close eye on how things develop to ensure that the bigger players do not abuse their market dominance and stifle any new companies that are striving to offer their services, hence why the net neutrality issue discussed earlier is so important.

Publishing

Jeff Bezos, founder and CEO of Amazon.com is a man who achieved the seemingly impossible task of changing the way people have read for hundreds of years. He was faced with overwhelming scepticism at the time, but it wasn't the first time, and he pushed ahead with his idea anyway. In 2007, the *Kindle* was launched. People were pleasantly surprised by how similar to reading a printed book it was, and everyone loved that they could have thousands of books and magazines all on the one device. Naturally, it became a travellers' best companion. There have been many upgrades to the original Kindle, and a number of other e-book readers have appeared on the market. Today, e-book sales are a serious contender to printed books. In the US, Amazon has a 60 per cent market share of all e-books, and 30 per cent share of printed books.

Such dominance by Amazon of both e-readers (its Kindle) and e-books could spark claims of anti-competitive practices if things started to get messy with the publishers. Remember how Microsoft was investigated for bundling its *Internet Explorer* browser with *Windows* and was forced to separate the two and give customers the option of installing other browsers? Similarly, it could be argued that Amazon's Kindle should allow customers to install other e-readers on it that do not necessarily favour Amazon's e-books. This issue may come to the fore as e-books eclipse printed books.

According to professional services firm PwC[10], consumer e-book sales will overtake printed book sales by 2017. Together, the size of the consumer book industry will be $16 billion and PwC expects e-book sales to account for 38 per cent of all book sales, which includes trade and educational books.

[10] *Source: PwC Global entertainment and media outlook: 2013-217, Entertainment & media practice.*

Most publishers have adopted a head-in-the-sand approach to this disruption to their long-standing way of doing things, and as a consequence they will lose most of their market share to e-books. In the pre-e-book era, self-publishing was seen as "vanity publishing" for authors who had been unable to secure a traditional publisher. But that is no longer the case; self-published hits are increasing in frequency, cutting out not only the publisher but also the literary agent.

It wasn't long ago when the traditional publishing giants called the shots as to whether a book was going to be published or not, but nowadays it is quite common to find at least one self-published book in the best sellers' list. The now famous Fifty Shades of Grey by British author E L James was originally self-published as an e-book and a print-on-demand in 2011, but as its popularity spread across the internet and by word-of-mouth, it grabbed the attention of the big publishing houses, and the author was probably made an irresistible offer to sell her book rights, which she did to **Vintage Books,** a subsidiary of **Random House.**

The title has sold more than 90 million copies, both e-book and print combined and is also being made into a film to be released in 2015. The magnitude of success from E L James's book has been exceptional, and had it not been for the development of new channels to market, most notably Amazon.com, the self-publishing industry would have remained a small, niche market, and Fifty Shades of Grey would never have sold more than a handful of copies.

Amazon's industry dominance means it is able to squeeze its suppliers into submission on pricing. But some suppliers have hit back. **Hachette,** a book publisher that carries titles by renowned authors such as Malcolm Gladwell, JK Rowling, James Patterson and Stephen King, has rejected Amazon's aggressive pricing terms, especially for its e-books, which Amazon would like to see capped at $9.99. In retaliation, Amazon refused to accept pre-sale orders of Hachette's titles, as well as to understock existing ones.

The publishing landscape is undergoing a major transformation, and it is unclear which side will emerge as the victor. It is true that the consumer is the ultimate beneficiary of such ruthless treatment of suppliers by Amazon, but at the same time, if the publishing houses' margins are squeezed to the point that they can no longer make money, there will be little incentive to produce new products which means fewer new releases in the future, which is negative for society as a whole. Amazon is in a strong position given that it is the best revenue source for most publishers. There is a chance that this matter will have been resolved by the time you read this book; our guess is that Hachette will cave in to Amazon's terms but Amazon will make some sort of concession, otherwise its authors would lose out on royalties and switch to other publishing houses, and some may even select Amazon as its publisher.

The interesting thing about this dispute is that publishers themselves cannot do much collectively to stand up to Amazon as that would be a conspiracy to price fix. There was a 2012 ruling by the US Justice Department against five publishers for conspiring to raise e-book prices, and yet Amazon is legally permitted to squeeze publishers. Clearly, Hachette's legacy cost structure is not suited to the new publishing business model and drastic measures must be taken if Hachette and others are to survive in the medium to long-term. Other publishers are no doubt closely watching the Hachette-Amazon stand-off to see who blinks first, as they are in the same boat and it is just a matter of time before they are faced with the same tough decisions that will determine their future existence.

In July 2014 HarperCollins, another major publisher owned by Rupert Murdoch's News Corporation, took the unprecedented step of selling its titles directly to customers online.

This was probably done partly to test the waters and partly as an act of frustration with Amazon's strong-arming of publishers. Indeed other publishers have started doing the same thing. Even Hachette is now allowing customers to buy e-books of some of its titles directly from its website. Clearly though, publishers don't have the customer relationship and sophistication that Amazon has. This is very evident if you try and go through the process of checking out after selecting a title. Still, it is a shot across the bow of Amazon and the long term sustainability of its dominance of retailing books.

These disputes and the debates they trigger are important because they reveal the dark side of the internet - an environment in which a few giant companies, armed with cash, enormous reach, logistics centres (Amazon has 92 giant facilities around the world), unsurpassed bandwidth and bright minds dominating the landscape for years to come. This means that it will be harder - but not impossible - for start-ups to grow into investable companies, partly because the big boys will just snap them up if they show any signs that they may be a future threat.

Also in publishing, but specialising in academic papers, privately-held **Academia.edu** is worth a mention. Based in San Francisco, Academia is opening science up to free access for all interested in research around the world. The company has 10 million members - a remarkable achievement, and a ringing endorsement of the positive disruptive potential of the internet.

The Rise of E-books

Thanks to Amazon's brave launch of the Kindle, e-books have become a widely accepted alternative reading medium to printed books, some readers even preferring them over printed books altogether. There are many advantages of e-books over printed books, even for authors and publishers. This has resulted in many new start-ups with business models that attempt to capitalise on the growing acceptance of e-books. At the 2014 London Book Fair, entrepreneurs presented their plans to disrupt the publishing industry, possibly even giving Amazon a run for its money. Here are a couple of examples.

In 2009, Ricardo Almeida launched a self-publishing platform called **Clube de Autores.** What makes this platform so attractive is that authors do not have to pre-pay any production costs; they only have to pay once a book order has been placed and paid for - a pay-as-you-go approach. This has proved so popular that Clube de Autores has now published 24,000 titles by 21,000 authors, making it the largest such platform in Latin America.

Another award winning company is **Bookmate** from Russia, an e-book distributor targeting areas other than North America, Western Europe and Australia. It is already the largest e-book distributor in Russia with a million users. It plans to enter 30 new markets by the end of 2014, including South America. The unique subscription-based model of Bookmate is that it streams the content, thus preventing users from selling it on or sharing it with others, so it is an ideal model for markets with high piracy rates.

With so much change going on in the publishing industry, no player is immune to becoming irrelevant, with the old publishing houses under the greatest threat. Even Amazon's dominance is not assured in the years to come, which is why the company continues to innovate in an effort to define the market of the future, rather than get dragged along by it.

As authors ourselves, we have experienced first-hand how the industry has been evolving since we published our first book *Wake Up!* in 2005. We have seen e-book sales become stronger with each subsequent title release, and we have also seen Amazon become more critical as a sales channel for book sales, both in the US and the UK site. Conversely, we have witnessed the role of the publisher diminish, making it increasingly difficult for a publisher to justify its 80 to 85 per cent sales commission; a legacy from a time when publishers played bigger roles in the promotion and distribution of book titles.

Indeed, for this book we decided to part ways with our long-standing publisher, *Wiley* to adopt a more modern approach to publishing that we believe gives us better flexibility and more control to distribute and promote *Fast Forward.*

Education

The way students are taught has finally started to change, largely thanks to the internet which is playing a key role in the education revolution. Today, the way children are learning is radically different to how most of us were taught.

Universities and schools around the world are embracing these new learning channels, which is more tailored to the individual student. So-called *MOOCS* allow anyone with internet access to receive a free university education. This is particularly beneficial to society when it comes to offering an education to all, not just the wealthy. Over the past 30 years, tuition fees to attend private schools and universities have soared, far outpacing the rate of inflation. MOOCS could be the solution to levelling the playing field in university education. Never before has such democratisation of education taken place.

What are MOOCS?

A strange sounding acronym, MOOCS stands for **Massive Open Online Courses.** It is a term first coined in 2008 by Dave Cormier from the University of Prince Edward Island, Canada.

MOOCS are free, short online courses that are direct descendants of correspondence courses. Their recent popularity may finally be changing the old fashioned reputation of distance learning. But given that they are relatively new, the limitations of MOOCS are still unclear; whilst they may work well for a subject such as mathematics, for other fields such as the social sciences it may not. For a subject such as philosophy, it may result in only a couple of "super-star" lecturers teaching the subject, limiting other lecturers' interpretations and viewpoints and narrowing the field of philosophy as a whole. No doubt these issues will be addressed and MOOCS will eventually find their place.

The Technology Platform Behind MOOCS

Most learning institutions prefer to outsource the technology platform for their MOOCS to a company specialising in such things. There are quite a few such platforms emerging; we will cover the main three organisations.

One of the leading companies that academic institutions turn to when looking at setting up MOOCS is **Coursera,** a privately held for-profit company. It was founded in 2012 by two Stanford University professors, Andrew Ng and Daphne Koller. Over 100 institutions use Coursera to run their MOOCS along with over seven million users. The universities comprise some of the world's leading establishments, especially the Ivy League universities in the US. But there are also non-university institutions such as National Geographic Society and The World Bank. For the time being, Coursera offers the broadest range of courses.

A rival platform to Coursera is **edX.** Founded by Harvard and MIT also in 2012 but unlike Coursera, as a not-for-profit organization, its mission is twofold: to give access to high quality education to as many people as possible; and secondly to improve the learning experience on campus by understanding how people learn. Through edX, anyone can enrol in an unlimited number of courses on virtually any subject, from algebra to Chinese history. EdX has been gathering momentum and its xConsortium network has over 30 learning partners.

In 2014, edX in partnership with Google, launched **mooc.org** to *"...help educational institutions, businesses and teachers easily build and host courses for the world to take."*

The third company offering a MOOCS technology platform is called **Udacity.** Originally offering computer science classes through Stanford University in 2011, it grew and developed into a broader MOOCS platform. Udacity is a for-profit organization with over 1.5 million users, and has received over $15 million in venture capital.

In the UK, it is the Open University that is leading the charge in MOOCS, setting up the country's first platform under the name **Future Learn.**

We're somewhat sceptical about the future prospects of the for-profit MOOCS platforms, such as Coursera and Udacity, simply because the open source, free option is usually the one that tends to prevail in the long-term. By essentially removing the technology barrier to entry, MOOCS are set to explode as the new way to learn, and with backing from Google, mooc.org stands to become the Android of open source learning. So whilst we do believe that MOOCS are going to seriously disrupt education, the open source free delivery platform of MOOCS will make it an unattractive area of investment.

Universities are waking up to the fact that their reputations cannot be assured in the future and they cannot afford not to take part in the MOOCS movement, even though nobody knows where it will lead. At the moment, an education from MOOCS does not have the same prestige and recognition as a bricks and mortar education, even if it is from the same university, so it is not yet a substitute for enrolling at a university in the traditional way. This may change in the coming years.

One of the main challenges that MOOCS face is how to recreate the interactivity that goes on in a real classroom, face-to-face between fellow students and the lecturer. They have tried to address this by establishing discussion groups, but again it is all online, which doesn't quite capture the same buzz. This may change in the future as virtual reality and video technology improves, allowing some of that face-to-face feeling to be captured virtually.

For the time being, the really incredible potential for MOOCS is with remote, poor countries, as for the first time, they can receive a world class education for free. Anyone with a device and internet access has a plethora of courses to choose from. However things develop, MOOCS are widely seen as a major part of a larger disruptive process taking place in education. We discuss a couple more education disruptors in the next sections of this chapter.

Interactive Learning

Another new development in education is that of game-based learning. If kids love playing games, why not make them educational ones that have a useful application?

Nolan Bushnell, an American engineer, entrepreneur and founder of the now defunct gaming console company, **Atari** has decided to re-engage himself in the field of teaching, through a new company called **Brainrush.**

Brainrush is focused on smarter learning techniques through adaptive games. Taking advantage of children's desire to play video games, Mr Bushnell hopes to exploit this by designing video games that actually teach children. Mr Bushnell believes that children can be taught almost anything through games, because games engage children and are fun to play, so it won't feel like they are being taught. The company is still in its infancy so we shall have to wait and see with Mr Bushnell is successful in his approach.

Another interesting development in education is interactive language learning. Our favourite company in this space is called **Duolingo,** which has a free app that helps teach users new languages. The app is intuitive, with rewards and prompts to keep users engaged. As more users populate the system (around 30 million at the time of writing), they add to its depth, enriching the vast language learning programme. There is also a voice recognition feature in the app, which tests the user's pronunciation of words and sentences. We love Duolingo and highly recommend our readers give it a try.

The Khan Academy

Arguably the pioneer in this learning revolution is a man called Salman Khan. Whilst working as a hedge fund analyst, Mr Khan was remotely trying to help his 12 year old cousin with some mathematics problems that she was struggling with. And because she was living in different part of the US, he was trying to explain things to her over the phone and sometimes with a digital blackboard. But then more cousins started asking for help, and so one of Mr Khan's friends suggested that he make video of himself explaining the topic and post it on YouTube so he didn't have to keep explaining the same thing over and over again. This he did and within a few months, something totally unexpected started to happen: many people who were not Mr Khan's cousins started watching his YouTube videos. The number of viewers grew and he recognised that he was onto something big, so he quit his well-paid job with the hedge fund and decided to give this cause his full-time attention, and so the Khan Academy was born.

After struggling to support himself and his young family for a year or so, the Khan Academy was noticed by none other than the richest man in the world, Bill Gates who, unbeknownst to Mr Khan had become a huge fan and so Mr Gates decided to provide financial support to the not-for-profit academy of free learning, and not long after that, so did Google.

That marked the end of The Khan Academy's financing problems.

Mr Khan is passionate about reinventing the way we teach, which he says is about 200 years old. Technology now allows us to dramatically transform the dated one-size-fits-all approach to education. We can personalise every student's curriculum and pace it to suit their comfort levels.

In what initially started out as a few mathematics videos, the Khan Academy library now contains thousands of videos covering many subjects, no longer just mathematics. Students can learn about science, economics, finance, computing, even history. There is literally no limit to what can be taught through the Khan Academy. Each subject is broken down neatly into small, bite-sized videos, usually around 10 minutes long. Students can watch these videos by themselves at home; they can pause them, rewind them and watch them over and over again if necessary until they have thoroughly grasped the topic being taught. They are then required to answer correctly a series of questions on that topic, before they can move on to the next one. This ensures that each building block of learning is sound before moving on, thus preventing students from missing something critical early on in their learning that causes them to struggle with a related, more complicated topic several weeks, or even years later.

The Khan Academy's mission is to provide free world-class education to anyone, anywhere. Salman Khan founded the company in 2008 and by 2014 it was attracting over 10 million users per month from virtually every country in the world. In just a few years, the Khan Academy has become the world's largest school, and there is no sign of it slowing down any time soon.

What makes the Khan Academy so popular and effective is its self-paced learning with on-demand tutoring videos for whenever students find themselves stuck on something.

The Khan Academy's popularity is not limited to students; there are now thousands of schools around the world that have also started using it as part of their education curriculum. In a practice known as flipping the classroom, teachers assign Khan Academy videos to students to watch at home, and then the teachers use the classroom time to do the traditional homework of solving problems, allowing teachers to-provide on-the-spot assistance and support as students work through their assignments.

As disruptive as the Khan Academy has been and will continue to be, it is as we mentioned earlier a not-for-profit organization, so investors cannot participate in its continued growth and success.

However, there will almost certainly be spin-off and complementary business around the Khan Academy in the coming years, and these may be for profit businesses. Readers should continue to follow the Khan Academy's evolution as its adoption rate at schools around the world continues to increase.

At some point in the future, it is just possible that the schools of today end up becoming the bricks and mortar presence of the Khan Academy itself.

Figure 34: Salman Khan, the man pioneering the education revolution, pictured speaking at TED 2011. **Source:** Steve Jurvetson for Wikimedia Commons

ETWORK SEARCH
-INTERNET
-LIVE CHAT
-MEDIA
-MESSAGES
-SHOW
-ASIA

Summary

Having always been fascinated by technology and all the amazing ways it has improved our lives, we were keen to write a book on the subject.

The difficult part was deciding on which technologies to cover, as there are thousands of exciting things out there, but only a handful of them will make it out of laboratories and really impact all of our lives.

As part of our research, we sieved through countless articles and books covering all sorts of technologies, and we spoke at length with friends and with various tech companies before we finally decided on the topics to cover. Initially, we were going to write the entire book on robotics and automation, but then decided that there were too many other exciting things going on in tech to ignore, so we broadened the scope. After some deliberation and debate, we managed to whittle down the areas we wanted to cover into 8 themes, each one covered in the chapters you have just read.

As with our previous books, we have included information in each section on the leading companies behind these disruptive technologies in order to give readers ideas on how to invest in those that are publically traded. We also highlighted some interesting private companies that might one day go for an IPO.

We started off with robotics and automation in Chapter 1, recognising that robots have been with us in factories and assembly lines for several decades already, especially in the auto industry. These robots perform precise, repetitive tasks at speed.

Like
Like
Like
Like
Like
Like

However, they lack intelligence and have limited flexibility in being able to be reassigned to perform other tasks.

Thanks to smarter software and the development of haptics, or touch sensitivity, robots are starting to develop a level of intelligence that makes them more flexible in the work they undertake. Industrial robots have up till now not been human friendly, and if someone happened to get in the way of a working industrial robot, they might have got seriously injured or even killed. This is changing with the new generation of working robots, such as Baxter by Rethink Robotics; they are able to sense the presence of another human and immediately stop before any harm can be done.

We also wrote at length about Google's robotic ambitions, demonstrated by its acquisition of numerous robotics companies (8 at the last count) and its establishment of a new robotics group headed up by the former head of its Android division.

The increased variety and sophistication of robots has already started to impact the workforce, and the theme of human redundancy as a result of mass automation in most sectors is a widely discussed scenario. However, we maintained a more optimistic tone, taking the view that as many traditional jobs are replaced with robots, new jobs will be created in industries that do not yet exist. We do acknowledge, however, that there is a danger of large scale human redundancy in regions that have relied on cheap unskilled labour for their economic growth, such as China.

In our chapter on life sciences, we highlighted the areas we believe will see the biggest breakthroughs in the coming decade, which is where we hope to find the greatest investment returns.

Cancer is still a field that science has yet to conquer despite some great achievements in treatments and life extension. Billions of dollars are still pouring into cancer therapeutics and we expect more types of cancers to become treatable in the next few years, and we mentioned some companies that are making progress towards treating lung and pancreatic cancer, both of which currently have low survivability rates.

Lifestyle diseases are on the rise, in particular those associated with a lack of physical activity and eating an unhealthy diet, such as obesity, type 2 diabetes, chronic kidney disease and fatty liver disease. Developing countries are seeing the highest growth rates of these lifestyle diseases, as their populations grow richer and develop a taste for western-style fast food. Clearly, the best medicine is to educate populations to lead active lifestyles and balanced diets, but in the meantime, a country like China has a serious health crisis on the horizon.

The overuse of antibiotics over the years has resulted in a growing incidence of so-called superbugs, particularly in hospitals. These superbugs, such as MRSA and C. difficile, have acquired resistance to our latest generation of antibiotics, creating serious concerns amongst the medical community. In response, a number of drug companies have been working on new drugs and new approaches to combat bacterial infections. One such approach has been resurrected from the Soviet era, known as bacteriophage, which uses a virus that infiltrates and feeds off the targeted bacteria. The two great advantages of using bacteriophages is that they do not attack the healthy bacteria that live inside us, which is one of the negative side effects of today's antibiotics. The other is that the virus evolves to combat any resistance that their host bacteria may develop.

Genetic engineering, although in its infancy, is making steady progress with techniques using zinc finger nucleases, synthetics nucleases (TALENs) and CRISPRS.

These techniques could well be used to cure genetic diseases, starting with ones that only have a small number of defective base pairs in the DNA, such as sickle cell anaemia, the type of disease that results from only one defective base pair and hence would be easier to identify and repair.

We also provided an update on RNAi therapeutics, stem cells and synthetic organ growth, which will allow us to replace defective organs with newly grown ones without the need for organ waiting lists and the risk of rejection by the body, as the synthetic organs will be seeded with the patient's own *stem cells.*

As the world's population continues to age, particularly in developed countries, diseases that tend to affect the elderly are on the rise, which has companies redoubling their efforts to find cures and treatments for the most common ones, namely Alzheimer's, Parkinson's, rheumatoid arthritis and osteoporosis. Not only will successful drugs address a desperate need in the market, they will also make the companies behind the drugs billions of dollars.

The last section in the life sciences chapter was about orphan diseases, which are rare, genetic diseases affecting a small percentage of the general population. In the US, this is defined as a disease affecting fewer than 200,000 people in the country. Because these diseases are rare, governments encourage companies to develop treatments for orphan diseases by offering them favourable taxation, longer patent protection and higher margins. We used the drug Solaris as an example, which treats a life-threatening, rare condition that affects only 5,000 people worldwide, where the cost of treatment of the drug is $450,000 per year!

The next chapter was about all the exciting things going on in what is being dubbed as The Internet of Things, or IOT. Over the past two decades the internet has created entirely new industries and pure play corporate giants have emerged. Consequently, the internet has created more billionaires than at any other time in history, and it continues to do so.

Cheap, broadband internet access and the mass adoption of smartphones and tablets is allowing new applications to emerge, especially in the so-called Sharing Economy space. This allows individuals and companies to maximise the utility of an asset by renting it out when they are not using it. Sectors that are benefiting from the sharing economy are property and automobiles. Airbnb has become a leader in facilitating the renting out of rooms, apartments and homes of individuals around the world, amassing a portfolio of 600,000 listings in 30,000 cities worldwide. We also used the example of RelayRides that is the car equivalent of Airbnb.

Microchips are getting so cheap that we are approaching the point where they can be embedded in most items, including packaged foods. Each item can be assigned a unique IP address and can be connected to the internet. This will lead to an explosion in the amount of data being stored on the internet, most of which is in a virtual setting known as the cloud. All this data can be analysed to predict our wants and needs based on our behavioural history, which may lead to a general backlash by people who are against being under constant surveillance by an omnipresent "big brother."

As the IOT inevitably grows, it will require an ever increasing amount of data centres, which by some estimates already accounts for about 10 per cent of the world's energy consumption. We suggested a few companies that are key players in providing infrastructure for the internet as a way for readers to capitalise on this trend.

Next we moved onto the transportation industry where there has been a recent resurgence in public sector and private investment interest. The most exciting development in this sector without a doubt is that of driverless cars, where Google has been a pioneer, its cars clocking up over a million accident-free kilometres on the roads in California. Driverless cars are very close to being on our roads, starting with the US, but with other developed countries quickly following suit.

The other exciting developments in transportation relate to space travel.

Despite the retirement of the Space Shuttle fleet and the upcoming retirement of the International Space Station by the end of the decade, there has been renewed public interest in space travel and exploration. Perhaps it has something to do with Virgin Galactic's upcoming first commercial space flight; or it is related to the recent mission successes of the Space X rocket, founded by entrepreneur Elon Musk. Whatever the reason, there is a level of interest in space not seen since the Apollo missions of the 1960s and 70s. There are even plans for a manned one way mission to Mars by 2025, which has received some 200,000 applicants.

In aviation, we described how aircraft haven't really changed much since the 1960s in terms of their shape and cruising speeds, although big advances have been made in engine technology and avionics. Since the retirement of Concorde, there has been no commercial supersonic mode of travel. Even when Concorde was in service, it was not permitted to fly at supersonic speed over populated areas because of the shockwaves it created during flight, known as the sonic boom. We identified a few companies that believe they found a way to mask or supress the sonic boom, thus enabling aircraft to travel at supersonic speeds over populated areas.

We also mentioned a British company that has plans to build an aircraft capable of cruising at Mach 5, i.e. five times the speed of sound. The first test flights are not expected until 2017, but if it proves to deliver on this promise and is able to do so in a commercially viable way, it would certainly revolutionise aviation, which is long overdue an upgrade.

Other interesting areas that are seeing a pick-up in activity include airships and drones, the former because of their incredible lifting capacity, the latter in military applications, but also surveillance, communications and delivery. This chapter also covered trains and ships, both of which have so far been slow to take advantage of new technologies.

In Chapter 5 we addressed the more fundamental topic of energy. With the global human population forecast to reach 9 billion

by 2050, we need to find a way to address the growing energy demands. We provided an overview of where our energy comes from today (mainly fossil fuels unfortunately), and we also explained why nuclear energy (fission) is the only practical, reliable and clean energy source that will address our energy shortfalls in the coming decade until more alternatives come online, and that as exciting as nuclear fusion may be in solving the entire planet's energy needs, it is still at least two decades away from becoming a reality.

We covered at length solar and wind energy, which are slowly gaining popularity as the cost of generating a kilowatt hour falls. However, the Achilles heel of both solar and wind energy is their unpredictability, which then led us onto energy storage. It is here that we believe the most interesting developments will be taking place in energy, and we described some novel technologies with ambitions to address this need.

A development we couldn't ignore in the energy sector is the growing use of fracking, particularly in the US. This is a good news / bad news story; good news in the sense that the US will likely have energy independence as a result of fracking for the foreseeable future; bad news because this cheap fossil fuel will mean there is less incentive to invest in and use more renewable energy, which is what is needed to reduce carbon dioxide and other greenhouse gas emissions.

Chapter 6 was all about electronic payment systems and how paying for things using notes and coins is very inefficient given where we are technologically today. We highlighted some of the new developments in this space, such as near field communication and gave examples of how it is being used around the world today. Payment systems are on the cusp of big change, thanks to the latest models of smartphones – the iPhone 6 is, for instance, NFC-enabled. There is a lot at stake in electronic payments which is why all the big retailers and all the big banks are experimenting with various forms of it. The big credit card companies, namely Visa and MasterCard, are doing their best to ensure that they remain relevant in the future landscape, whatever it may be, by partnering with a number of payment systems being trialled or under roll-out. There are also many new entrants trying to carve a market for themselves. But it's still too early in the game to declare with certainty who the winners will be.

Given how much media coverage Bitcoin has received, we included a section on crypto-currencies, explaining in detail what they are and how they work. We also mentioned a number of other players competing with Bitcoin. Still under development are a new generation of crypto-currencies that are being built to incorporate an additional layer of code to facilitate specific transactions, such as buying and selling stocks, or buying a car or other big ticket items where an encrypted code is attached to each asset. This code can be transferred to the new owner when a purchase is made, allowing only the rightful owner to use or sell the asset.

The internet has liberated the lending of money and access to capital in general, and this has seen the rise of numerous peer-to-peer lending and crowdsourcing companies, giving individuals and businesses the opportunity to raise capital in cases where traditional banks have declined their loan applications. There is a whole new world in finance in the making and the comfortable positions of the traditional banks are being seriously threatened.

The penultimate chapter was about a subject that only a few years ago no one had heard of – 3D printing. Once again it is thanks to faster computers that printers are now able to print out 3D objects of any shape in a reasonable time. We explained why we believe that by the end of the decade, we can expect to see 3D printers in most homes, just as we do today with 2D Inkjet printers. This will potentially turn every home into a mini-manufacturer, allowing anyone to buy and print any object they like from the internet. This will lead to many patent infringement issues that the industry is currently not set-up to address. Manufacturers will become marginalised as it gets cheaper and quicker to print an item at home rather than to order it online, pay for shipping and wait for delivery. Of course some items will be too difficult to print at home, but eventually home printers will be able to print just about anything. We used some interesting examples of what 3D printers are being used to make today, including houses and food. We concluded the chapter with a section on graphene, the new wonder-material that stands to revolutionise what things are made from because of its abundance, strength, flexibility and conductance. Scientists are still trying to figure out how to make it in large quantities given that it is just one atom thick.

In our final chapter we focused on how the internet has shaken the up media, publishing and education. In media, it has always been about ad revenue and the big media empires are seeing much of that ad spending get reallocated to online advertising. We explained how the way people consume media is changing, with mobile devices being the fastest growing sector. We emphasized just how dominant Google was in this space, given that its annual revenues are around $50 billion and growing and total global ad spending is around $500 billion (print and online). That's an impressive market share for Google, especially when considering that all of its ad revenue - at least for now - is from online advertising.

In publishing, the other online giant Amazon is eating the lunch of the traditional publishers with ongoing legal battles over which party gets to control the price of books. We pointed out that e-books are becoming so popular that they are set to overtake printed books by 2017. Indeed, we expect that over half the sales of this book will be electronic.

In education, MOOCS have become widely available to anyone with internet access for free. But universities remain wary of cannibalising their own business, so MOOCS don't currently offer degrees, only courses. This may change as things develop, as no one seems to know how things will play out. We also wrote about the Khan Academy, which has quietly become the world's largest school with over 10 million students using it every month. Its customised teaching approach and series of short videos is helping students learn at their own pace and within their abilities. It is the most exciting thing to happen to education.

So there you have it, our summary of the technologies shaping our future. The pace of tech is heating up and the big boys with their deep pockets have been snapping up innovative companies with an insatiable appetite. At the time of writing, Google had made a total of 168 acquisitions and Facebook had made 49, with its most expensive acquisition being WhatsApp in 2011 for $19 billion. We mentioned this to make the point that it is no longer as easy to invest in promising, high-growth tech companies, as they are often swallowed up before they ever get a chance to go public. The only sector where big gains can still be had is in the life sciences, where smaller companies with promising drugs still go public to finance their clinical trials. Those that are successful then fall under the radar of big pharma and become potential acquisition targets or become stellar companies in their own right.

Pulling all this information together in a packaged, digestible way has been a fun challenge. We hope it has given our readers a clearer glimpse of what it happening out there in emerging tech, as well as some ideas on how they can invest in this fascinating and ever-changing arena. We will keep you updated through our website and our quarterly newsletters.

SUCCESS
IDEA
Think outside The box
TARGET MARKET
ATTRACT
Integrated
VALUE
PROFITABILITY
30%
17%
10%
18%
25%

Glossary of Abbreviations & Terms

ADR: American Depository Receipt; a US dollar denominated certificate issued in the US that represents one or more shares in a foreign stock that is listed on a US exchange.

EIA: United States Energy Information Administration

Bar: a non-SI unit of pressure approximately equal to atmospheric pressure. In SI units, it is equal to 100,000 Pascal (Pa).

FCC: The US Federal Communications Commission.

DARPA: The Defence Advanced Research Projects Agency is an agency of the United States Department of Defence for the development of new technology for use by the military.

Exabyte: 1018 bytes.

FDA: The Food and Drug Administration is an agency of the United States Department of Health and Human Services.

IOT: Internet of Things

IP: Internet Protocol or Intellectual Property.

ISP: Internet Service Provider.

ISS: International Space Station.

Kph: Kilometres per hour.

Mach: The speed of sound.

MB: Megabyte or million bytes.

Mbps: Megabits per second.

Mph: Miles per hour.

Nanobot, nano-robot: a very small self-propelled machine of the nano scale (of the order of 10-9 metres) that has a degree of autonomy.

NSCLC: Non-small cell lung cancer.

OEM: Original Equipment Manufacturer.

Quinone: a class of organic compounds that occur naturally, the prototypical member of the class is 1,4-benzoquinone.

NASA: The National Aeronautics and Space Administration, an agency of the United States government.

P2P: Peer-to-peer, or person-to-person.

PIN: Personal Identification Number, usually used as a form of security for card-based transactions.

POS: Point of Sale.

RFID: Radio Frequency Identification is the wireless use of electromagnetic fields to transfer data.

QR code: Quick Response code, a matrix type of barcode.

SEC: The US Securities and Exchange Commission.

SIM Card: SIM stands for Subscriber Identity Module, which is an integrated circuit that securely stores the subscriber identity of a mobile phone or mobile device.

SMS: Short Message Service, also known at texting.

Appendix A

Performance of Life Sciences Portfolios Suggested in Cracking the Code from 31 Jul 2012 - 31 Jul 2014.

Conservative

Company	Weighting	Currency	31/07/2012	31/07/2014	% Change
1. Allergan	8	USD	82.07	165.94	102%
2. Alnylam	8	USD	18.69	54.11	190%
3. Amgen	8	USD	82.6	127.39	54%
4. Astellas	8	JPY	746	1415.5	90%
5. Biogen-Idec	8	USD	145.83	334.56	129%
6. GlaxoSmithKline	8	GBP	1468.5	1437	-2%
7. Johnson & Johnson	8	USD	69.22	100.11	45%
8. Medicis	8	USD	32.92	44	34%
9. Pfizer	8	USD	19.74	28.71	45%
10. Roche	8	CHF	173.3	265.7	53%
11. Shire	8	USD	86.18	246.51	186%
12. Arrowhead Research	3	USD	3.7	12.66	242%
13. Complete Genomics	3	USD	2.27	3.15	39%
14. Inifinity	3	USD	17.46	9.1	-48%
15. Medivation	3	USD	49.85	74.23	49%

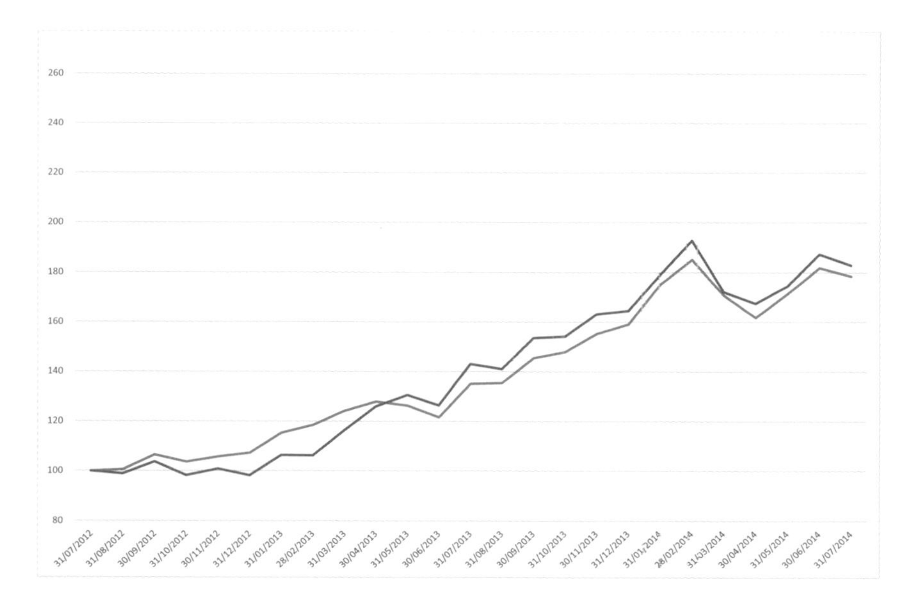

Conservative Portfolio Performance (blue), Jul 2012 - Jul 2014, compared to NASDAQ Biotech Index (orange) - underperformed by 4.4%

Balanced

Company	Weighting	Currency	31/07/2012	31/07/2014	% Change
1. Alnylam	6.5	USD	18.69	54.11	190%
2. Amgen	6.5	USD	82.6	127.39	54%
3. Astellas	6.5	JPY	746	1415.5	90%
4. Celgene	6.5	USD	34.23	87.16	155%
5. Forest Labs	6.5	USD	33.55	89.48	167%
6. Gilead	6.5	USD	27.17	91.56	237%
7. GlaxoSmithKline	6.5	GBP	1468.5	1437	-2%
8. ISIS	6.5	USD	12.12	30.99	156%
9. Pfizer	6.5	USD	19.74	28.71	45%
10. Rigel	6.5	USD	10.94	3.27	-70%
11. Roche	6.5	CHF	173.3	265.7	53%
12. Shire	6.5	USD	86.18	246.51	186%
13. Vertex	6.5	USD	48.51	88.92	83%
14. AmpliPhi	3.25	USD	0.19	0.335	76%
15. Arrowhead Research	3.25	USD	3.7	12.66	242%
16. Complete Genomics	3.25	USD	2.27	3.15	39%
17. Medivation	3.25	USD	49.85	74.23	49%
18. Nano-Viricides	3.25	USD	0.51	40.7	698%

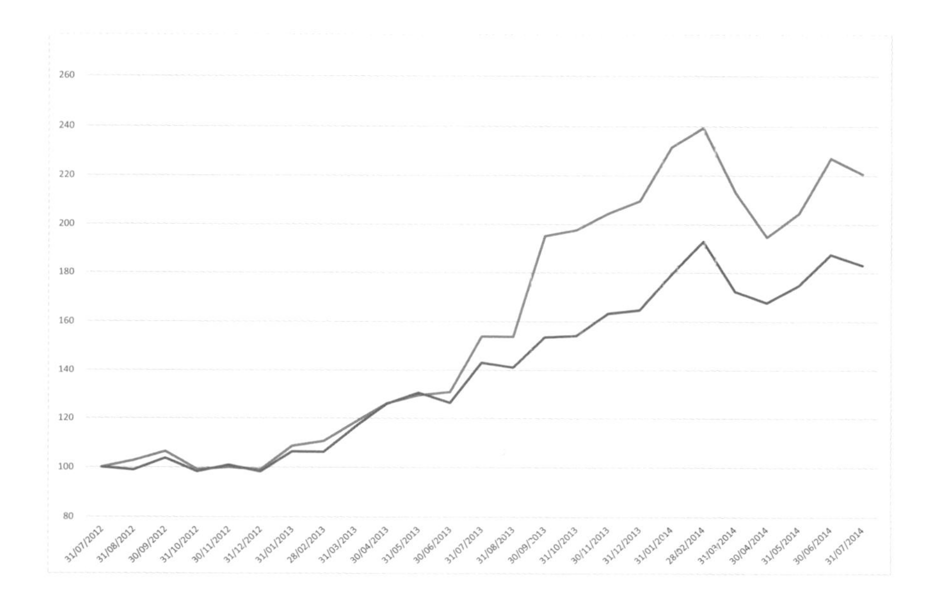

Balanced Portfolio Performance (blue), Jul 2012 - Jul 2014, compared to NASDAQ Biotech Index (orange) - outperformed by 37.6%

Speculative

Company	Weighting	Currency	31/07/2012	31/07/2014	% Change
1. Alnylam	5	USD	18.69	54.11	190%
2. AmpliPhi	5	USD	0.19	0.335	76%
3. Arrowhead Research	5	USD	3.7	12.66	242%
4. BioTime	5	USD	3.86	2.54	-34%
5. Cellceutix	5	USD	0.645	1.65	156%
6. Complete Genomics	5	USD	2.27	3.15	39%
7. Cubist	5	USD	43.06	60.91	41%
8. CytRx	5	USD	4.68	3.27	-30%
9. Cynavax	5	USD	3.86	1.47	-62%
10. Infinity	5	USD	17.46	9.1	-48%
11. Isis	5	USD	12.12	30.99	156%
12. Medivation	5	USD	49.85	74.23	49%
13. Nano-Viricedes	5	USD	0.51	4.07	698%
14. Nektar	5	USD	8.52	10.55	24%
15. Optimer	5	USD	13.66	10.75	-21%
16. Pacific Biosciences	5	USD	1.81	4.58	153%
17. Pharmacyclics	5	USD	53.21	120.49	126%
18. Rigel	5	USD	10.94	3.27	-70%
19. Star Scientific	5	USD	3.78	0.3738	-90%
20. Vertex	5	USD	48.51	88.92	83%

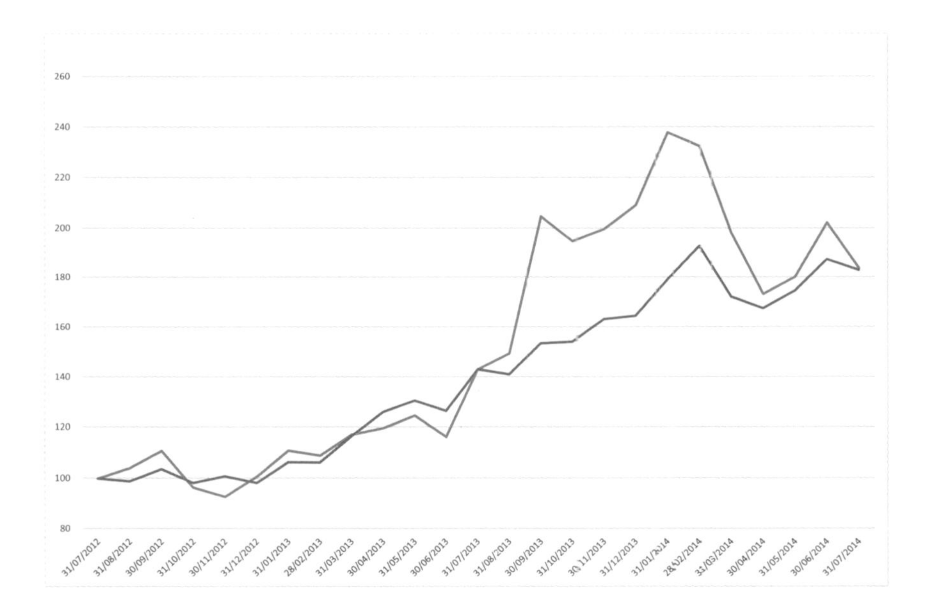

Speculative Portfolio Performance (blue), Jul 2012 - Jul 2014, compared to NASDAQ Biotech Index (orange) - outperformed by 0.8%

Appendix B

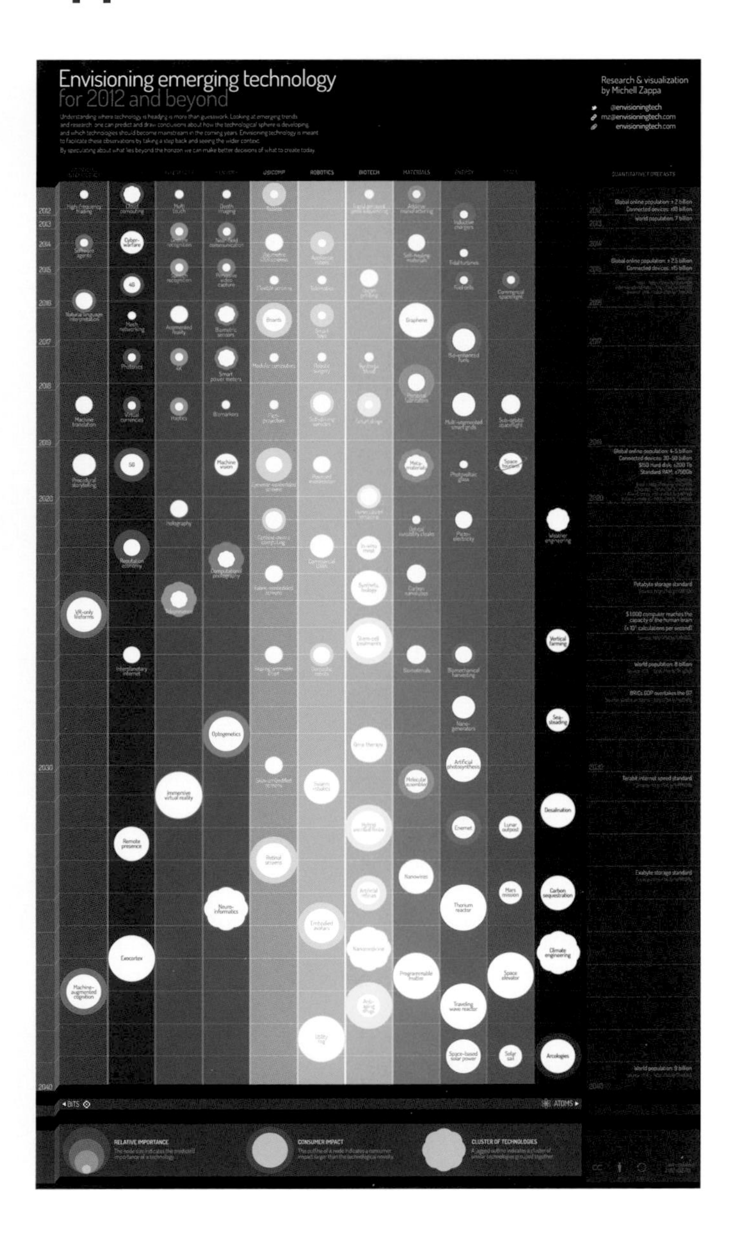
Envisioning emerging technology
for 2012 and beyond
Understanding where technology is heading is more than guesswork. Looking at emerging trends and research, one can predict and draw conclusions about how the technological sphere is developing and which technologies should become mainstream in the coming years. Envisioning technology is meant to facilitate these observations by taking a step back and seeing the wider context.
By speculating about what lies beyond the horizon we can make better decisions of what to create today.
Research & visualization
by Michell Zappa
@envisioningtech
mz@envisioningtech.com
envisioningtech.com
UBICOMP
ROBOTICS
BIOTECH
MATERIALS
QUANTITATIVE FORECASTS
Global online population: ≈2 billion
Connected devices: ≈10 billion
World population: 7 billion
Cyber-warfare
4G
5G
Graphene
Machine vision
Space tourism
Optogenetics
Immersive virtual reality
Remote presence
Exocortex
Neuro-informatics
Programmable matter
Thorium reactor
Traveling wave reactor
Space-based solar power
Space elevator
Mars mission
Lunar outpost
Solar sail
Enernet
Artificial photosynthesis
Weather engineering
Vertical farming
Sea-steading
Desalination
Carbon sequestration
Climate engineering
Arcologies
VR-only lifeforms
Machine-augmented cognition
BITS
ATOMS
RELATIVE IMPORTANCE
CONSUMER IMPACT
CLUSTER OF TECHNOLOGIES

Appendix C

Listed companies mentioned in the chapters

Chapter 1

Company	Exchange	Ticker	Market Cap (USD Millions)
iRobot	NASDAQ	IRBT	894.3
Fanuc Corp	TYO	6954	43,658
Kuka AG	XETRA	KU2	2,000
Google	NASDAQ	GOOG	388,210
Amazon	NASDAQ	AMZN	146,680
Hon Hai Precision Industy	TPE	2354	48,301
Apple	NASDAQ	APPL	593,880
Walmart	NYSE	WMT	245,300
McDonalds	NYSE	MCD	92,490
IBM	NYSE	IBM	186,720
Intuitive Surgical	NASDAQ	ISRG	16,640
Hansen Medical	NASDAQ	HNSN	131.27
Rex Bionics Plc	LON	RXB	41.19
Softbank Corporation	TYO	9984	84,223
Krones	XETRA	KRN	2,750
Hiwin Technologies Corp.	TPE	2049	2,316

Chapter 2

Company	Exchange	Ticker	Market Cap (USD Millions)
Pfizer Inc.	NYSE	PFE	184,800
AstraZeneca	LON	AZN	87,600
Arrowhead Research Corporation	NASDAQ	ARWR	728
Alynlam Pharmacueticals Inc.	NASDAQ	ALNY	5,880
Merrimack Pharmacueticals	NASDAQ NASDAQ	MACK	885.86
NewLink Genetics Corporation	NASDAQ NASDAQ	NLNK	640.51
Medivation Inc.	NASDAQ	MDVN	7,710
Amgen	NYSE	AMGN	105,450
Bristol-Myers Squibb	NYSE	BMY	83,770
Merck & Co.	NASDAQ	MRK	169,360
Incyte Corporation	NASDAQ	INCY	8,070
Novartis AG	NASDAQ	NVS	254,470
Pharmacyclics	NYSE	PCYC	8,720
Johnson & Johnson	VTX	JNJ	294,160
Roche Holding AG	NASDAQ	ROG	246,560
Kite Pharma	NASDAQ	KITE	897.77
ImmunoGen Inc	NASDAQ	IMGN	495.04
Orexigen Therapeutics Inc	NYSE	OREX	72,710
Eli Lilly and Company	NASDAQ	LLY	2,060
Insulet Corporation	NASDAQ	PODD	2,310
Mannkind Corporation	NYSE	MNKD	101,750
Novo Nordisk	NYSE	NVO	148,520
Sanofi	NASDAQ	SNY	101,750
Akebi Therapeutics	NASDAQ	AKBA	419.44
La Jolla Pharmaceuticals Company	NASDAQ	LJPC	140.76
Intercept Pharmaceuticals Inc	NASDAQ	ICPT	5,000

Chapter 2

Company	Exchange	Ticker	Market Cap (USD Millions)
Genefit SA	EPA	GNFT	1,168
Gilead Sciences	NASDAQ	GILD	159,620
GSK	NYSE	GSK	111,170
Cubist Pharmaceuticals	NASDAQ	CBST	4,900
Summit Plc	LON	SUMM	97.4
Ampliphi BioSciences Corp.	OTCMKTS	APHB	41.4
Uniqure	NASDAQ	QURE	171.09
Bluebird Bio Inc.	NASDAQ	BLUE	991.13
Sangamo BioSciences Inc	NASDAQ	SGMO	739.58
ISIS Pharmaceuticals Inc.	NASDAQ	ISIS	4,460
Sarepta Therapeutics	NASDAQ	SRPT	895.41
Cellular Dynamics International Inc.	NASDAQ	ICEL	95.52
Mesoblast	ASX	MSB	1,210
Teva Pharmaceuticals	NYSE	TEVA	50,720
ReNeuron Plc	LON	RENE	97.7
AbbVie	NYSE	ABBV	91,180
Impax Laboratories	NASDAQ	IPXL	1,660
Acadie Pharmaceuticals	NASDAQ	ACAD	2,430
Alexion Pharmaceuticals	NASDAQ	ALXN	33,070

Chapter 3

Company	Exchange	Ticker	Market Cap (USD Millions)
ASOS	LON	ASC	2,639
Ocado	LON	OCDO	2,300
Facebook Inc	NASDAQ	FB	199,030
Ebay	NASDAQ	EBAY	68,840
Twitter	NYSE	TWTR	30,800
LinkedIn Corporation	NYSE	LNKD	24,960
Netflix	NASDAQ	NFLX	26,370
ARM Holdings Plc	LON	ARM	19,900
FireEye Inc	NASDAQ	FEYE	4,280
Avis Budget Group	NYSE	CAR	5,533
Salesforce.com	NYSE	CRM	35,120
Microsoft Corporation	NASDAQ	MSFT	378,210
Oracle Corporation	NYSE	ORCL	168,790
Rockwell Automation	NYSE	ROK	15,080
Honeywell	NYSE	HON	71,730
Cisco Systems Inc.	NASDAQ	CSCO	128,160
Comcast	NASDAQ	CMCSA	136,900
Verizon Communications	NYSE	VZ	204,900
Vodafone Group Plc	LON	VOD	86,060
Telefonica	NYSE	TEF	70,130
Mail.RU Group Limited	LON	MAIL	5,403
Naspers Limited	JHB	NPN	37.05
Tencent	HKG	0700	140,000

Chapter 4

Company	Exchange	Ticker	Market Cap (USD Millions)
Orbital Sciences Corporation	NYSE	ORB	1,640
BAE Systems	LON	BA/	23,240
Alstom	EPA	ALO	10,440
Siemens	XETRA	SIE	102,760
Bombardier	TSE	BBD/B	5,860
Hitachi Ltd	TYO	6501	37,347
Volvo	STO	VOLVB	22,735
Audi	FRA	NSU	32,560
NCC Group	LON	NCC	623.29
Continental AG	XETRA	CON	37,143
Nissan Motor Co Ltd	TYO	7201	43,035
BMW AG	XETRA	BMW	67,827
Tesla Motors	NASDAQ	TSLA	29,940
Toyota Motor Corp.	TYO	7203	197,279
Triton Minerals Ltd	ASX	TON	92.42
Critical Elements Corporation	CVE	CRE	34.53
GS Yuasa Corporation	TYO	6674	2,341
Daihatsu	TYO	7262	6,605
Alcoa Inc.	NYSE	AA	18,090
Intelligent Energy Holdings Plc	LON	IEH	689.28
Suzuki Motor Corporation	TYO	7269	17.801
AFC Energy Plc	LON	AFC	51.71
Maersk	OTCMKTS	AMKBY	25,410
Alibaba	NYSE	BABA	218,780

Chapter 5

Company	Exchange	Ticker	Market Cap (USD Millions)
ConocoPhilips	NYSE	COP	91,840
Jinkosolar	NYSE	JKS	826.29
Renesola Ltd	NYSE	SOL	302.42
Trina Solar Limited	NYSE	TSL	1,070
Yingli	NYSE	YGE	556.2
Soitec	EPA	SOI	596.36
Solar City Corp	NASDAQ	SCTY	5.310
Ilika	LON	IKA	120
RWE AG	XETRA	RWE	22,259

Chapter 6

Company	Exchange	Ticker	Market Cap (USD Millions)
Vodacom Group Ltd	JHB	VOD	16,841
Safaricom Ltd	NAI	SCOM	5,759
Monitise	LON	MONI	853.7
HSBC	LON	HSBA	194,578
GLI Finance	LON	GLI	133.64
Identive Group Inc	NASDAQ	INVE	129.38
Worldline	EPA	WLN	2,637
Clear Channel Outdoor	NYSE	CCO	2,400
Coupon.com	NYSE	COUP	954.7

Chapter 7

Company	Exchange	Ticker	Market Cap (USD Millions)
General Electric	NYSE	GE	252,050
Stratasys	NASDAQ	SSYS	5,820
3D Systems Corporation	NYSE	DDD	4,800
ExOne	NASDAQ	XONE	274.41
Autodesk	NASDAQ	ADSK	13,120
HP	NASDAQ	HP	64,410
Renishaw Plc	LON	RSW	2,003
Arcam	STO	ARCM	435.18
Voxeljet	NYSE	VJET	259.27
Organovo Holdings	NYSE	ONVO	460.68
Dassault Systemes	EPA	DSY	16,427
Proto Labs Inc	NYSE	PRLB	1,750

Chapter 8

Company	Exchange	Ticker	Market Cap (USD Millions)
Rocket Fuel	NASDAQ	FUEL	588.36

Suggested Portfolio for Fast Forward Theme

Company	Allocation within portfolio (%)
IRobot	1
Fanuc	3
Kuka	2
Google	7
IBM	3
Intuitive Surgical	2
Arrowhead Research	2
Merrimack	1
Bristol-Myers Squib	5
Incyte Corporation	2
Novartis AG	2
Pharmacyclics	2
Kite Pharma	2
Insulet Corp	2
Mannkind	1
Novo Nordisk	3
Intercept Pharmaceuticals	1
Genefit SA	2
Gilead Sciences	3
Summit Plc	2
Sangamo Biosciences	2
ISIS Pharmaceuticals	2
Mesoblast	1
Reneuron Plc	1
Impax Labs	2
Acadia Pharmaceuticals	2
ARM Holdings	3
Rockwell Automation	4
Honeywell	4
Cisco Systems Inc.	3
Comcast	4
Verizon Communications Plc	4
Naspers Limited	1
Orbital Sciences Corporation	2
Alstom	3
Siemens	4
Bombardier	2
Hitachi Ltd	3
Critical Elements Coporation	2
GS Yuasa Corporation	2
SolarCity Corp	1

References

Brynjolfsson, Erik and McAfee, Andrew (2014) The Second Machine Age: Work, Progress, and Prosperity in a Time of Brilliant Technologies, W. W. Norton & Company.

CB Insights: https://www.cbinsights.com

Ford, Martin (2009) The Lights in the Tunnel: Automation, Accelerating Technology and the Economy of the Future, CreateSpace Independent Publishing Platform.

Meyer, Renee and Schuyler, Dean (2011) Old Age and Loneliness, Prim Care Companion CNS Disord 2011;13(2):e1–e2.

Piketty, Thomas (2014) Capital in the Twenty-First Century, Belknap Press.

Wikipedia Commons (www.commons.wikimedia.org)

Wohlers , Terry (2014) Wohlers Report 2014, 3D Printing and Additive Manufacturing, State of the Industry

Canalys, independent analyst company. "3D printing market to grow to US$16.2 billion in 2018" Press Release, 31 March 2014.

Kinsley, Michael (May 2014) The Front Page 2.0, Vanity Fair.

Global Wind Energy Council, Global Wind Report, Annual Market Update 2013.

The Economist, No Loopy Idea. Elon Musk, electric-car entrepreneur and proponent of private colonies on Mars, now plans to redesign the railway, 17 August 2013.

Rifkin, Jeremy (2014) The Zero Marginal Cost Society: The Internet of Things, the Collaborative Commons, and the Eclipse of Capitalism, Palgrave Macmillan Trade.

Kotler, Steven and Diamandis, Peter H. (2012) Abundance: The Future Is Better Than You Think, Free Press.

Kurzweil, Ray (2006), The Singularity Is Near: When Humans Transcend Biology, Penguin Books.

Schulte, Brigid (2014), Overwhelmed: Work, Love, and Play When No One Has the Time, Sarah Crichton Books.

Ammori, Marvin, Foreign Affairs, July/August 2014 Issue, The Case for Net Neutrality - What's Wrong With Obama's Internet Policy.

Ferguson, Niall, The Ascent of Money: A Financial History of the World, 13 Nov 2008, Penguin Books.

Citigroup Research: http://www.citigroup.com

Wikimedia Commons: http://commons.wikimedia.org

PwC Research Reports: http://www.pwc.com

McKinsey Quarterly and McKinsey Research Reports: http://www.mck-insey.com

Adyen: http://www.adyen.com

The Nilson Report: http://www.nilsonreport.com

Talkin' Cloud: http://talkincloud.com

Teal Group Corporation: http://www.tealgroup.com

The Economist: http://www.economist.com

Sanford C. Bernstein: http://www.bernsteinresearch.com

Bibliography

National Bureau of Statistics of China: http://www.stats.gov.cn/english

United Nations, Department of Economic and Social Affairs, Population Division: http://www.un.org/en/development/desa/population

U.S. Department of Energy - National Renewable Energy Laboratory (NREL): http://www.nrel.gov

Renewable Energy World - http://www.renewableenergyworld.com

America Makes - http://americamakes.us

International Monetary Fund: (http://www.imf.org) Energy Subsidy Reform: Lessons and Implications, January 28, 2013

European Wind Energy Association: http://www.ewea.org

Intergovernmental Panel on Climate Change: http://www.ipcc.ch

Global Wind Energy Council: http://www.gwec.net

Energy Fair: http://www.energyfair.org.uk

Wind Energy Foundation: http://www.windenergyfoundation.org

The Guardian: http://www.theguardian.com

The Wall Street Journal: http://online.wsj com

The Sunday Times: http://www.thesundaytimes.co.uk

The Telegraph: http://www.telegraph.co.uk

Nature: http://www.nature.com

Smart Card Alliance: http://www.smartcardalliance.org

Here is a list of publications that we found useful during our research:

BioWorld: http://www.bioworld.com

FierceBiotech Research: http://www.fiercebiotechresearch.com

Jefferies: http://www.jefferies.com

JP Morgan: http://www.jpmorgan.com

The Lancet: http://www.thelancet.com

National Center for Biotechnology Information http://www.ncbi.nlm.nih.gov

Neuron: http://www.cell.com/neuron/home

The New England Journal of Medicine: http://www.nejm.org

Singularity University: http://singularityu.org

The New York Times: http://www.nytimes.com

The Financial Times: http://www.ft.com

Science Daily: http://www.sciencedaily.com

New Scientist: http://www.newscientist.com

PubMed Central® (PMC) at the US National Institutes of Health's National Library of Medicine: http://www.ncbi.nlm.nih.gov/pmc

International Energy Agency (IEA): http://www.iea.org

International Monetary Fund. Energy Subsidy Reform: Lessons and Implications. 28 January 2013. Multiple staff authors, led by Benedict Clements.

Global Wind Energy Council: http://www.gwec.net

The US Energy Information Administration: http://www.eia.gov

Wind Energy Foundation: http://www.windenergyfoundation.org

Bloomberg: http://www.bloomberg.com

Centres for Disease Control and Prevention (CDC): http://www.cdc.gov

Gartner: http://www.gartner.com

European Photovoltaic Industry Association: http://www.epia.org

The US Department of Energy (DOE) SunShot Initiative: http://energy.gov/eere/sunshot/sunshot-initiative

GTM Research: http://www.greentechmedia.com/research

Nature: http://www.nature.com

BBC News: http://bbcnews.com

iReserach Consulting Group: http://www.iresearchchina.com

The Crowdfunding Centre: http://thecrowdfundingcentre.com

AT Kearney: http://www.atkearney.com

Xinhua News Agency: http://www.xinhuanet.com/english

Index